R. M. Garavito

THE MOLECULAR REPLACEMENT METHOD

A COLLECTION OF PAPERS

ON THE USE OF NON-CRYSTALLOGRAPHIC SYMMETRY

INTERNATIONAL SCIENCE REVIEW SERIES
Edited by LEWIS KLEIN
National Bureau of Standards

VOLUME I – LEWIS KLEIN, *Editor*. Dispersion Relations and the Abstract Approach to Field Theory

VOLUME II – HARRY L. MORRISON, *Editor*. The Quantum Theory of Many-Particle Systems

VOLUME III – D. McINTYRE and F. GORNICK, *Editors*. Light Scattering from Dilute Polymer Solutions

VOLUME IV – N. N. BOGOLIUBOV, *Editor*. The Theory of Superconductivity

VOLUME V – P. K. KABIR, *Editor*. The Development of Weak Interaction Theory

VOLUME VI – M. E. ROSE, *Editor*. Nuclear Orientation

VOLUME VII – P. H. E. MEIJER, *Editor*. Group Theory and Solid State Physics (In Two Volumes)

VOLUME VIII
- Part 1: C. TRUESDELL, *Editor*. The Mechanical Foundations of Elasticity and Fluid Dynamics
- Part 2: C. TRUESDELL, *Editor*. The Rational Mechanics of Materials
- Part 3: C. TRUESDELL, *Editor*. Foundations of Elasticity Theory
- Part 4: C. TRUESDELL, *Editor*. Problems of Non-Linear Elasticity

VOLUME IX – J. WEBER, *Editor*. Lasers (In Two Volumes)

VOLUME X – J. WEBER, *Editor*. Lasers (In Two Volumes)

VOLUME XI – EDWARD H. KERNER, *Editor*. The Theory of Action-at-a-Distance in Relativistic Particle Dynamics

VOLUME XII – EDWARD H. KERNER, *Editor*. Gibbs Ensemble: Biological Ensemble

VOLUME XIII – M. G. ROSSMAN, *Editor*. The Molecular Replacement Method

Additional Volumes in Preparation

THE MOLECULAR REPLACEMENT METHOD

A COLLECTION OF PAPERS

ON THE USE OF NON-CRYSTALLOGRAPHIC SYMMETRY

Edited by

M. G. ROSSMANN

Department of Biological Sciences
Purdue University

GORDON AND BREACH, SCIENCE PUBLISHERS

New York London Paris

440 Park Avenue South, New York, N.Y. 10016

Library of Congress Catalog Card Number: 79-109088

Editorial office for Great Britain:
Gordon and Breach, Science Publishers Ltd.
12 Bloomsbury Way
London W.C. 1

Editorial office for France:
Gordon & Breach
7-9 rue Emile Dubois
Paris 14e

Printed in the United States of America

A COLLECTION OF PAPERS ON

THE USE OF NON-CRYSTALLOGRAPHIC SYMMETRY

Introduction and Sectional Comments: M.G. Rossman

THE MOLECULAR REPLACEMENT METHOD

After completion of the initial commentary to the collected papers, the manuscript languished somewhere between the publishers and binders for a period of two years. Eventually it was agreed that I might add some of the many important results which had appeared in the interval. While many of these considered vital improvements in technique, such as Crowther's fast rotation function, their primary impact has been in the successful application of the rotation and translation function to the analysis of structurally related proteins. Indeed, it has given me deep satisfaction to observe that the molecular replacement concept, which I first proposed in 1960, is now accepted not only as theoretically feasible, but also as a useful tool in the examination of biological structure.

The additional papers are included in the appendix.

Michael G. Rossmann
Purdue University
Lafayette, Indiana
November, 1971

INTRODUCTION

Although W. L. Bragg, D. J. Bernal, M. F. Perutz, and others started their crystallographic investigation of proteins in the late 1930's, it was not until 1953 that Perutz demonstrated the power of the isomorphous replacement method (Green, Ingram, Perutz, 1954; Bragg and Perutz, 1954). The specific substitution of one amino acid residue in the asymmetric unit of the crystals of horse hemoglobin with a heavy-atom-containing organic group produced small but measurable differences in the diffraction pattern. Thus it became possible to determine phases of the protein structure factors. For the first time there was promise of an atom-by-atom structure determination of a complete protein, involving the positioning of thousands of atoms.

By mid 1969 at least ten different proteins have been solved, all by the isomorphous replacement method, and many more are likely to be solved in the near future. However in the summer of 1960 only two proteins had been solved: myoglobin at 2.0 Å resolution (Kendrew, Dickerson, Strandberg, Hart, Davies, Phillips, Shore, 1959) and hemoglobin at 5.5 Å resolution (Perutz, Rossmann, Cullis, Muirhead, Will, North, 1959). A number of other proteins were being studied but none had given up its secrets. The principal difficulty lay in the preparation of good single-site heavy atom derivatives. It was necessary either to make some advance in the alchemy used in the preparation of the derivatives or to find an alternative method if the two respiratory proteins were not to stand unchallenged for many years. Some handle was needed which was a natural property of these large molecules and which did not depend on some artificial device as is implied in the isomorphous replacement technique.

D. M. Blow and I had already shown that much could be done with only one heavy atom derivative (Blow and Rossmann, 1961), but the enormity of the impasse was still considerable. While discussing these problems with colleagues, at the time of the International Congress of Crystallography held in Cambridge in 1960, it occurred to me that both the ability of proteins to crystallize in different space groups and their frequent property of being made up of identically folded polypeptide chains might form a basis for an alternative process in the solution of the phase problem.

Many larger protein molecules are made of identical, or closely similar subunits. Plausible causes for such aggregates of the protein parts of virus structures were set out by Crick and Watson (1956) whose predictions have been amply confirmed in studies of spherical and rod-shaped viruses. The subunit building blocks of larger proteins are similarly restricted to sizes less than approximately 40,000 M.W. In hemoglobin (Muirhead, Cox, Mazzarella, Perutz, 1967 and Perutz, Muirhead, Cox, Goaman, 1968) and in lactate dehydrogenase (Adams et al, 1969) the interactions between the subunits have been shown to play a role in the function of the protein and control of biological activity (Monod, Changeux, and Wyman, 1965). Amino acid changes in the primary sequence of functionally similar proteins taken from differing species produce only minor structural alterations (Perutz, 1965; Scouloudi, 1969; Huber, Formanek, Epp, 1968), indicating that the evolution of divergent functions can occur without large changes in structure, or even that proteins with related functions converge to similar structures.

Molecular replacement utilizes the similarity or identity of structure in different parts of the crystallographic asymmetric unit caused by a repetition of the same subunit structure in the formation of a whole molecule. Molecular replacement may also utilize the relationship between differing crystal forms of the same or similar molecules. The problem divides itself into three parts for which reason the method has been referred to as "The Rocket." These stages are:

A. Determination of the relative orientation of the independent molecules, or subunits of molecules, within one crystal lattice or between different crystal forms. This may be done by a systematic inspection of the Patterson function(s), particularly in the region nearer the origin where there are more vectors arising from within subunits than vectors between subunits.

B. Given the relative orientation, the translation of the subunits must be determined with respect to designated crystallographic symmetry elements. Again this may be done by a systematic inspection of the Patterson(s). At the completion of stage A and B the exact equivalence between point $\underline{x}$ in the standard molecule or subunit and the point $\underline{x}'$ in any of the other subunits will be known and can be expressed as

$$\underline{x}' = [\underline{C}]\underline{x} + \underline{d}$$

where $[\underline{C}]$ is the rotation matrix determined in stage A and $\underline{d}$ is the translation vector determined in stage B. The above relationship will be true only within the volume U of the standard subunit.

C. Setting up and solving of the Molecular Replacement Equations. These equations represent the condition that, for the observed set of structure amplitudes, the electron density distribution within the volume U is identical in all subunits related by both crystallographic and non-crystallographic symmetry, and that it is zero or constant outside these volumes.

The occurrence of many identical structures not related by the crystal symmetry has given rise to the concept of "non-crystallographic symmetry." Its presence signals the possible application of the Molecular Replacement Method.

Crystallographic and non-crystallographic symmetry are differentiated by the property that an operator applies throughout the whole infinite crystal for the former, whereas a non-crystallographic symmetry element relates only to a localized volume within a crystal. For instance, in Figure 1 there are non-crystallographic two-fold axes in the plane of the paper valid only in the immediate vicinity of each line. However, the crystallographic two-fold axes perpendicular to the plane of the paper apply to every point within the crystal. Two types of non-crystallographic symmetry can occur. A "proper" element is independent of the sense of rotation. An example of this kind is a five-fold axis in a virus. Clearly a rotation of the crystal either left or right by one-fifth of a revolution will leave all parts of a given virus coat (but not the whole crystal) in equivalent positions. Improper rotation axes are found if two molecules are arbitrarily oriented in the same asymmetric unit or are in two entirely different crystal lattices. For instance, in Figure 2, the object A_1B_1 can be rotated by $+\theta$ about the axis at P to orient it identically with A_2B_2. However, the two objects will not be lined up after a rotation of A_1B_1 by $-\theta$ or of A_2B_2 by $+\theta$. It follows that any non-crystallographic operator that possesses an element of translation must be improper for, if it were proper, it must be a crystallographic translation.

The properties of a non-crystallographic rotation-translation element have been discussed in paper B1 by Rossmann, Blow, Harding, Coller (1964), where it is shown that only the component of translation parallel to the axis of rotation has a "precise" meaning. The two com-

Figure 1. Two-dimensional periodic design shows crystallographic two-fold axis perpendicular to the page and local non-crystallographic rotation axes in the plane of the paper.

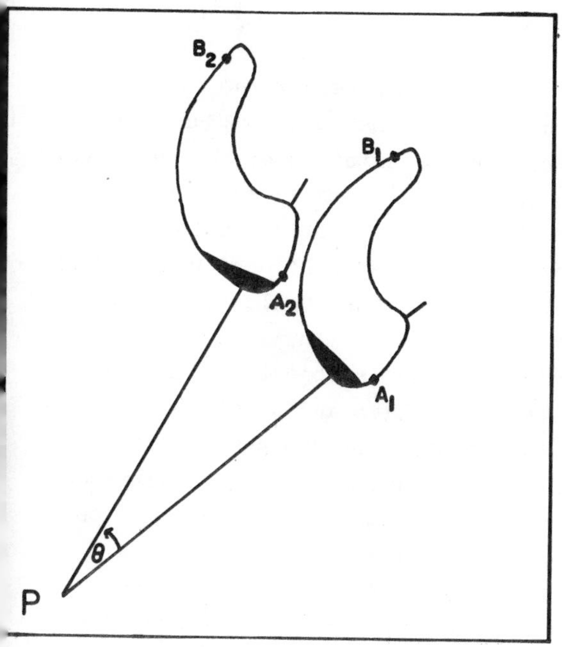

Figure 2. The objects A_1B_1 and A_2B_2 are related by an improper rotation θ, since it is necessary to consider the sense of rotation to achieve superposition of the two objects.

ponents perpendicular to the rotation axis are dependent on the arbitrary positioning of the axis, and can be defined only by the volumes within which the objects to be related are confined.

Proteins consist only of levo amino acids. The introduction of a mirror glide plane would produce dextro amino acids which is highly improbable. For this reason only rotations and translations of non-crystallographic symmetry operators are discussed in the papers included in this book. In the application of the method to non-biological materials, reflection planes will also have to be considered.

It was fortunate that, by the time I had formulated the general concepts of molecular replacement, I had also established a remarkable collaboration with D. M. Blow. His natural caution and skepticism caused me to put rigor into my derivations; his willing ear and astute criticisms gave me sufficient encouragment to proceed.

Encouragement came also from M. F. Perutz who first suggested to D. C. Hodgkin that the rotation function might determine the relative orientation of the two crystallographically independent molecules in rhombodhedral insulin. The peak in the ensuing rotation function of R3 insulin was most pronounced (paper D3) and was the beginning of a happy collaboration on the application of the molecular replacement method to insulin.

There were, however, formidable objections to the solution of the translation problem and possibly even greater obstacles in the solution of the phase problem. F. H. C. Crick was active in pointing out that the amount of translation required to superimpose two identical objects, after they had been similarly oriented, would depend on the position of the axis of rotation. How then could there be a unique solution of the translation problem at all? For a time this appeared to be an insurmountable hurdle, but gradually, as we considered the specific translation problem of R3 insulin, the difficulties became less formidable. Nevertheless, some of the biggest unsolved problems still lie in the determination of equivalent origins in differing crystal forms of equivalent molecular species; that is in the solution of the translation problem in the presence of improper non-crystallographic symmetry.

F. H. C. Crick and M. F. Perutz had in addition serious objections to the third stage, the solution of the phase problem. It had been pointed out that the information presented by identical subunits which were different crystallographically was similar to that obtained by sampling the reciprocal lattice at non-integral lattice points. The situation was indeed similar to the hemoglobin shrinkage stages investigated by Perutz (1952). When the sign of the molecular transform in the centric $h0\ell$ zone changes, then a discontinuity results in the plot of its magnitude. Since various shrinkage stages permitted the sampling of the transform's magnitude at points far closer than its anticipated minimum wave length, it became possible to determine the position of these discontinuities and hence the sign of the transform at every point. Crick pointed out that, in the more general non-centric case, there would be no discontinuities in the function $\sqrt{A^2 + B^2}$, as might be present separately in the real, A, or imaginary, B, parts. That is, even if the magnitude of a transform of a molecule is known at every point in space, Crick argued, the structure of the molecule could not be determined. These arguments were powerful, indeed sufficiently so that I found myself working alone for some time.

The first ideas were based on equating the electron density, ρ, at points in the asymmetric unit which were equivalent chemically. Thus, if the non-crystallographic relationship is expressed as (using the same notation as previously)

$$\underline{x}' = [\underline{C}]\underline{x} + \underline{d} \,,$$

then $$\rho(\underline{x}') = \rho(\underline{x}) \,.$$

Each side can be expressed as a Fourier summation where the unknowns are the phase angles, α_h. Hence

$$\sum_h |\underline{F}_h| \exp 2\pi i(\underline{h}.\underline{x}' - \alpha_h) = \sum_h |\underline{F}_h| \exp 2\pi i(\underline{h}.\underline{x} - \alpha_h).$$

As many equations of this type can be written as there are unknown phases to be determined. Each expresses the equality of electron density at a different pair of points $\underline{x}$ and $\underline{x}'$. The problem is then one of solving this non-linear system of equations for the unknown phases. In order to decide which points to select for setting up the observational equations, both a system based on the sampling of points covering the single molecule on a regular grid, and a system of selecting sufficient points from random number tables were employed. When neither of these processes worked it was felt that the lack of success might have been due to not sampling enough points. Therefore a very fine grid was employed next. This gave many more observational equations than there were unknown phases. These were normalized by a least squares procedure. From here it was only a small step to employ a continuous integration over the volume of one molecule (Rossmann and Blow, 1963, in paper C1). Yet no success was encountered in the solution of the equations.

The cause of failure was not in the physical content of the equations but in the method of their solution. All attempts so far had been based on separating real and imaginary parts and then solving these two families of equations separately for $\cos\alpha$ and $\sin\alpha$. Solutions arrived at in this way did not in general satisfy the condition $\cos^2\alpha + \sin^2\alpha = 1$. Others, in particular Main and Woolfson (1963), had also encountered the same problem. Crowther (1967), in paper C5, has shown that the cause lies with ill conditioning of equations of this type. Even more significant was that the structure amplitudes could be shown to cancel out altogether when these equations were derived by an analytical integration over the molecular volume.

In September, 1961, I spent a week of enforced meditation together with the family on the sunny beaches of Pembrokeshire, haunted by the problems I had tried to lay aside. The structure amplitudes cancelled out only when the real and imaginary parts of the equations were separated. Furthermore, the unknowns were not the two variables $\cos\alpha$ and $\sin\alpha$, but the single variable α. The kernel of an alternative technique of solution started to form itself in my mind. On returning to Cambridge, D. M. Blow permitted me to elaborate these thoughts to him over a cup of tea in a dingy café in Free School Lane. As usual, our joint discourse resulted in many improvements and within a month or two the first limited success had been encountered in solving a simple two-dimensional problem (paper C1). Nevertheless, we had not solved a protein and clearly many felt that time would have been better spent in tackling real problems by more certain techniques.

Attempts at applying the method to insulin and chymotrypsin were only partially successful. It was essential to try some other problems and in addition I now had the responsibility of creating my own laboratory. For a while I spent my time learning a little chemistry as a more certain approach to the problems of molecular biology.

Most of the derivations had only considered the special problem of two independent molecules per asymmetric unit in a given crystal. P. Main generalized the ideas contained in Appendix II of Rossmann and Blow (1963) (paper C1). The advantage of Main's equations was the insight obtained both by their simplicity and their generality, but the method of solution was still basically that conceived by D. M. Blow and myself. We were now convinced that, in general, there was a unique solution to problems of molecular replacement. Various hypothetical structures in space groups P1 and in R3 (as insulin) were set up and solved.

In the meantime, R. A. Crowther in Cambridge was reconsidering the application of linear algebra to the solution of the Molecular Replacement Equation (paper C5). He showed that the conditions of non-crystallographic symmetry were given by a family of solutions represented by the complex Eigen vectors of the equations' complex coefficients. The Eigen values were shown to lie in the range 0 to 1. Only those vectors whose values were close to unity fulfilled the necessary non-crystallographic conditions. Experimental error in measurement of structure amplitudes or representation of non-crystallographic symmetry permitted the acceptance of solutions slightly less than one. Suitable linear combinations of these solutions maintain not only the non-crystallographic symmetry but also approach the set of observed structure amplitudes. This technique, while still in its infancy, gives not only greater insight into the method of solution, but is surely far more powerful than the statistical devices employed by Blow, Main, and myself.

The success of Main and Crowther, the heightened interest in functional proteins whose biological activity frequently depends in part on communication between identical subunits, and advances in structural studies of viruses have created a lively interest in the Molecular Replacement Method. However, at the time of writing, the final test of the method, namely the solution of an unknown protein, still lies in the future. It may be hoped that the collection and editing into a single volume of the principal papers which together describe the Molecular Replacement Method will hasten a totally successful application.

The papers are arranged in four groups, A, B, C, and D. The first three groups A, B, and C correspond to the three stages of the method outlined earlier in this introduction. The last group, D, contains papers where a partial application of the method has been accomplished.

In concluding these remarks I would particularly like to express my gratitude to Mrs. Jill Dawes and Mrs. Angela Mott who so ably assisted me through the initial difficult years at Cambridge, to Dr. Aaron Klug whose words of encouragement and advice were most welcome, and to Dr. Patrick Tollin who helped stimulate my embryonic group at Purdue. The text has already made clear my debt to Drs. David M. Blow and Peter Main in their participation in this adventure and the warm encouragement given by Dr. Max F. Perutz and Prof. Dorothy C. Hodgkin. Thanks must also go to Mrs. Judy Jacobson for help in preparation of this volume. Finally I must make mention of my wife Audrey, who not only drew some of the diagrams, but also showed forbearance in the face of frequent nocturnal orgies with various computers.

References

Adams, M. J., Haas, D. J., Jeffery, B. A., McPherson, A. Jr., Mermall, H. L., Rossmann, M. G., Schevitz, R. W., Wonacott, A. J., J. Mol. Biol. (1969) 41, 159.

Blow, D. M., and Rossmann, M. G., Acta Cryst. (1961) 14, 1195.

Bragg, Sir L., and Perutz, M. F., Proc. Roy. Soc. (1954) A225, 315.

Crick, F. H. C., and Watson, J. D., Nature (1956) 177, 473.

Green, D. W., Ingram, V. M., and Perutz, M. F., Proc. Roy. Soc. (1954) A225, 287.

Huber, R., Formanek, M., Epp, O., Naturwissenschaften (1968) 55, 75; and (1969) 56, 362.

Kendrew, J. C., Dickerson, R. E., Strandberg, B., Hart, R. G., Davies, D. R., Phillips, D. C., and Shore, V. C., Nature (1959) 185, 422.

Main, P., and Woolfson, M. M., Acta Cryst. (1963) 16, 1046.

Monod, J., Changeux, J-P., Wyman, J., J. Mol. Biol. (1965) 12, 88.

Muirhead, H., Cox, J. M., Mazzarella, L., Perutz, M. F., J. Mol. Biol. (1967) 28, 117.

Perutz, M. F., Muirhead, H., Cox, J. M., Goaman, L. C. G., Nature (1968) 219, 131.

Perutz, M. F., Rossmann, M. G., Cullis, A. F., Muirhead, H., Will, W., and North, A. T. C., Nature (1959) 185, 416.

Perutz, M. F., Proc. Roy. Soc. (1952) 213A, 425.

Perutz, M. F., J. Mol. Biol. (1965) 13, 646.

Scouloudi, H., J. Mol. Biol. (1969) 40, 353.

THE ROTATION PROBLEM

A1. The Detection of Sub-Units within the Crystallographic Asymmetric Unit.
Rossmann, M. G., Blow, D. M., Acta Cryst. (1962) 15, 24.

A2. A Description of Various Rotation Function Programs.
Tollin, P., Rossmann, M. G., Acta Cryst. (1966) 21, 872.

A3. The Symmetry of the Rotation Function.
Tollin, P., Main, P., Rossmann, M. G., Acta Cryst. (1966) 20, 404.

A4. The Differential Rotation Function.
Sasada, Y., Acta Cryst. (1964) 17, 611.

A5. Vector Space Search and Refinement Procedures.
Nordman, C. E., Trans. Am. Cryst. Assoc. (1966) 2, 29.

A6. Programmed "Faltmolekül" Method.
Huber, R., In Crystallographic Computing Proc. (1969) Ed., F. R. Ahmed, Munksgaard, Copenhagen, p. 96.

A7. The Fast Rotation Function.
Crowther, R. A., Specially prepared for this volume. (1971).

A8. Optimal Sampling of the Rotation Function.
Lattman, E. E., Specially prepared for this volume. (1971).

PLEASE NOTE--Reprints of the above articles are on pages 43 to 74.

THE ROTATION PROBLEM

In the application of the Molecular Replacement Technique it is first necessary to determine the relative orientation of subunits either within the same crystal structure or between differing crystals. This may be done by a direct inspection of the Patterson (paper A5, Nordman, 1966) or by methods based on the Patterson but utilizing the original structure amplitudes instead of the Patterson calculated from these same amplitudes (paper A1, Rossmann and Blow, 1962). In all cases the basic concept is one of comparing Pattersons in different orientations to match the identical vector sets of variously oriented subunits.

Tollin and Cochran (1964) have described a two-dimensional search of a Patterson applicable to the case when a significant proportion of the structure is known to be roughly planar. The procedure determines planes of high vector density and thus locates the orientation of the plane in the unknown structure. Nordman and his co-workers (papers A5, D4, D5) compare the unknown Patterson with a point Patterson prepared on the basis of knowledge of at least part of the molecular structure. Both these methods are novel in that they systematically utilize known chemical information. Hoppe (1957), Huber (1965), and Huber and Hoppe (1965) have also developed a similar technique for searching the observed structure amplitudes with known molecular transforms.

Rossmann and Blow (paper A1, 1962) define the rotation function

$$R\ (\theta_1,\theta_2,\theta_3) = \int_U P_2(\underline{x}_2)\ P_1(\underline{x}_1)\ d\underline{x}_1$$

which compares any unknown Patterson P_1 to any other unknown Patterson P_2 within the volume U for a given set of rotation angles $\theta_1,\theta_2,\theta_3$. It is therefore the most general situation and one that will normally be encountered in the true application of the molecular replacement method.

Section 2 of the Rossmann and Blow 1962 paper contains the important mathematical procedure of evaluating the above function in terms of the structure amplitudes on which each of the two Pattersons are based. The derivation is more general than need be for the problem in hand, but only here is it written out in full detail. Similarly section 4 of the paper is the only place where we have a full treatment of the procedure for rotating two crystal systems relative to each other. These two sections of paper A1 thus contain the essence of many of the other papers in this volume and should be studied carefully. Various corrections to paper A1 are given in the appendix to paper A2.

While paper A2 contains no basic information which is not already present in A1, useful strategies in the application of the rotation function and preparation of a suitably program are discussed. It has been experienced that lack of attention to details has frequently led to poor results.

Section 7 of paper A1, an analysis of the symmetry of the rotation function, is amplified and generalized by Tollin, Main, and Rossmann, 1966 (paper A3). The rotation function can be plotted in terms of three suitable chosen angles. Clearly the function will repeat itself after integral increments of 2π in any angle. We therefore have a periodic function in three dimensions. The symmetry of each of the two Pattersons under comparison, together with the properties of the selected rotation variables, demand greater symmetry within the unit cell of the rotation function plot. While paper A1 considers these problems only for one special case, paper A3 develops an easy set of general rules which determine the "rotation space group. An interesting problem can arise under certain conditions which require a non-linear relationship between equivalent points in different asymmetric units. These difficulties are avoided if Eulerian angles are chosen except if one or both Pattersons have cubic symmetry. In any event, the prior determination of the angular ranges which determine the limits of the asymmetric unit of the rotation function will save much time. In addition checking for correct symmetry is a good test for gross errors. These symmetry considerations apply equally to Nordman's search procedures (paper A5).

A major difficulty in the application of any kind of rotational search procedure is that each point of the function has to be evaluated separately. Hence, the computation times are quite considerable. Strategies to reduce times are discussed by Tollin and Rossmann (paper A2, 1966), but a substantially different approach is given by Sasada (paper A4, 1964). He uses the slope of the rotation function to determine the position of the peak maximum by an iterative refinement procedure. Hence, provided a rough approximation to the rotation function is first computed from a few terms, each peak can then be explored quickly. Another approach is being developed by Crowther (private communication, 1969) who expands each Patterson in terms of spherical harmonics. In this form it is possible simultaneously to compute the contribution to all points in a plane of rotation space. Tollin (private communication, 1969) has used a sum function instead of the product implied in the rotation function for the case when one of the two structures can be expressed as a set of point vectors. This has yielded a ten-fold increase in speed with some improvement of contrast.

Nordman (paper A5, 1966) discusses the removal of the origin prior to any rotation search. This is unquestionably a useful procedure as has also been found by Burnett and Rossmann (1971), by Zwick (1969) who determines the orientation of α-helices in myoglobin, and by Lattman and Love (1970) who use an altered form of the rotation function to determine the orientation of lamprey hemoglobin given the structure of sperm whale myoglobin.

References

Burnett, R. M. and Rossmann, M. G., Acta Cryst. (1971) B27, 1378.

Hoppe, W., Elektrochem. (1957) 61, 1076.

Huber, R., Acta Cryst. (1965) 19, 353.

Huber, R., and Hoppe, W., Chem. Ber. (1965) 98, 2403.

Lattman, E., Love, W. E., Acta Cryst. (1970) B26, 1854.

Tollin, P., and Cochran, W., Acta Cryst. (1964) 17, 1322.

Zwick, M., Ph.D. Thesis, Massachusetts Institute of Technology, (1969).

THE TRANSLATION PROBLEM

B1. The Relative Positions of Independent Molecules within the Same Asymmetric Unit.
Rossmann, M. G., Blow, D. M., Harding, M. M., Coller, E., Acta Cryst. (1964) 17, 338.

B2. On the Determination of Molecular Location.
Tollin, P., Acta Cryst. (1966) 21, 613.

B3. A Method of Positioning a Known Molecule in an Unknown Crystal Structure.
Crowther, R. A., Blow, D. M., Acta Cryst. (1967) 23, 544.

B4. A Comparison of the Q-Functions and the Translation Function of Crowther and Blow.
Tollin, P., Acta Cryst. (1969) A25, 376.

PLEASE NOTE--Reprints of the above articles are on pages 75 to 92.

THE TRANSLATION PROBLEM

The largest unsolved problem of the Molecular Replacement Method lies in the determination of the translation vector between two molecules related by an improper non-crystallographic symmetry rotation, as may occur if there are two or more independent molecules per asymmetric unit in one crystal structure. A possible approach is discussed by Rossmann et al (paper B1, 1964) under the paragraph heading "General rotation," but it would seem unlikely that there is much power in this technique. The problem also occurs if the same molecule has crystallized in different crystal forms as might be the case for an enzyme extracted from a variety of differing species. Luckily it is probable that the Molecular Replacement Technique will be most useful when one molecule contains many identical subunits whose symmetry relationships are likely to be pure rotations (Monod, Changeaux, Wyman, 1965).

The methods separate themselves, as they also did for the rotation problem, into two classes: one where none of the molecular structure is known (paper B1) and a second where some or all of the molecular configuration may be assumed (papers B2, B3, and B4). In both classes the relative orientation of the molecules must first be established. While we are only truly interested in the first class for the Molecular Replacement Technique, nevertheless the similarity of so many protein structures has stimulated the use of the first two stages of the method for the solution of related structures, where a good approximation to the unknown structure is already at hand. Such techniques have been used by Tollin (1969) to relate seal and sperm whale myoglobin and by Lattman and Love (1970) to compare lamprey hemoglobin with myoglobin. Muirhead, Cox, Mazzarella, Perutz (1967) applied similar techniques to relate the known structures of reduced and oxy-hemoglobin.

Tollin (paper B2, 1966) and Crowther and Blow (paper B3, 1967) each develop apparently independent methods for solving the translation problem when the structure of the molecule, or a significant part of the molecule, is already known. Tollin (paper B4, 1969), however shows these two methods to be virtually identical. Nordman (paper A5, 1966) has also a rather similar approach but he develops a simultaneous refinement procedure to improve his fitting model. It has been observed (Burnett and Rossmann, 1971) that Tollin's Q function can give poor results if the model is inaccurate although not false. Hence Nordman's refinement procedures may be rather important.

Rossmann et al (paper B1, 1964) give a rather cumbersome derivation of the translation function. The following derivation is both more general and lends more insight. We shall follow the procedure and notation of paper A1.

Let us compare a volume around the point $\underline{S}$ in the periodic function $\rho_1(\underline{x})$ with an equivalent region around $\underline{S}'$ in the function $\rho_2(\underline{x}')$. Since $\underline{S}$ and $\underline{S}'$ are said to be related by non-crystallographic symmetry, it follows from (1) of paper A1 that $\underline{S}' = [\underline{C}]\underline{S}+\underline{d}$. Now we can define the translation function as

$$T(\underline{S},\underline{S}') = \int_U \rho_1(\underline{x})\cdot\rho_2(\underline{x}')\, d\underline{x}$$

where T is a six-variable function given by each of the three scalars that define $\underline{S}$ and $\underline{S}'$. Following the same procedure as in paper A1 and substituting Fourier summations for $\rho_1(\underline{x})$ and $\rho_2(\underline{x}')$ we have

$T(\underline{S},\underline{S}') =$

$$\frac{1}{V^2}\sum_h\sum_p |F_h|\cdot|F_p| \exp\left[i(\alpha_h+\alpha_p-2\pi\underline{p}.\underline{d})\right]\cdot\left\{\int_U \exp\left[-2\pi i(\underline{h}+\underline{p}[\underline{C}])\right].\underline{x}.d\underline{x}\right\}$$

Expression (5) of paper A1 shows that the integral in brac[kets] may be written as $G_{hp}\exp\left[-2\pi i(\underline{h}+\underline{p}[\underline{C}]).\underline{S}.\right]$ if the volume U is bounded by a surface whose center of symmetry is at $\underline{S}$. Hence,

$$T(\underline{S},\underline{S}') = \frac{1}{V^2}\sum_h\sum_p |F_h|\cdot|F_p|\,G_{hp}\exp\left[i\left\{\alpha_h+\alpha_p-2\pi\left\langle\underline{h}.\underline{S}+\underline{p}.\left([\underline{C}].\underline{S}+\underline{d}\right)\right\rangle\right\}\right] ,$$

$$\text{or } T(\underline{S},\underline{S}') = \frac{1}{V^2}\sum_h\sum_p |F_h|\cdot|F_p|\,G_{hp}\exp\left[i\left\{\alpha_h+\alpha_p-2\pi(\underline{h}.\underline{S}+\underline{p}.\underline{S}')\right\}\right]$$

By application of Friedel's Law we have

$$T(\underline{S},\underline{S}') = \frac{2}{V^2}\sum_h\sum_p |F_h|\cdot|F_p|\cdot G_{hp}\cos\left\{\alpha_h+\alpha_p-2\pi(\underline{h}.\underline{S}+\underline{p}.\underline{S}')\right\} .$$

If we can reduce this expression to one of only three variables then it is possible to explore these by means of a normal Fourier program.

If the position of a non-crystallographic two-fold ax[is] is to be found, then paper B1 (see Figure 3) shows that it is necessary to compare a volume in the Patterson at $\underline{S}$ wit[h] one (after rotation) at $-\underline{S}'$. That is $\underline{S} = -\underline{S}'$. Hence the translation function becomes

$$T(\underline{S}) = \frac{2}{V^2}\sum_h\sum_p F_h^2\,F_p^2\,G_{hp}\cos\left\{2\pi(\underline{h}-\underline{p}).\underline{S}\right\},$$

which is expression (8) of paper B1. Alternatively, if we wish to find the position of a two-fold axis in real space then T will be large when $\underline{S} = \underline{S}'$, and represent the locus of points on the two-fold axis. In this case

$$(\underline{S}) = \frac{2}{V^2} \sum_h \sum_p |F_h| \cdot |F_p| \; G_{hp} \cos\{\alpha_h + \alpha_p - 2\pi(\underline{h}+\underline{p}).\underline{S}\} .$$

imilar results may be obtained in real space by fixing he value of $\underline{S}'$ and allowing $\underline{S}$ to move. This function as employed by Blow et al (paper D2, 1964, Figure 7). inally the function can be reduced to the rotation unction since $\alpha_h = \alpha_p = 0$ for the Pattersons and as $= \underline{S}' = 0$ for the volumes under comparison.

---

ote these corrections to paper B1:

p. 340, expression before eq. 8.: $2\pi i$ is omitted.
3 lines and 4 lines before eq. 8.: $G_{h,p}$ and $\Omega_{h,p}$ (commas to separate h and p had been omitted, contrary to the notation of this paper).
expression after eq. 8. should read:

$$\sum_{\underline{p}} F^2_{\underline{H}+\underline{p}} \; F^2_{\underline{p}} \; G_{\underline{H}+\underline{p},\underline{p}}$$

p. 341, similar expression should have $\underline{H} + \underline{p}$ subscripts.

p. 342, 4th line, expression should read

$$m_{\underline{p}} = -\frac{U'}{V}.G_{\underline{p},0}$$

Condition of summation in expression (10) should be $\underline{p} \neq 0$.

References

Burnett, R. M., and Rossmann, M. G. Acta Cryst. (1971) B27, 137

Lattman, E. E., and Love, W. E., Acta Cryst. (1970), B26, 1854.

Monod, J., Changeux, J-P., Wyman, J., J. Mol. Biol. (1965) 12, 88.

Muirhead, M., Cox, J. M., Mazzarella, L., Perutz, M. F., J. Mol. Biol. (1967) 28, 117.

Tollin, P., J. Mol. Biol., (1969) Acta Cryst. (1969) A25, 376.

THE MOLECULAR REPLACEMENT EQUATIONS AND THEIR SOLUTIONS

1. The Determination of Phases by the Conditions of Non-Crystallographic Symmetry.
Rossmann, M. G., Blow, D. M., Acta Cryst. (1963) 16, 39.

2. Solution of the Phase Equations Representing Non-Crystallographic Symmetry.
Rossmann, M. G., Blow, D. M., Acta Cryst. (1964) 17, 1474.

3. Relationships among Structure Factors due to Identical Molecules in Different Crystallographic Environments.
Main, P., Rossmann, M. G., Acta Cryst. (1966) 21, 67.

4. Phase Determination Using Non-Crystallographic Symmetry.
Main, P., Acta Cryst. (1967) 23, 50.

5. A Linear Analysis of the Non-Crystallographic Symmetry Problem.
Crowther, R. A., Acta Cryst. (1967) 22, 758.

6. Applications of the Molecular Replacement Equations to the Heavy Atom Technique.
Rossmann, M. G., Acta Cryst. (1967) 23, 173.

7. The Use of Non-Crystallographic Symmetry for Phase Determination.
Crowther, R. A., Acta Cryst. (1969) B25, 2571.

PLEASE NOTE--Reprints of the above articles are on pages 93 to 125

THE MOLECULAR REPLACEMENT EQUATIONS AND THEIR SOLUTION

Some of the historical development of this section has already been related in the introduction. Paper C1 (Rossmann and Blow, 1963) represents the first success in deriving and solving conditions which impose non-crystallographic symmetry on the phases. Section 2 of this pape sets up a series of conditions based on finding phases which maximize the function $\int_U \rho(\underline{x}) . \rho(x').d\underline{x}$. Appendix II of the same paper strengthens these conditions by showing that partial sums of the function to be minimized must be proportional to corresponding structure factors. Paper C (Main and Rossmann, 1966) generalizes this approach. The equation (10) gives for the first time the Molecular Replacement Equations in the completely general form

$$|\underline{F}_p| \exp\{i\alpha_p\} = \frac{U}{V}\sum_h |\underline{F}_h| \exp\{i\alpha_h\} \sum_{n=1}^{N} G_{hpn} \exp\{2\pi i(\underline{p}.\underline{S}_n - \underline{h}.$$

The N identical subunits centered at $\underline{S}_n$ (n=1,2...N) are related by crystallographic and non-crystallographic symmetry to the standard subunit at $\underline{S}$. A series of appen dices to paper C3 formally demonstrate that these equatio obey all normal crystallographic requirements. Another derivation of basically the same set of equations is give by Crowther (1967) in paper C4. The summation over N can be completely evaluated subject to the availability of al necessary rotation matrices and translation vectors. Hence, we can simplify the appearance of the Molecular Replacement Equations to the form

$$\underline{F}_p = \sum_h \underline{H}_{hp} \underline{F}_h$$

where the elements $\underline{H}_{hp}$ of the complex matrix $[\underline{H}]$ are all known. Crowther (paper C5) shows that the matrix $[\underline{H}]$ is ermitian about its leading diagonal (i.e. $\underline{H}_{pr} = \underline{H}^*_{pr}$).

Although the computing and storage of the elements of atrix [$\underline{H}$] is time consuming and requires large amounts of omputer storage, there is no basic difficulty. The real roblem is the finding of a good method for solving these on-linear equations for the phase angles α_h and α_p. Two rincipal techniques have been devised. The first is an ntuitive procedure based on the physical properties of the lements of matrix [$\underline{H}$]. Due to the rapid convergence of he G_{hp} function only the elements with $\underline{h} \simeq \underline{p}$ can attain ny significant amplitude. Hence each equation can be xpressed in terms of only a few relatively large coeffi- ients which themselves can be arranged in a rapidly de- reasing sequence of amplitude. A first crude approxima- ion can be made by neglecting all but the largest coeffi- ient. Other terms can gradually be included as the phase f the corresponding structure factors becomes known. The hole process must be initiated from the center of recip- ocal space where the F(000) has the known phase of 0°. he probability of each phase determination is considered n section 4 of paper C1 and again more elegantly in paper 2 (Rossmann and Blow, 1964). The method is again describ- d in paragraph 2 of paper C4 (Main, 1967) where the con- ept of intermediate cycles of refinement of the current hase solution is also introduced. After each such refine- ent knowledge of the phases is extended further into eciprocal space.

The intuitive procedure was shown to work well in two paper C3, 1964) and in three (paper C4, 1967) dimensions rovided a sufficient number of identical subunits were resent. Application to rhombohedral insulin and to α- hymotrypsin (see papers D2 and D3) did not produce useful esults presumably because only two identical subunits were resent in either case. Attempts at utilizing the relation- hip between the two types of rhombohedral insulin forms escribed in paper D3 failed due to an inability to solve the translation problem relating the insulin monomers wit in these two forms. Crowther (1969) also arrives at the conclusion that non-crystallographic symmetry can be a sufficient constraint to yield useful phase information when the ratio (nU/V) is sufficiently small. Here n is th number of crystallographically equivalent units, U is the volume of one subunit and V the volume of the unit cell. His discussion supersedes that of the last section in pap C5 starting with the paragraph "To discover the informati content...", Crowther (1969) suggests that (nU/V) should probably be at least less than 0.18 for a successful solution. However, Main (paper C4) solved a three-dimensional problem for which this ratio was 0.185 and Main and Rossmann (paper C3) solved a one-dimensional problem with (nU/V) equal to 0.28 without finding the false minima reported by Crowther (1969).

An elegant alternative approach has been outlined by Crowther (1967) in paper C5 based on the techniques of linear algebra. His results have already been summarized in the introduction. The major advantage in his method is that the necessity of dealing with probabilities is avoid and that some insight is obtained into the uniqueness of the solution under given conditions. Two major problems must, however, be considered: (i) the computing time of determining the eigenvectors of complex matrices of dimensions of some thousands is prohibitive and (ii) the subsequent determination of the relatively few scalars, μ, used as weights in combining a selected set of eigenvecto remains a non-linear problem. Nevertheless, the elegance of Crowther's method is so intriguing that it will be advantageous to consider techniques to surmount these two problems. Crowther (1969) compares and contrasts the power of these two methods.

It can be shown (see Main, paper C4) that either method of solution will lead to results similar to successive averaging of electron density in real space. An xample of the latter procedure was used by Muirhead, Cox, azzarella, and Perutz (1967). A roughly recognizable lectron density distribution of reduced human hemoglobin ad been obtained by the method of isomorphous replacement. he molecular two-fold axis does not coincide with a rystallographically two-fold axis in these crystals. ence, the electron density distribution was improved by veraging between the two independent molecular halves ithin the selected molecular boundary. An advantage of he real space approach is that the molecular boundary need ot be a simple geometrical shape. The averaged density an then be used to calculate structure factors whose hases are combined with the observed amplitudes to compute he electron density distribution for the next cycle of efinement. The calculated and observed structure amplitudes may be used to define an R factor (paper C2 and rowther, 1969) as a measure of the rate of progress of efinement.

In the initial stages of solving the molecular replaceent equations care must be taken in selecting only one of he two possible enantiomorphs and only one of a number of ifferent possible origins. In some cases the problem can e avoided by selecting an asymmetric distribution of olecular envelopes centered at $\underline{S}_i$ (i=1,2,3...n). If this s feasible then the envelope arrangement has itself aleady designated the desired choice of hand and origin. he examples given in papers C3 and C5 are of this kind. f a more symmetric envelope arrangement has had to be hosen, then the equations will be satisfied by one of a umber of different solutions corresponding to different nantiomorphs or origin selections of the same structure. hese have to be differentiated by the initial arbitrary election of the phase of well chosen structure factors.

If the non-crystallographic symmetry elements are roper, it may be more convenient to define a single enelope around the whole structure instead of around each monomer. In this way it is possible to avoid the selectio of a surface between monomers, a division which can only have chemical but no geometrical significance. Provided the sum of the structures confined by the monomer envelopes equals the structure within the polymer envelope the equations can be shown to be identical.

In principle it has thus been shown that the Molecula Replacement Method is workable in each of its three stages Obstacles which may be encountered in an application are discussed in section 4 of paper C4 (Main, 1967). Mention should also be made of one of the principal objections raised by critics when the method was first proposed, that is the exact equivalence of non-crystallographically relat ed molecules. These will have different environments whic may cause significant surface perturbations of the molecul and in turn may cause alterations of more deeply buried structure. That this is not the case for α-chymotrypsin has been demonstrated by Sigler, Blow, Matthews, Henderson (1968) where no significant structural changes between the two crystallographically independent molecules have yet been observed (Blow, 1969). On the other hand, insulin at 3.0Å resolution reveals some structural changes between th two independent monomers in the crystallographic asymmetri unit (Dodson, 1969 private communication).

Many problems in crystallography can be reduced to equations of the type $\underline{F}_h = [\underline{H}][\underline{F}]$. A study of techniques for solving these non-linear equations is therefore likely to be rewarding and may also have some bearing on the solution of Sayre's equations (1952), although they are in a somewhat different form. A further example of an application is presented in paper C6 (Rossmann, 1967). Here is derived a set of equations expressing the relationship between structure amplitudes and known (heavy atom) positions. Refinement of an approximate set of phases, based on the known structural information, to satisfy these equations should yield the correct electron density of the emaining unknown structure. No search for chemically eaningful peaks in successive electron density maps will hen be required. A similar procedure of phase refinement n the presence of molecular symmetry has been discussed y Maslen (1968). Pawley (1969) reverses the procedure y retaining identity between different parts of the rystallographic asymmetric unit during least squares re-inement.

References

low, D. M., (1969) Private communication.

rowther, R. A., Acta Cryst. (1969) B25, 2571.

aslen, E. N., Acta Cryst. (1968) B24, 1165.

uirhead, H., Cox, J. M., Mazzarella, L., Perutz, M. F., J. Mol. Biol. (1967) 28, 117.

awley, G. S., Acta Cryst. (1969) A25, 531.

ayre, D., Acta Cryst. (1952) 5, 60.

igler, P. B., Blow, D. M., Matthews, B. W., Henderson, R., J. Mol. Biol. (1968) 35, 143.

APPLICATIONS

D1. The Relative Orientation of Molecules of Crystallize Human and Horse Oxyhaemoglobin.
Prothero, J. W., Rossmann, M. G., Acta Cryst. (1964) 17, 768.

D2. The Arrangement of α-Chymotrypsin Molecules in the Monoclinic Crystal Form.
Blow, D. M., Rossmann, M. G., Jeffery, B. A., J. Mol. Biol. (1964) 8, 65.

D3. The Crystal Structure of Insulin. Evidence for a 2-fold Axis in Rhombohedral Zinc Insulin.
Dodson, E., Harding, M. M., Hodgkin, D. C., Rossmann M. G., J. Mol. Biol. (1966) 16, 227.

D4. Interpretations of the Patterson Function of Crystal Containing a Known Molecular Fragment. The Structure of an Alstonia Alkaloid.
Nordman, C. E., Nakatsu, K., J. Am. Chem. Soc. (1963) 85, 353.

D5. The Structure of Villalstonine.
Nordman, C. E., Kumra, S. K., J. Am. Chem. Soc. (196 87, 2059.

D6. Application of Patterson Methods to the Solution of Molecular Crystal Structures Containing a Known Rigid Group.
Harrison, H. R., Joynson, M. A., Acta Cryst. (1970) A26, 692.

D7. The Determination of the Crystal Structure of Trans- 4-Dihydroxy-2, 4-Dimethyl-Cyclohexane-trans-1-Acetic Acid-γ-Lactone, $C_{10}H_{16}O_3$, Using Rotation and Translation Functions in Reciprocal Space.
Burnett, R. M., Rossmann, M. G., Acta Cryst. (1971) B27, 1378.

D8. Determination of the Orientation and Position of the Myoglobin Molecule in the Crystal of Seal Myoglobin.
Tollin, P., J. Mol. Biol. (1969) 45, 481.

D9. A Rotational Search Procedure for Detecting a Known Molecule in a Crystal.
Lattman, E. E., Love, W. E., Acta Cryst. (1970) B26, 1854.

D10. Crystallographic Evidence for the Tetrameric Subunit Structure of L-Asparaginase from Escherichia coli.
Epp, O., Steigemann, W., Formanek, H., Huber, R., Eur. J. Biochem. (1971) 20, 432.

D11. Structure of Yellow Fin Tuna Metmyoglobin at 6Å Resolution.
Lattman, E. E., Nockolds, C. E., Kretsinger, R. H.
Love, W. E., J. Mol. Biol. (1971) 60, 271.

D12. Low-resolution Studies on the Relationship between the Triclinic and Tetragonal Forms of Lysozyme.
Joynson, M. A., North, A. C. T., Sarma, V. R., Dickerson, R. E., Steinrauf, L. K., J. Mol. Biol. (1970) 50, 137.

D13. An X-ray Crystallographic Study of Dematallized Concanavalin A.
Jack, A., Weinzierl, J., Kalb, A. J., J. Mol. Biol. (1971) 58, 389.

D14. Subunit Structure of Aldolase: Chemical and Crystallographic Evidence.
Eagles, P. A. M., Johnson, L. N., Joynson, M. A., McMurray, C. H., Gutfreund, H., J. Mol. Biol. (1969) 45, 533.

PLEASE NOTE--Reprints of the above articles are on pages 127 to 164.

APPLICATIONS

The first major success of the rotation function was in determining the relationship of the two independent insulin molecules in the rhombohedral modification (Dodsor et al, 1966, paper D3). The subsequent development and application of the translation function showed that insuli aggregates as a hexamer with point symmetry 32. Possible modes of arrangement of the monomers in such a hexamer are discussed in section 3 of this paper but pure rotations without translations are preferred. This has recently been confirmed by an isomorphous replacement solution of R3 insulin to 3.0 Å (Hodgkin, 1969, private communication). A similar hexameric aggregate can also be shown to exist in $P2_1$ insulin which contains six independent insulin mon- omers per asymmetric unit. The editor of these papers computed a rotation function for this form of insulin base on data collected by G. Ferguson and D. Hodgkin. Figures and 2 are plots of the rotation function onto stereograms when the Patterson has been rotated by 180° and 120° re- spectively. In order to save time the function was first evaluated with only 10 Å data and then the major peaks we explored with 6 Å data. These results are superimposed in Figures 1 and 2. Figure 3 shows the Laue point group arrangement of non-crystallographic symmetry elements in monoclinic insulin. A further rotation function, not sho here, verified that the Pattersons of R3 insulin and $P2_1$ insulin are indeed very similar when the crystallographic three-fold axis of R3 insulin is superimposed on one of th non-crystallographic three-fold axes in $P2_1$ insulin.

The second application of the rotation and translati functions was in the work on α-chymotrypsin (Blow et al, 1964, paper D2) where there are again two independent

MONOCLINIC INSULIN K=180° R=30A

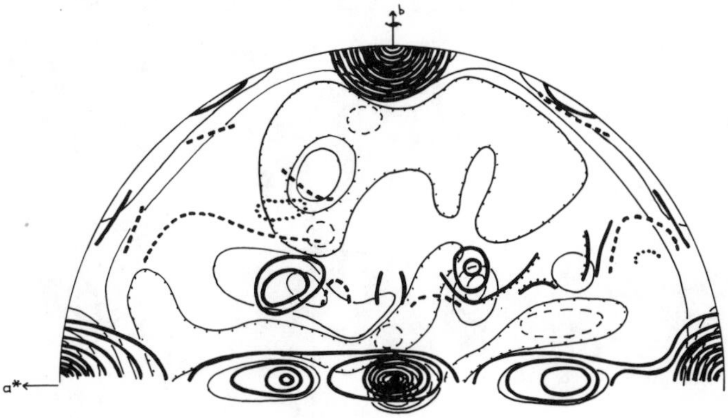

Figure 1

MONOCLINIC INSULIN K=240° R=30A

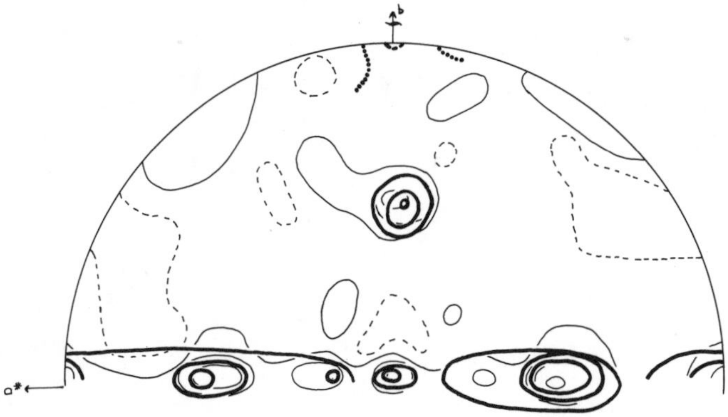

Figure 2

Figures 1 and 2. Rotation functions of $P2_1$ insulin shown as stereograms for rotations of $\kappa = 180°$ and 240°. Data limited to 10 Å (thin lines) was used to search the whole function while complete 6 Å data (thick contours) was used only to explore higher regions of the rotation function with more care.

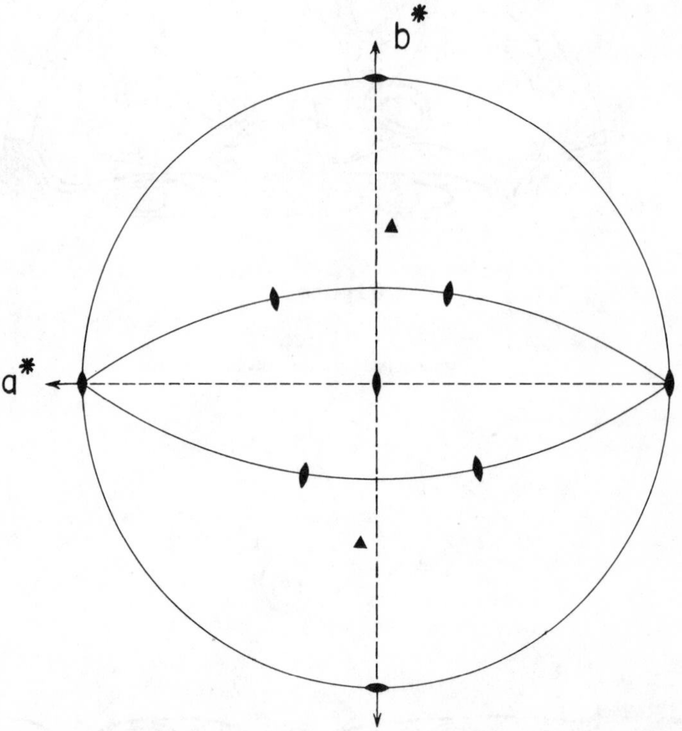

Figure 3. Stereographic representation of non-crystallographic and crystallographic symmetry elements for $P2_1$ insulin.

molecules per asymmetric unit. A rather special position of the non-crystallographic diad caused some special difficulties (Fig. 5 of paper D2) which were not anticipated in the theory of the translation function. A systematic investigation of the conditions under which such problems arise is lacking. The relationship between the two independent chymotrypsin molecules was fully confirmed later (Sigler, Blow, Matthews, Henderson, 1969). An endeavour to apply molecular replacement to the 6 Å data of α-chymotrypsin failed because the method itself had not been sufficiently developed and also the nature of the structure of proteins was not well enough understood at that time.

Paper D1 (Prothero and Rossmann, 1964) shows an application to relate molecules of the same protein from different species, a problem which will occur with increasing frequency as our structural knowledge of proteins increases. An improvement on the method used in this paper would have been to compute a new "synthetic" horse oxyhemoglobin Patterson based on its known structure in a sufficiently large unit cell to avoid overlap of self-Pattersons at neighboring origins (Burnett and Rossmann, 1971). Alternatively, J. Cox (private communication, 1969) has compared the orientation and position of these hemoglobin molecules in real space by exploring its rotation about the two-fold axis and translation along this axis. When phases were subsequently computed, based on the known molecule correctly placed in the unknown cell, the heavy atoms of a certain derivative could be positioned.

Lattman and Love (1970) have recently used a slightly modified rotation function to compare the unknown lamprey hemoglobin with known whale myoglobin structure. Tollin (1969) has used in succession the rotation and Q functions to determine the structure of seal myoglobin. His results can be compared with Scouloudi's (1969) isomorphous replacement work. A comparison of real space and reciprocal space rotation search procedures has been made in determining the unknown triclinic lysozyme given the known tetragonal structure (Joynson, North, Sarma, 1969). It should be emphasized that a real space search can only be made in a triclinic cell where there are no translation problems relative to symmetry elements.

Brew, Vanaman, and Hill (1967) have shown, on the basis of sequence homology and structural consistency, that α-lactalbumin is probably similar in structure to lysozyme. Support for these conclusions has now come in an interesting application of the rotation function by Joynson and North (Phillips, 1969, private communication). It was first shown that the relationship between the two independent goat α-lactalbumin molecules in their own cell is a non-crystallographic diad. Subsequently a systematic comparison of calculated structure amplitudes based on the known lysozyme structure with the unknown α-lactalbumin structure amplitudes showed pairs of orientations in which a good fit was obtained. These orientations are consistent with the two, diad related, α-lactalbumin molecules.

Eagles et al (1969) applied the rotation function to show that the molecular symmetry of the subunit arrangement in aldolase is most probably 222. The significance of such symmetry was reviewed in the introduction.

Nordman's method (see paper A5) is equally useful for determining the orientation of known groups in unknown cells, particularly if atomic resolution data is available. The power of his method is demonstrated in papers D4 and D5. In the latter paper his search group consisted of only 11 out of a total of 48 non-hydrogen atoms. In unpublished work both he and Zwick claim to have determined the orientations of the α-helices in myoglobin by the use of the Nordman technique and the rotation function respectively.

Application of rotational and translational search procedures to smaller molecules, apart from the two Nordman papers D4 and D5, are fairly numerous.

Palmer, and Dickerson (1964) determined the orientation of the chromophore in actinomycin by means of the rotation function. Burnett and Rossmann (1971) determined the orientation and position of a known molecular fragment which was then used for phasing the structure factors. Tollin and his collaborators have published numerous results of the use of the $I(\theta,\phi)$ function in tandem with the Q function to determine the orientation and position of known molecular planes, respectively (Tollin and Munns, 1969; Tollin, Wilson and Young, 1968; Watson, Sutor and Tollin, 1965; Young, Tollin and Sutherland, 1968; Young, Tollin and Wilson, 1969).

References

Blow, D. M., Biochem. J. (1969) 112, 261.

Brew, K., Vanaman, T. C., Hill, R. L., J. Biol. Chem. (1967) 242, 3747.

Burnett, R. M., and Rossmann, M. G., Acta Cryst. (1971) B27, 1378.

Eagles, P. A. M., Johnson, L. N., Joynson, M. A., McMurray, C. H., Gutfreund, H. (1972) in preparation.

Joynson, M. A., North, A. T. C., Sarma, V. R., Dickerson, R. E., Steinrauf, L. K., J. Mol. Biol. (1970) 50, 137.

Lattman, E. E., and Love, W. E., Acta Cryst. (1970) B26, 1854.

Palmer, H. T., Palmer, R. A., and Dickerson, R. E., Nature (1964) 202, 1052.

Sigler, P. B., Blow, D. M., Matthews, B. W., Henderson, R., J. Mol. Biol. (1968) 35, 143.

Scouloudi, H., J. Mol. Biol. (1969) 40, 353.

Tollin, P., J. Mol. Biol. (1969) 45, 481.

Tollin, P., and Munns, A. R. I., Nature (1969) 222, 1170.

Tollin, P., Wilson, H. R., and Young, D. W., Nature (1968) 217, 1148.

Watson, D. G., Sutor, D. J., and Tollin, P., Acta Cryst. (1965) 19, 111.

Young, D. W., Tollin, P., and Sutherland, H. H., Acta Cryst. (1968) B24, 161.

Young, D. W., Tollin, P., and Wilson, H. R., Acta Cryst. (1969) B25, 1423.

A. THE ROTATION PROBLEM

Reprinted from *Acta Crystallographica*, Vol. 15, Part 1, January 1962

Acta Cryst. (1962). **15**, 24

The Detection of Sub-Units Within the Crystallographic Asymmetric Unit

BY MICHAEL G. ROSSMANN AND D. M. BLOW

M. R. C. Unit for Molecular Biology, Cavendish Laboratory, Cambridge, England

The number of structurally identical units within one unit cell often exceeds the number of general positions. The angular relationships between any two units, not related by space-group symmetry, can be found by rotating the Patterson function until the rotated and original Patterson functions are brought into maximum coincidence. For such a rotation, the rotation function

$$R = \sum_{\mathbf{h}} [|F_{\mathbf{h}}|^2 \{\sum_{\mathbf{p}} |F_{\mathbf{p}}|^2 G\}]$$

has a maximum value. G is an interference function which has large values only when the point **p** in reciprocal space is brought close to **h** by the rotation.

Application of the R function to horse haemoglobin gives a dominant peak that corresponds accurately to the relative orientation of the α and β chains.

Evidence is accumulating that many of the larger protein molecules are made up of identical, or closely similar sub-units. The reasons for expecting this for the protein part of virus structures were set out by Crick & Watson (1956), and the prediction has been amply confirmed in crystallographic studies of spherical viruses (Caspar, 1956; Finch & Klug, 1959; Klug & Finch, 1960; Magdoff, 1960) and of one rod-shaped virus (Watson, 1954; Franklin & Holmes, 1958). Harrison (1959) has given crystallographic evidence that the large protein, ferritin, is made up of a number of sub-units. By far the most remarkable example, however, is haemoglobin (Perutz *et al.*, 1960). Although this protein has four polypeptide chains, four times the molecular weight and exactly four times the iron content of the related protein myoglobin, chemical evidence showed that there were two distinct kinds of polypeptide chain and that their composition was quite different from that of myoglobin. It was therefore a surprise, (strongly supporting the view that the spatial configuration of a protein is important) to find that the haemoglobin molecule consisted of four similar units, each very like the myoglobin molecule as determined by Kendrew and his collaborators (Bodo *et al.* (1959)), and arranged in a roughly tetrahedral manner. It may be noted that in every case referred to above, the sub-unit has a molecular weight of the order $2 \,.\, 10^4$.

While the viruses represent examples of exact but non-crystallographic symmetry of the independent particles (e.g. five-fold rotation symmetry and non-integral screw operations), the haemoglobin structure may be said to have partial, approximate symmetry. The symmetry is approximate as the two chains are chemically distinct, and to a small extent they have different configuration. Moreover the operation which superimposes one chain on to another, does not necessarily superimpose the other back on to the first, so that this symmetry operation, which is only satisfied by a part of the molecule, is called partial.

In this paper we describe how we have detected the existence of this partial, approximate symmetry from a knowledge of the intensities alone. The effect of non-crystallographic symmetry, whether partial or total, results in decreasing the size of the structure to be determined, while the number of observable intensities remains the same. This 'redundancy' in information might be used to help solve a structure. Also, the ideas presented here are as applicable to finding the relationship between similar molecules in different crystal lattices, as they are to finding the relative orientation of molecules (or sub-units within a molecule) in the same crystal lattice.

1. The rotation of Patterson syntheses

Consider a structure of two identical units which are in different orientations. The Patterson function of such a structure consists of three parts. There will be the self-Patterson vectors of one unit, being the set of interatomic vectors which can be formed within that unit, with appropriate weights. The set of self-Patterson vectors of the other unit will be identical, but they will be rotated from the first due to the different orientation. Finally, there will be the cross-Patterson vectors, or set of interatomic vectors which can be formed from one unit to another. The self-Patterson vectors of the two units will all lie in a volume extending from the origin by the overall dimensions of the units. Some or all of the cross-Patterson vectors will lie outside this volume.

Suppose the Patterson function is now superposed on a rotated version of itself. There will be no particular agreement except when one set of self-Patterson vectors of one unit has the same orientation as the self-Patterson vectors from the other unit. In this position, we would expect a maximum of agreement or 'overlap' between the two.

These ideas have often been used by workers

looking for evidence about the orientation of symmetrical groups like benzene rings in simple structures. Perutz *et al.* (1955) used similar considerations for predicting a structural resemblance between reduced human haemoglobin and horse methaemoglobin.

In § 2 an expression will be developed which allows the overlap to be calculated directly from the observed intensities, for a given rotation. In § 3 the physical significance of the expression obtained will be considered.

2. The rotation function

Consider a point whose position **r** may be specified relative to three crystallographic axes $\mathbf{a}_1, \mathbf{a}_2, \mathbf{a}_3$ by $\mathbf{r}=x_1\mathbf{a}_1+x_2\mathbf{a}_2+x_3\mathbf{a}_3$. The position relative to another set of axes $\mathbf{a}_1', \mathbf{a}_2', \mathbf{a}_3'$ is given by

$$\begin{aligned} x_1' &= c_{11}x_1+c_{12}x_2+c_{13}x_3+d_1 \\ x_2' &= c_{21}x_1+c_{22}x_2+c_{23}x_3+d_2 \\ x_3' &= c_{31}x_1+c_{32}x_2+c_{33}x_3+d_3 \,. \end{aligned} \quad (1)$$

Alternatively we can consider x_1', x_2', x_3' as the coordinates of the point in the same axes, after it has been rotated and translated. For simplicity and brevity, matrix notation is preferable. All three of the above equations may then be written

$$\mathbf{x}'=[\mathrm{C}]\mathbf{x}+\mathbf{d}\,.$$

The d_i $(i=1, 2, 3)$ form a vector **d** which represents the translation between the origins of the two systems, while the c_{ij} form a matrix [C] representing rotation about the origin of the unprimed system. In the application considered here, the translation **d** will always be zero, but it will be retained for generality.

Now consider any function $\varrho(x_1, x_2, x_3)$ periodic in a cell defined by $\mathbf{a}_1, \mathbf{a}_2, \mathbf{a}_3$. We define the *overlap*, R, of this function with a rotated and translated version of ϱ, within some volume U as

$$R=\iiint_U \varrho(x_1, x_2, x_3)\varrho(x_1', x_2', x_3')\,dx_1\,dx_2\,dx_3\,. \quad (2)$$

It is clear that R will take large values if the transformation relating the primed and unprimed systems has the property that $\varrho(x_1, x_2, x_3)$ tends to be equal to $\varrho(x_1', x_2', x_3')$ within the volume U.

Since ϱ is a periodic function it may be expanded in a Fourier series:

$$\varrho(x_1, x_2, x_3)=(1/V)\sum_{h_1}\sum_{h_2}\sum_{h_3}|F(h_1, h_2, h_3)| \times \exp\{i\alpha(h_1, h_2, h_3)\}\exp\{-2\pi i(h_1x_1+h_2x_2+h_3x_3)\}$$

or more briefly

$$\varrho(\mathbf{x})=(1/V)\sum_{\mathbf{h}}|F(\mathbf{h})|\exp[i(\alpha_{\mathbf{h}}-\varphi_{\mathbf{h},\mathbf{x}})]\,,$$

where

$$\varphi_{\mathbf{h},\mathbf{x}}=2\pi\sum_{i=1}^{3}h_ix_i\,.$$

Similarly we may write

$$\varrho(\mathbf{x}')=(1/V)\sum_{\mathbf{p}}|F(\mathbf{p})|\exp[i(\alpha_{\mathbf{p}}-\varphi_{\mathbf{p},\mathbf{x}'})]\,,$$

where the Fourier coefficient with indices (p_1, p_2, p_3) is written as $|F(\mathbf{p})|\exp[i\alpha_{\mathbf{p}}]$.

Since only the exponents $\varphi_{\mathbf{h},\mathbf{x}}, \varphi_{\mathbf{p},\mathbf{x}'}$ depend upon **x**, the overlap may thus be written

$$R=(1/V^2)\sum_{\mathbf{h}}\sum_{\mathbf{p}}\Big[|F_{\mathbf{h}}||F_{\mathbf{p}}|\exp[i(\alpha_{\mathbf{h}}+\alpha_{\mathbf{p}})] \times\Big\{\iiint_U \exp[-i(\varphi_{\mathbf{h},\mathbf{x}}+\varphi_{\mathbf{p},\mathbf{x}'})]\,dx_1\,dx_2\,dx_3\Big\}\Big]\,.$$

Writing the exponents more fully we have

$$\begin{aligned}(\varphi_{\mathbf{h},\mathbf{x}}+\varphi_{\mathbf{p},\mathbf{x}'}) &= 2\pi(\sum_i h_ix_i+\sum_i p_ix_i') \\ &= 2\pi\sum_i (h_i+h_i')x_i+2\pi\sum_i p_id_i\,,\end{aligned}$$

where

$$\begin{aligned} h_1' &= c_{11}p_1+c_{21}p_2+c_{31}p_3 \\ h_2' &= c_{12}p_1+c_{22}p_2+c_{32}p_3 \\ h_3' &= c_{13}p_1+c_{23}p_2+c_{33}p_3 \end{aligned} \quad (3)$$

or more briefly

$$\mathbf{h}'=[\tilde{\mathrm{C}}]\mathbf{p}\,,$$

where $[\tilde{\mathrm{C}}]$ is the transpose of [C], obtained by interchanging its rows and columns.

Substituting back in the expression for R, we now have

$$R=(1/V^2)\sum_{\mathbf{h}}\sum_{\mathbf{p}}\Big[|F_{\mathbf{h}}||F_{\mathbf{p}}|\exp[i(\alpha_{\mathbf{h}}+\alpha_{\mathbf{p}}-2\pi\sum_i p_id_i)] \times\Big\{\iiint_U \exp[-2\pi i\sum_i (h_i+h_i')x_i]\,dx_1\,dx_2\,dx_3\Big\}\Big]\,.$$

The bracketed integral is an interference function familiar in crystallography (see especially Patterson, 1939). We will write its solution as

$$(U/V)\times G_{\mathbf{h},\mathbf{h}'}\exp[i\Omega_{\mathbf{h},\mathbf{h}'}],$$

so that we have, finally

$$R=(U/V^3)\sum_{\mathbf{h}}\sum_{\mathbf{p}}|F_{\mathbf{h}}||F_{\mathbf{p}}|G_{\mathbf{h},\mathbf{h}'} \times\exp[i(\alpha_{\mathbf{h}}+\alpha_{\mathbf{p}}-2\pi\sum p_id_i+\Omega_{\mathbf{h},\mathbf{h}'})]\,. \quad (4)$$

We quote as examples the expressions for G and Ω when the integral is bounded by the faces of a parallelepiped between $A_i^- \le x_i \le A_i^+$; and by the surface of a sphere radius r with centre at $(A_i^+ + A_i^-)/2$.

In both cases

$$\Omega_{\mathbf{h},\mathbf{h}'}=-\pi\sum_{i=1}^{3}(h_i+h_i')(A_i^-+A_i^+)\,.$$

For the parallelepiped

$$G_{\mathbf{h},\mathbf{h}'}=\prod_{i=1}^{3}\frac{\sin\pi(h_i+h_i')(A_i^+-A_i^-)}{\pi(h_i+h_i')(A_i^+-A_i^-)} \quad (5)$$

and for the sphere

$$G_{\mathbf{h},\mathbf{h}'}=\frac{3(\sin 2\pi Hr-2\pi Hr\cos 2\pi Hr)}{(2\pi Hr)^3}$$

where H is the distance of the point

$$((h_1+h_1'),\ (h_2+h_2'),\ (h_3+h_3'))$$

from the origin in reciprocal space.

In the application of R with which we are concerned, the above, generalized, form for R may be simplified. Since it is desirable to have a form dependent only on the intensities, we choose to calculate the overlap of the two Patterson functions. The Fourier coefficients are all real, and, according to convention, will be written $|F_\mathbf{h}|^2$, $|F_\mathbf{p}|^2$, while $\alpha_\mathbf{h}$ and $\alpha_\mathbf{p}$ are zero. Translations of the origin are not required; thus $\mathbf{d}=0$. The symmetry of the Patterson function means that it is always convenient to integrate over a volume U symmetrical about the origin so that $\Omega \equiv 0$. Thus for overlap of the Patterson function without translation, we have

$$R=(U/V^3)\sum_\mathbf{h}\sum_\mathbf{p}|F_\mathbf{h}|^2|F_\mathbf{p}|^2 G_{\mathbf{h},\mathbf{h}'}\,. \tag{6}$$

The vector $\mathbf{h}'$, given by (3), is the position of the reciprocal-lattice point $\mathbf{p}$ after a rotation specified by the matrix [C]. For this reason the above expression is referred to as the rotation function.

The result (6) has been given by Patterson (1952) in a context chiefly concerned with *crystallographic* symmetry. He shows that the generalized Faltung integrals, of which R is an example (equation (2)), may be regarded as symmetry functions which show the extent to which given symmetry operations are obeyed by the structure. In this paper, we show that the extension to non-crystallographic symmetry operations has a useful application.

3. The physical significance of the *R* function

The maximum value of $3(\sin 2\pi x-2\pi x\cos 2\pi x)/(2\pi x)^3$ is 1·00 (see Fig. 1). It is never greater than 0·086 outside the range $-0{\cdot}725<x<+0{\cdot}725$. Hence all terms in (6) for which $|Hr|>0{\cdot}725$ may well be neglected if U is assumed to be a sphere of radius r. Conversely, G will be a maximum when $H=0$. Now H is the distance of the point $(h_1+h_1',\ h_2+h_2',\ h_3+h_3')$ from the origin of reciprocal space. Therefore, from (3), $G=1$

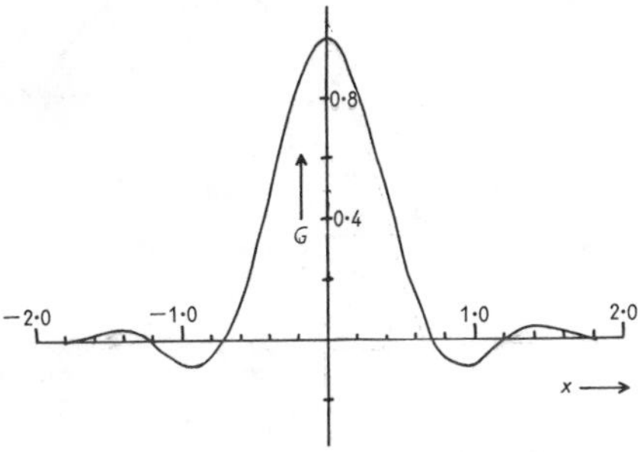

Fig. 1. The interference function
$G=3\,(\sin 2\pi x-2\pi x\cos 2\pi x)/(2\pi x)^3$
applicable for roughly spherical sub-units.

for the non-integral values of (p_1, p_2, p_3) which satisfy the three simultaneous equations

$$\begin{aligned} p_1c_{11}+p_2c_{21}+p_3c_{31}&=-h_1\\ p_1c_{12}+p_2c_{22}+p_3c_{32}&=-h_2\\ p_1c_{13}+p_2c_{23}+p_3c_{33}&=-h_3\,. \end{aligned} \tag{7}$$

In other words the integral reciprocal-lattice point h_1, h_2, h_3 has been rotated to the non-integral reciprocal-lattice position (p_1, p_2, p_3). The summation (6), however, includes terms only for which (p_1, p_2, p_3) are all integral, where $|F_\mathbf{p}|^2$ can be measured. At integral values of (p_1, p_2, p_3) *close* to the non-integral point given by the solution of the above three simultaneous equations, H will be small, and only at such points can G have a large value.

The argument in the preceding sections has been put in terms of the rotation of the self-Patterson function of the sub-units. An identical argument might be given in terms of the rotation of the Fourier transform of the self-Patterson function within an infinite unit cell. This would be a continuous transform. We would rotate the point h_1, h_2, h_3 to the point p_1, p_2, p_3 in order to superimpose the transform of two identical units. The limitations of the finite unit cell require us to interpolate the value of the continuous transform at non-integral points by means of

$$(U/V)\sum_\mathbf{p}|F|^2 G_{\mathbf{h},\mathbf{h}'}\,.$$

The actual number of significant terms in the summation over $\mathbf{p}$ depends on the rapidity with which the transform changes.

If r is large, causing Hr to increase rapidly as H increases, then most of the terms in the summation are negligible. That is, when r is large the rate of change of the transform between reciprocal-lattice points is small, necessitating the inclusion of fewer terms in the interpolation process. Generally r designates the limits of the self-Patterson function, so that the size of the sub-unit determines the number of terms in the interpolation summation.

4. Rotation of a set of oblique axes

In order to calculate the rotation function R corresponding to any desired rotation, all that remains is to calculate the corresponding matrix [C]. This problem has been treated from the crystallographic standpoint by Patterson (1959). The crystallographic axes will in general be unequal and oblique, and the least clumsy procedure appears to be:

(i) to transform the coordinates to a Cartesian form;

(ii) to transform the resulting coordinates to a rotated set of axes*;

* Note that new coordinates are defined by reference to a set of axes which has been rotated right-handedly. This means that the new coordinates, used with the original axes, result in *left*-handed rotation of the structure. The convention was used in Patterson's (1959) paper.

Table 1

(*a*) Matrix ρ in terms of Eulerian angles θ_1, θ_2, θ_3

$-\sin\theta_1\cos\theta_2\sin\theta_3 + \cos\theta_1\cos\theta_3$	$\cos\theta_1\cos\theta_2\sin\theta_3 + \sin\theta_1\cos\theta_3$	$\sin\theta_2\sin\theta_3$
$-\sin\theta_1\cos\theta_2\cos\theta_3 - \cos\theta_1\sin\theta_3$	$\cos\theta_1\cos\theta_2\cos\theta_3 - \sin\theta_1\sin\theta_3$	$\sin\theta_2\cos\theta_3$
$\sin\theta_1\sin\theta_2$	$-\cos\theta_1\sin\theta_2$	$\cos\theta_2$

(*b*) Matrix ρ in terms of rotation angle $\varkappa$ and the spherical polar coordinates ψ, φ

$\cos\varkappa + \sin^2\psi\cos^2\varphi(1-\cos\varkappa)$	$\sin\psi\cos\psi\cos\varphi(1-\cos\varkappa) + \sin\psi\sin\varphi\sin\varkappa$	$-\sin^2\psi\cos\varphi\sin\varphi(1-\cos\varkappa) + \cos\psi\sin\varkappa$
$\sin\psi\cos\psi\cos\varphi(1-\cos\varkappa) - \sin\psi\sin\varphi\sin\varkappa$	$\cos\varkappa + \cos^2\psi(1-\cos\varkappa)$	$-\sin\psi\cos\psi\sin\varphi(1-\cos\varkappa) + \sin\psi\cos\varphi\sin\varkappa$
$-\sin^2\psi\sin\varphi\cos\varphi(1-\cos\varkappa) - \cos\psi\sin\varkappa$	$-\sin\psi\cos\psi\sin\varphi(1-\cos\varkappa) - \sin\psi\cos\varphi\sin\varkappa$	$\cos\varkappa + \sin^2\psi\sin^2\varphi(1-\cos\varkappa)$

(iii) to return these coordinates to their crystallographic form.

In matrix notation, this means

$$[\mathbf{C}] = [\alpha][\rho][\beta]\,. \tag{8}$$

In this equation

$$[\beta] = \begin{pmatrix} a_1\sin\alpha_3\sin\omega & 0 & 0 \\ a_1\cos\alpha_3 & a_2 & a_3\cos\alpha_1 \\ a_1\sin\alpha_3\cos\omega & 0 & a_3\sin\alpha_1 \end{pmatrix}, \tag{9}$$

is the matrix which transforms the oblique crystallographic fractional coordinates x_i to Cartesian coordinates X_i. α_i are the crystallographic interaxial angles and $\cos\omega = (\cos\alpha_2 - \cos\alpha_1\cos\alpha_3)/\sin\alpha_1\sin\alpha_3$. We have chosen to retain the direction of the X_2 axis along $\mathbf{a}_2$, and to set X_1 along $\mathbf{a}_2\times\mathbf{a}_3$, for convenience in the monoclinic system (see Fig. 2).

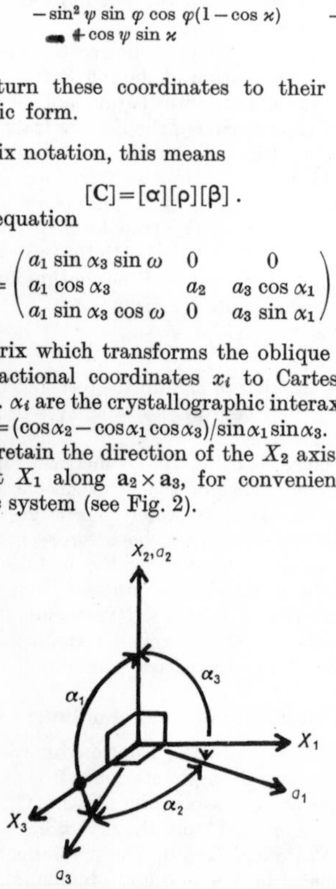

Fig. 2. Relationship of the orthogonal axes X_1, X_2, X_3 to the crystallographic axes x_1, x_2, x_3.

$$[\alpha] = \begin{pmatrix} 1/a_1\sin\alpha_3\sin\omega & 0 & 0 \\ 1/a_2\tan\alpha_1\tan\omega - 1/a_2\tan\alpha_3\sin\omega & 1/a_2 & -1/a_2\tan\alpha_1 \\ -1/a_3\sin\alpha_1\tan\omega & 0 & 1/a_3\sin\alpha_1 \end{pmatrix} \tag{10}$$

is the inverse of $[\beta]$. In the case where the rotation function is used to compare the orientation of units in two different crystal lattices, the a_i and α_i in [o and $[\beta]$ are different.

The matrix $[\rho]$ (Table 1) specifies the rotatio operation. $[\rho]$ depends on three variables, and in thi work, we have used two different forms of them.

A rotation can be specified by the three Euleria angles $\theta_1, \theta_2, \theta_3$, whose significance can be mos readily seen by reference to Fig. 3. The rotatio operation $[\rho]$ consists of (i) a rotation of the Cartesia axes by θ_1 about the X_3 axis, (ii) a rotation θ_2 abou the new position of the X_1 axis, and (iii) a rotation θ about the new X_3 axis. These angles are positive i they are clockwise when looking along the relevan axis, as in the usual right-handed convention. Table 1(*a*) gives $[\rho]$ in terms of Eulerian angles.

The Eulerian angles are somewhat difficult t visualise, and are preferred only because they sho up the symmetry of the rotation function in a con venient way, as is shown in the final section. It i equally possible to specify a single rotation by a

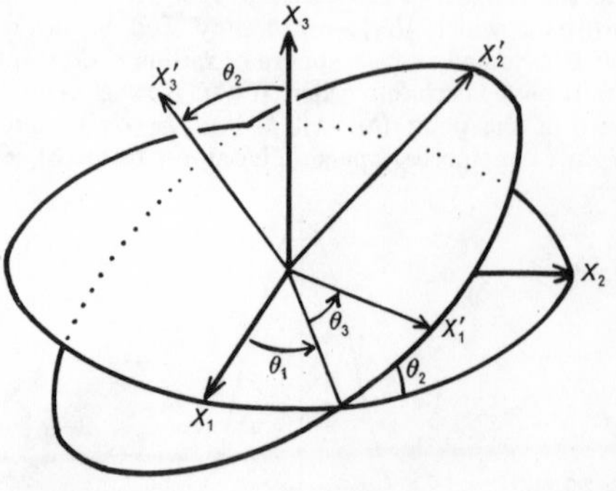

Fig. 3. The Eulerian angles θ_1, θ_2, θ_3 relating the rotated axe X_1', X_2', X_3' to the original unrotated orthogonal axe X_1, X_2, X_3.

* This convention agrees with that of Goldstein (1951) who gives a clear account of the Eulerian angles, togethe with an interesting discussion of the different sign convention adopted by various authors.

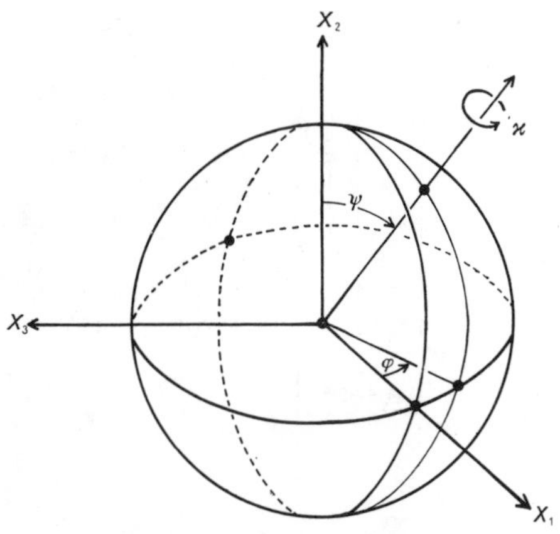

ig. 4. The variables ψ and φ, polar coordinates which specify a direction about which the axes may be rotated through an angle $\varkappa$.

ngle $\varkappa$ about a given axis. Patterson (1959) has quoted ıe [ρ] matrix in terms of this rotation and the irection cosines of the rotation axis. In the matrix f Table 1(*b*) we have reduced this to a system of ıree variables by writing the direction cosines in ɜrms of spherical polar coordinates ψ, φ of the rotaon axis (Fig. 4). For convenience in the monoclinic ɾstem, we have retained X_2 as the unique axis, hile $\varkappa$, ψ and φ again follow the right-handed conention.

The relationship between the two sets of variables ıay be established by comparison of the elements of ıe two matrices (Table 1(*a*) and (*b*)). One finds

$$\cos(\varkappa/2) = \cos(\theta_2/2)\cos\left(\frac{\theta_1+\theta_3}{2}\right)$$

$$\tan\varphi = -\cot(\theta_2/2)\sin\left(\frac{\theta_1+\theta_3}{2}\right)\sec\left(\frac{\theta_1-\theta_3}{2}\right)$$

$$\cos\varphi\tan\psi = \cot\left(\frac{\theta_1-\theta_3}{2}\right). \qquad (11)$$

Since φ and ψ can always be chosen in the range to π, these equations suffice to find $(\varkappa, \psi, \varphi)$ from ny set $(\theta_1, \theta_2, \theta_3)$.

5. Application to horse haemoglobin

Iorse haemoglobin crystallizes in space group $C2$ with alf a molecule per asymmetric unit. The two halves f the molecule are related by a crystallographic wo-fold axis. Perutz *et al.* (1960) have shown that ach half molecule consists of two similar configuraıons, each representing approximately the structure f myoglobin. Although these are not quite identical, he rotation function showed accurately their relative rientation.

About 1000 independent reflexions with a spacing greater than approximately 6 Å were used. The volume U for integration was a parallelepiped specified by the limits $x_1 = \pm a_1/4$, $x_2 = \pm a_2/2$, $x_3 = \pm a_3/2$ in the unrotated Patterson. For any one set of Miller indices (h_1, h_2, h_3) eight different sets of (p_1, p_2, p_3) were considered for interpolation. These eight reciprocal-lattice points lay at the corners of the reciprocal-lattice unit cell containing the non-integral position given by solution of (7). However, four of these eight points were always on the site of systematic absences. Thus, essentially, a four-point interpolation was used to determine the amplitude of the transform at the non-integral position given by (3).

The value of each intensity was packed in the store of the computer EDSAC 2 as ten binary bits. In this way all 1000 intensities could be accommodated in just over half the free store. The position of any one intensity in the store was entirely determined by its Miller indices. This method of packing not only avoided listing of indices, but avoided time-consuming hunting procedures to find any particular $|F_{\mathbf{p}}|^2$ value. It is important to note that, when (h_1, h_2, h_3) rotates to the non-integral position (h_1', h_2', h_3'), the point $(\bar{h}_1, h_2, \bar{h}_3)$ related by the monoclinic symmetry does not rotate to $(\bar{h}_1', h_2', \bar{h}_3')$. Thus a single summation involved approximately 2000 independent values of $|F_{\mathbf{h}}|^2$, each multiplied by the appropriate summation

$$\sum_{\mathbf{p}} |F_{\mathbf{p}}|^2 G_{\mathbf{h},\mathbf{h}'}$$

taken over four terms. The 8000-term summation needed to determine the value of R for a particular set of Eulerian angles took the machine $3\frac{3}{4}$ minutes.

Expression (6) shows that the rotation function, R, is a necessarily positive function, chiefly because of overlap of the origin peaks of the Pattersons. Values of R well away from the important peaks are mostly in the range 380 ± 40 units on the scale adopted. The origin peak of R (no rotation) is 621 units, and the peak at (85°, 40°, 95°) is 504 units. After subtracting the mean background, this peak is about half the origin peak, and considerably greater than the random fluctuations.

The results for points around the largest peak are shown in Fig. 5. Its maximum occurs at $\theta_1 = 85°$, $\theta_2 = 40°$, $\theta_3 = 95°$. The amount of rotation, and the direction of the rotation axes, can be found by substituting these, and symmetry-related Eulerian angles, into expressions (11). The following two pairs of axes are then found:

$$A_1, A_2:\ \varkappa = 180° \pm 3°,\ \psi = 90°,\ \varphi = 20°.$$
$$A_3, A_4:\ \varkappa = 180°,\ \psi = 90° \pm 2°,\ \varphi = 110°.$$

These four axes, whose positions are plotted on a stereogram in Fig. 6, are inter-related by the crystallographic two-fold axis. They are themselves close to being two-fold axes, and with the crystallographic

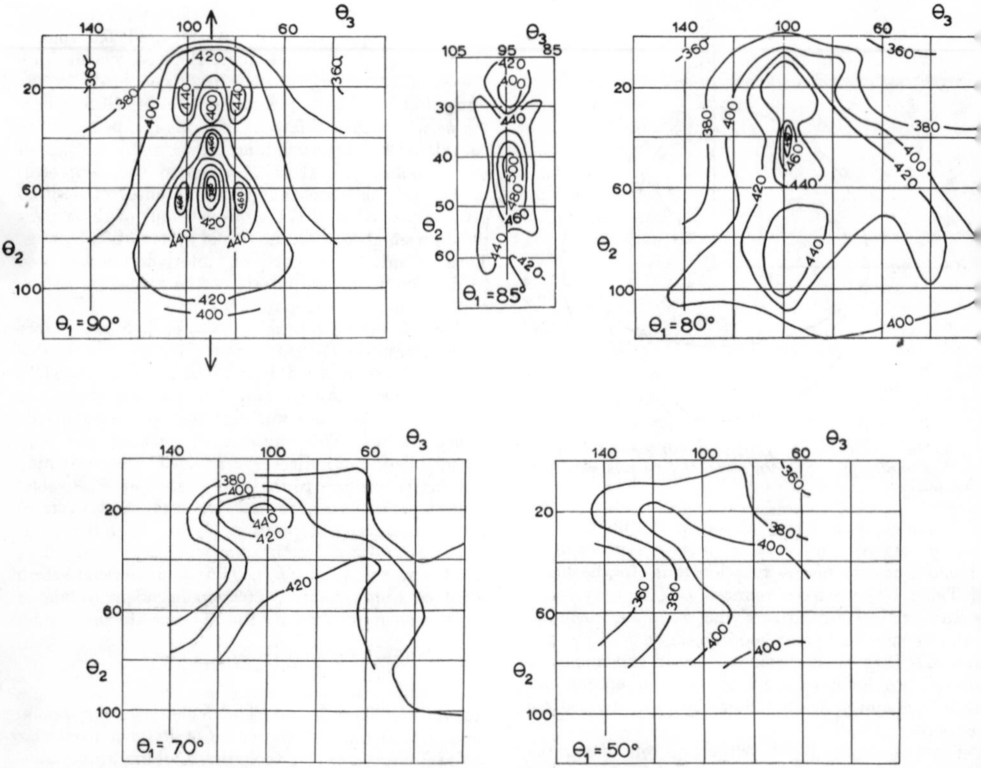

Fig. 5. A plot of the R function, for horse haemoglobin, in terms of the Eulerian angles θ_1, θ_2, θ_3 in the vicinity of the large peak. The peak corresponds to the non-crystallographic operation that rotates the α chain into the β chain. Heights are given on an arbitrary scale: one unit corresponds to 26·8 e.^{4}/Å^6. The origin has a height of 621 units.

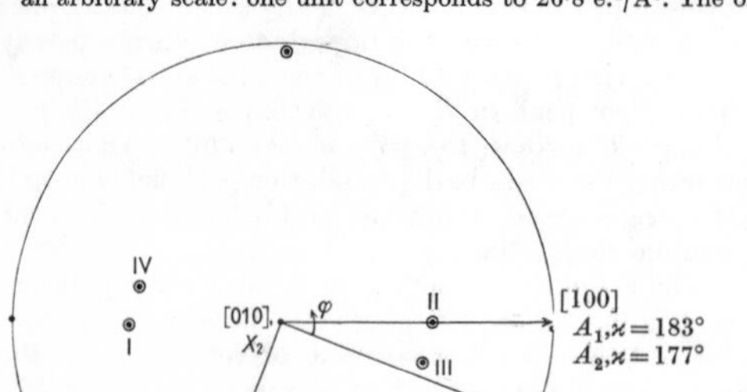

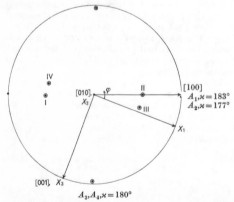

Fig. 6. Stereogram showing the directions of the non-crystallographic rotation axes $A_1 \ldots A_4$ of the horse haemoglobin molecule. The haem normal directions, I, II, III and IV, found from electron spin resonance data, are also shown. Points above the XZ plane are indicated by dots, points below by circles.

axis, form an almost orthogonal set. If the axes all passed through one point, the molecules would very nearly have the point group 222.

There are two sets of measurements with which these results may be compared. Associated with each quarter of the haemoglobin molecule is a planar haem group, whose orientation has been determined by electron-spin resonance (Ingram *et al.*, 1956). The directions of the haem normals are shown in Fig. 6, and are consistent within 6° with the directions of the pseudo axes found by the rotation function. Cullis *et al.* (1961) attempted to determine the direction of the pseudo rotation axes by examination of the polypeptide chain directions in the 6 Å resolution Fourier map of haemoglobin. The attempt showed up clearly the slight differences between the quarter-molecules, but the result agrees within 6° with the position of the rotation function peak.

The rotation matrix [C] corresponding to the peak of R is

$$\begin{pmatrix} -1{\cdot}0098 & -0{\cdot}0126 & +0{\cdot}3429 \\ +0{\cdot}0014 & -0{\cdot}9982 & -0{\cdot}0485 \\ -0{\cdot}0573 & -0{\cdot}0736 & +1{\cdot}0080 \end{pmatrix}$$

6. Resolution

The full range of Eulerian angles was not explored, using all the data. It would have taken about 50 hr. on EDSAC 2 to cover all independent Eulerian angles, taken at 20° intervals. Instead, a survey was made using a very restricted amount of data. Each summation was therefore much faster, and a smaller number of points needed to be evaluated. Complete coverage of all reflexions with spacing over 20 Å and at 30° intervals of the Eulerian angles took under 1 hr. The highest non-origin peak fell in the same region as the maximum of the rotation function, found by using all 1000 independent reflexions.

It is useful to know the smallest change of Eulerian angle which will give a significant effect. Roughly speaking, it is that rotation which moves the most distant reciprocal-lattice points through one reciprocal-lattice translation. If h is the highest h_1, h_2 or h_3 index, angles less than $2 \sin^{-1} (1/2h)$ are insignificant. This gives, in our case, 3·5°; the closest angular intervals used, namely 5°, are of the same order. A survey around the peak was first done with larger intervals of 20° and 10°; 5° intervals were used only to obtain the exact peak position.

The peak may be 'sharpened' in exactly the same way as a normal Fourier synthesis, by weighting down, or omitting, the inner reflexions of the reciprocal lattice. As an experiment, only those reflexions between 10 Å and 6 Å spacing were used. Fig. 7 shows a line section passing near the peak using this partial data, and, for comparison, all the data. The partial data shows greater background variations because of the smaller number of reflexions involved.

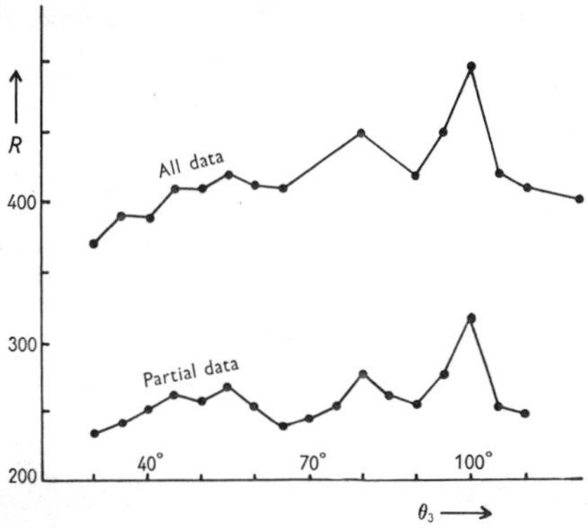

Fig. 7. A line section of $R(\theta_1=80°, \theta_2=40°, \theta_3)$ passing near the large peak. Upper line: All reflexions, with spacing greater than 6 Å. Lower line: Only reflexions with spacing between 10 and 6 Å included.

7. Symmetry properties of the rotation function, *R*

As the amount of computing required is critical, it is particularly important to know what range of angles needs to be explored before all independent rotation operations have been considered. This will depend on the point group of the rotated object, and in this final section, we explain how this range may be determined.

Although there are compelling reasons (which will appear) for carrying out the computation in terms of the Eulerian angles $(\theta_1, \theta_2, \theta_3)$, it is often much easier to think of the rotation in terms of $(\varkappa, \psi, \varphi)$. If the $(\theta_1, \theta_2, \theta_3)$ cannot be visualized directly, they can be interpreted in terms of $(\varkappa, \psi, \varphi)$ by the use of equations (11), or by comparing the elements of the matrix $[\rho]$.

In both systems, a given rotation operation can have several different expressions:

(*a*) If any angular variable lies outside the range 0 to 2π, it can be brought into this range by adding an integral multiple of 2π, without affecting the rotation operation. Thus we can write

$$[\rho(\varkappa, \psi, \varphi)] \equiv [\rho(\varkappa+2\pi n_1, \psi+2\pi n_2, \varphi+2\pi n_3)]\,,$$

where n_1, n_2, n_3 are integers.

(*b*) Referring to Fig. 4, if ψ is greater than π the rotation operation is the same as one in which φ is increased by π and ψ becomes $2\pi-\psi$. Thus

$$[\rho(\varkappa, \psi, \varphi)] \equiv [\rho(\varkappa, 2\pi-\psi, \varphi+\pi)]\,.$$

(*c*) Note that a rotation $\varkappa$ about any axis is equivalent to a rotation $-\varkappa$ about an oppositely directed axis. Thus

$$\rho[(\varkappa, \psi, \varphi)] \equiv [\rho(-\varkappa, \pi-\psi, \pi+\varphi)]\,.$$

All these identities can be checked by substituting into $[\rho]$ (Table 1(*b*)), and seeing that no element is changed.

All rotation operations are therefore included in

$$0 \le \varkappa < 2\pi\,,\quad 0 \le \psi \le \pi\,,\quad 0 \le \varphi < \pi\,.$$

The corresponding relationships in $(\theta_1, \theta_2, \theta_3)$ are:

$$[\rho(\theta_1, \theta_2, \theta_3)] \equiv [\rho(\theta_1+2\pi n_1, \theta_2+2\pi n_2, \theta_3+2\pi n_3)],$$
$$[\rho(\theta_1, \theta_2, \theta_3)] \equiv [\rho(\theta_1+\pi, -\theta_2, \theta_3+\pi)]\,.$$

The full range of rotation operations is

$$0 \le \theta_1 < \pi\,,\quad 0 \le \theta_2 < 2\pi\,,\quad 0 \le \theta_3 < 2\pi\,.$$

So far, we have considered physically identical operations, which lead to identical expressions of the $[\rho]$ matrix. In addition, point-group symmetry in the rotated object (in our case, the reciprocal lattice) will cause the same value of the rotation function to be found for physically distinct rotations. The point group of the haemoglobin reciprocal lattice ($2/m$) will be used for illustration.

(*d*) Equal rotations about directions related by the point group symmetry will give the same result.

Thus, in haemoglobin, where the dyad relates points with coordinates φ and $\varphi+\pi$, we have

$$R(\varkappa, \psi, \varphi)=R(\varkappa, \psi, \varphi+\pi)\ .$$

Taking this in conjunction with (*c*), we find that the mirror-plane symmetry

$$R(\varkappa, \psi, \varphi)=R(-\varkappa, \pi-\psi, \varphi)$$

is automatically produced, showing that the rotation operations have the same symmetry for point groups 2 and $2/m$. This is true because only *proper* rotations (rotation without inversion) are considered.

The corresponding relationship for the Eulerian angles is

$$R(\theta_1, \theta_2, \theta_3)=R(\pi-\theta_1, \theta_2, \pi-\theta_3)\ .$$

(*e*) Two consecutive rotations about different axes are always equivalent to a single rotation about some other axis, given by multiplication of the two rotation matrices. If $[\rho_1]$ represents the crystallographic rotation of π about $\mathbf{a}_2$, and $[\rho]$ a general rotation $(\varkappa, \psi, \varphi)$, then the rotation $[\rho][\rho_1]$ is a complicated function of $\varkappa, \psi, \varphi$. However, in Eulerian angles such relationships take a simple form. For a two-fold rotation about X_2 before a general rotation one finds

$$R(\theta_1, \theta_2, \theta_3)=R(\theta_1, \theta_2+\pi, \pi-\theta_3)\ ,$$

so that the range of rotations can be expressed quite simply. For this reason the required range of angles can only be expressed conveniently in terms of the Eulerian angles, and for this reason they are preferred for computation.

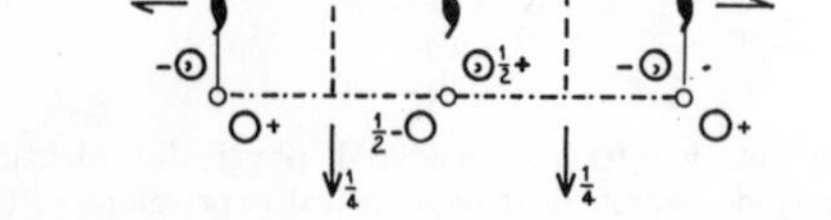

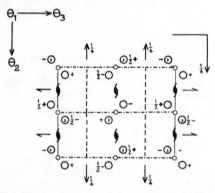

Fig. 8. Diagram showing equivalent values of the Eulerian angles for rotations of an object with point group symmetry $2/m$.

To collect all these relationships together in a form familiar to crystallographers, it is convenient to consider the symmetry of R in a three-dimensional space with orthogonal coordinates $\theta_1, \theta_2, \theta_3$. Postulate (*a*) above tells us that equivalent points lie on a lattice with spacing 2π in each direction, and the other relationships may be indicated by constructing a conventional space-group diagram (Fig. 8). The space group in this case is No. 56 (*Pbnb* retaining the order $\theta_1, \theta_2, \theta_3$). The size of the asymmetric unit, giving the range of angles which needs to be explored, may be expressed

$$0 \le \theta_1 \le \pi/2$$
$$0 \le \theta_2 < \pi$$
$$0 \le \theta_3 < 2\pi\ .$$

We are indebted to Dr M. F. Perutz for allowing us to use the three-dimensional 6 Å haemoglobin data and to the Director of the University of Cambridge Mathematical Laboratory for making the EDSAC computer available. We are grateful for most useful discussions with Dr V. Heine and Dr A. Klug, and to Mrs D. Thomas who has given assistance in the preparation of this manuscript.

References

BODO, G., DINTZIS, H. M., KENDREW, J. C. & WYCKOFF, H. W., (1959). *Proc. Roy. Soc.* A **253**, 70.
CASPAR, D. L. D. (1956). *Nature, Lond.* **177**, 475.
CULLIS, A. F., MUIRHEAD, H., NORTH, A. T., PERUTZ, M. F. & ROSSMANN, M. G. (1961). *Proc. Roy. Soc.* (In press.)
CRICK, F. H. C. & WATSON, J. D. (1956). *Nature, Lond.* **177**, 473.
FINCH, J. T. & KLUG, A. (1959). *Nature, Lond.* **183**, 1709.
FRANKLIN, R. E. & HOLMES, K. C. (1958). *Acta Cryst.* **11**, 213.
GOLDSTEIN, H. (1951). *Classical Mechanics*, p. 107. Cambridge, Mass.: Addison–Wesley Press.
HARRISON, P. M. (1959). *J. Mol. Biol.* **1**, 69.
INGRAM, D. J. E., GIBSON, J. F. & PERUTZ, M. F. (1956). *Nature, Lond.* **178**, 907.
KLUG, A. & FINCH, J. T. (1960). *J. Mol. Biol.* **2**, 201.
MAGDOFF, B. S. (1960). *Nature, Lond.* **185**, 673.
PATTERSON, A. L. (1939). *Phys. Rev.* **56**, 972.
PATTERSON, A. L. (1952). In *Computing methods and the phase problem*, p. 29. Pennsylvania State College.
PATTERSON, A. L. (1959). *International Tables for X-ray Crystallography*, **2**, 52. Birmingham: Kynoch Press.
PERUTZ, M. F., ROSSMANN, M. G., CULLIS, A. F., MUIRHEAD, H., WILL, G. & NORTH, A. C. T. (1960). *Nature, Lond.* **185**, 416.
PERUTZ, M. F., TROTTER, I. F., HOWELLS, E. R. & GREEN, D. W. (1955). *Acta Cryst.* **8**, 241.
WATSON, J. D. (1954). *Biochim. Biophys. Acta.* **13**, 10

Reprinted from *Acta Crystallographica*, Vol. 21, Part 6, December 1966

:ta *Cryst.* (1966). **21**, 872

A Description of Various Rotation Function Programs

BY PATRICK TOLLIN AND MICHAEL G. ROSSMANN

Department of Biological Sciences, Purdue University, Lafayette, Indiana 47907, *U.S.A.*

Various closely related programs for the calculation of the rotation function are described. The latter explores systematically the amount of overlap between two differently oriented Patterson syntheses, and can be used to relate similar molecules or structures in the same or different crystals. The calculations require only the intensities rather than the Patterson sections. It is shown that (i) neglecting all but 10% of the largest intensities for one of the structures and (ii) construction of a table of the transform *G*, of the spherical volume within which the Patterson functions are being compared, sampled in a 5×5×5 grid within the reciprocal unit cell, gives considerable improvement in computing time without excess loss of accuracy. The effect of premature truncation or coarseness of the *G* table is discussed, together with other considerations which are important in the successful application of this technique.

1. Introduction

e shall describe the flow diagram of various closely lated programs for the calculation of the rotation nction (Rossmann & Blow, 1962) (RB). Even with isting fast computers the time involved in exploring e three rotation angles at reasonable intervals is fordable and a number of techniques are here presented ich significantly improve the speed of the computans. We also discuss strategic considerations required the application of these techniques to various types problem.

The rotation function is defined (RB) as

$$R=\int_U P_2(\mathbf{x}_2)\,.\,P_1(\mathbf{x}_1)\,d\mathbf{x}_1\,. \qquad (1)$$

measures the degree of coincidence when the Pattern function P_1 is rotated on the Patterson function . Any point $\mathbf{x}_1$ in P_1 is related to any other point in P_2 through the rotation matrix [C] by the relationp

$$\mathbf{x}_2=[\mathbf{C}]\mathbf{x}_1\,.$$

e above integral (1) can be shown (RB) to reduce the double summation

$$R=\sum_{\mathbf{p}}|F_{\mathbf{p}}|^2\{\sum_{\mathbf{h}}|F_{\mathbf{h}}|^2\,G_{\mathbf{h},\mathbf{h}'}\} \qquad (2)$$

where $|F_{\mathbf{p}}|$ and $|F_{\mathbf{h}}|$ are the structure amplitudes corresponding to the Patterson functions P_2 and P_1 respectively. $G_{\mathbf{h},\mathbf{h}'}$ is an interference function whose magnitude depends on the reciprocal lattice vectors **h** and **h**′ as well as the volume U within which the integral (1) is evaluated. The non-integral reciprocal lattice vector **h**′ is given by

$$\mathbf{h}'=\mathbf{p}[\mathbf{C}]\,.$$

The rotation function is particularly useful for the following problems:

(*a*) To determine the relative orientation of identical or similar rigid chemical groups in two different crystals. P_1 and P_2 must then represent the Patterson functions of the two crystals.

(*b*) To determine the orientation of a known rigid group in a molecular crystal. Here P_1 is the Patterson function of the unknown crystal, while P_2 is the Patterson function calculated from a model of rigid group in a known orientation.

(*c*) To determine the relative orientation of identical or similar groups of molecules within the same crystallographic asymmetric unit. Now P_1 and P_2 both represent the same Patterson function of the unknown crystal.

In all cases the integration is performed over the volume U equal to the volume around the origin of the Patterson functions within which P_1 and P_2 are expected to show similarity. We have invariably chosen U to be a sphere of radius r_0; $G_{\mathbf{h},\mathbf{h}'}$ is then determined entirely by the magnitude of the vector $\mathbf{H}=\mathbf{h}+\mathbf{h}'$, and is then given by the expression

$$G_{\mathbf{h},\mathbf{h}'}=\frac{3(\sin 2\pi H.r_0-2\pi Hr_0\cos 2\pi Hr_0)}{(2\pi Hr_0)^3}.$$

It has previously been observed (RB) that $G_{\mathbf{h},\mathbf{h}'}$ has a large value only if H is small. Thus the inner summation $\{\sum_{\mathbf{h}}|F_{\mathbf{h}}|^2 G_{\mathbf{h},\mathbf{h}'}\}$ in (2) need only be performed over those points $\mathbf{h}$ which are close to the non-integral point $-\mathbf{h}'$. In order to maintain the exact rotation symmetry (Tollin, Main & Rossmann, 1966) it is important to select a set of symmetrically disposed points around $\mathbf{h}$. The number, n, of points which need be included in this summation will depend on the magnitude of the radius, r_0, and the reciprocal unit cell dimensions of the crystal P_2. A discussion of the best value of n is given in §5, but for most purposes 27 points seems satisfactory.

2. The large term program*

Examination of equation (2) indicates that R will have a large value when large values of $|F_{\mathbf{h}}|^2$ and $|F_{\mathbf{p}}|^2$ are associated by large values of $G_{\mathbf{h},\mathbf{h}'}$. Since R is approximately proportional to $|F|^4$ it seems unlikely that the sum of the products of many small intensities will outweigh the contribution of a few large products. Also, since the time to compute R is directly proportional to the number of $|F_{\mathbf{p}}|^2$ values, and is only slightly affected by the number of $|F_{\mathbf{h}}|^2$, a modification of the general program was written which uses a small number of the largest $|F_{\mathbf{p}}|^2$ values. The above argument has been tested by computing the rotation function of monoclinic insulin on itself along the line $\theta_1=90°$, $0\leq\theta_2\leq180°$, $\theta_3=90°$, where θ_1, θ_2, θ_3 are the Eulerian angles as defined by RB. This particular line is known to have significant peaks along it (Hodgkin, Dodson, Coller & Rossmann, unpublished). The results obtained are shown in Fig. 1. The top curve shows the form of R when all the data were used for both $|F_{\mathbf{p}}|^2$ and $|F_{\mathbf{h}}|^2$. The middle curve shows the form of the rotation function when only the 50 largest $|F_{\mathbf{p}}|^2$ values and all $|F_{\mathbf{h}}|^2$ data had been employed. The bottom curve shows the result of using only the 50 largest intensities of both the h (or first) and p (or second) crystals. Although using only the largest $|F_{\mathbf{h}}|^2$ intensities does not make a great saving in time of computation for our program on a $32K$ memory store machine, the fact that useful results were obtained might be helpful in constructing a fast rotation function program for a smaller computer.

A further indication that this approximation is justified was obtained in the comparison of seal and sperm whale myoglobin (Tollin & Scouloudi, 1966). In the latter example the time per point, using all the reflection data, was 24 seconds, while when using only the 47 largest $|F_{\mathbf{p}}|^2$ values the time per point reduced to 1·8 seconds. These times refer to a Fortran II program compiled and executed on an IBM 7094 computer. The latter has a cycle time of 2 μsec, requires on the average about 10 cycles per floating point operation, and has 32768 words of memory.

* The idea that using only the largest $|F|^2$ values would give useful results was arrived at independently by Dr D. M. Blow.

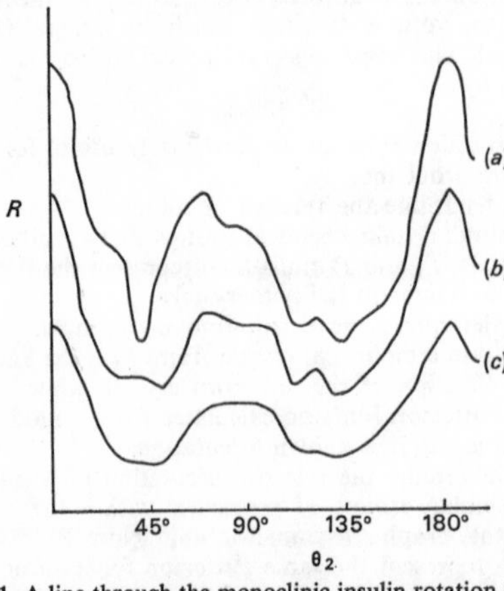

Fig. 1. A line through the monoclinic insulin rotation function in order to compare results using (a) full data, (b) only the 50 largest terms for the $|F_{\mathbf{p}}|^2$, and (c) the 50 largest terms for the $|F_{\mathbf{h}}|^2$ and $|F_{\mathbf{p}}|^2$ set of intensities.

3. The fine mesh program

Examination of the block diagram of the general program (Fig. 2) shows that most of the time is spent in calculating the magnitude of $\mathbf{H}$ in the innermost loop. Much of this time can be saved by noting that the point $-\mathbf{h}'$ can be written as

$$h_1+\Delta h'_1,\ h_2+\Delta h'_2,\ h_3+\Delta h'_3\ ,$$

where the nearest integral reciprocal lattice point to $-\mathbf{h}'$ has coordinates (h_1, h_2, h_3). A three-dimensional table can be constructed of values of $G_{\mathbf{h},\mathbf{h}'}$ with respect to a given integral point $\mathbf{h}$ and all values of $\Delta h'_1$, $\Delta h'_2$, $\Delta h'_3$, laid out as a fine grid within the reciprocal unit cell. In order to keep the size of this table within bounds each reciprocal length was divided into only five equal parts, and the summation over n was fixed at 27 points. Hence this table contained 27×125 entries. The computation of the inner loop is therefore reduced to determining $\Delta h'_1$, $\Delta h'_2$, $\Delta h'_3$ and then looking up the corresponding 27 values of $G_{\mathbf{h},\mathbf{h}'}$.

Fig. 3 shows the result of using this program for monoclinic insulin. The time per point, using this technique in the seal *versus* whale comparison was now only 1·0 sec when only the 47 largest $|F_{\mathbf{p}}|^2$ values were used.

4. The block diagram of the program

he block diagram of the general and large term pro- ·ams is given in Fig. 2(*a*). The modifications to pro- uce the 'fine mesh' program are shown in Fig. 2(*b*). number of explanatory notes are given below. Each ep in the program is represented by a block in the agram.

he general and large-term programs

Step 1. The cell data for both crystals, the Laue ·mmetry of reciprocal space, the limits of the rotation gles, the value of r_0 (the radius of the sphere of Pat- rson matching), and the maximum and minimum n θ/λ for the reflections to be used are read into the mputer.

Step 2. A table of $G_{\mathbf{h},\mathbf{h}'}$ is constructed as a function $(Hr_0)^2$. Values of G are listed for 400 equally spaced lues of $(Hr_0)^2$ between $0 \leq Hr_0 \leq 2{\cdot}0$.

Step 3. The $|\mathbf{F}|^2$ values for both crystals are read to the computer and a hemisphere in reciprocal space generated using their Laue symmetries. Reflections itside the given limits of (sin θ/λ) are rejected. The sition of any $|\mathbf{F}|^2$ value in the store is a function its Miller indices alone in order to give immediate ndom access to each structure amplitude. $|\mathbf{F}|^2$ values th the same Miller indices for both the first and cond crystals are packed into the same store location save space. However in the 'large-terms' program separate table lists the Miller indices and $|F_\mathbf{p}|^2$ values the largest terms. This gives the twofold advantage avoiding not only generating Miller indices in step of which approximately one-third will necessarily be tside the permitted limits of (sin θ/λ), but also the packing procedure while looking up each $|\mathbf{F}_\mathbf{h}|^2$ value.

Step 4. As indicated by RB, if x_1 and x_2 represent ctional coordinates with respect to the unit cell axes each crystal, we may express the rotation matrix **[C]** the triple product $[\boldsymbol{\alpha}][\boldsymbol{\varrho}][\boldsymbol{\beta}]$, where $[\boldsymbol{\beta}]$ converts $\mathbf{x}_1$ to orthogonal system and $[\boldsymbol{\alpha}]$ converts from an orthog- al system back to fractional coordinates. Matrix $[\boldsymbol{\beta}]$ then a function of the rotation angles alone. Ma- ces $[\boldsymbol{\alpha}]$ and $[\boldsymbol{\beta}]$ are set up here.

Step 5. The values of the rotation angles are gene- ed within the range defined by the data read in step Our present programs use only Eulerian angles as se lead, in general, to simple relationships between ferent asymmetric units in rotation space. The range angles to be computed is a function of the symme- s of the individual Patterson function as discussed Tollin, Main & Rossmann (1966).

Step 6. Matrices $[\boldsymbol{\varrho}]$ and hence **[C]** are calculated m the current values of the rotation angles.

Step 7. The Miller indices defined by **p** are generated tematically within a parallelepiped that completely ·elops a hemisphere of reciprocal space to the given its of (sin θ/λ). Corresponding $|F_\mathbf{p}|^2$ values are ab- acted from the array in the core store. In the case the 'large-term program' values of **p** and $|\mathbf{F}_\mathbf{p}|^2$ are

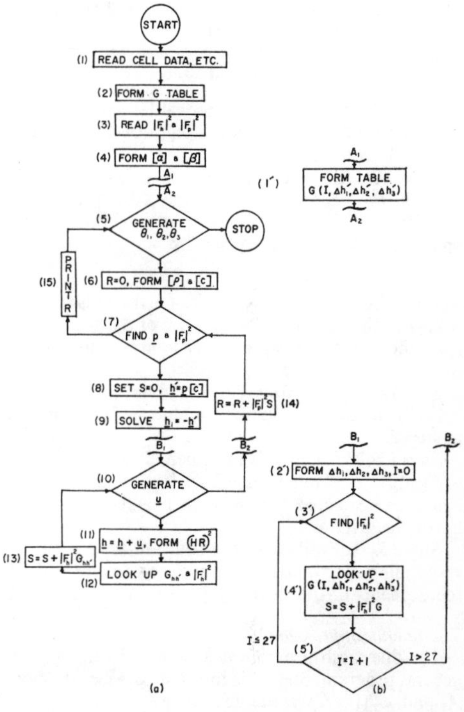

Fig. 2. Flow diagram of (*a*) the general program and (*b*) modification for the fine mesh program. For the latter program step 1′ is inserted between the points A_1 and A_2, and the inner loops between B_1 and B_2 are replaced by steps 2′ through 5′.

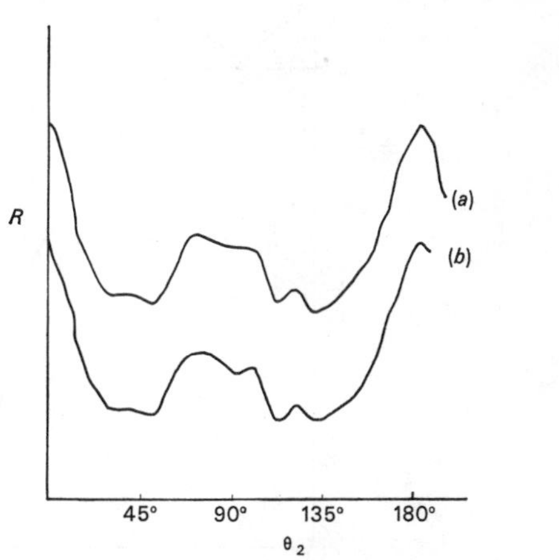

Fig. 3. Comparison of the monoclinic insulin rotation function results for (*a*) the large term program and (*b*) the fine mesh program.

not generated but are found by running sequentially through the list prepared in step 3.

Step 8. $\mathbf{h}'$ is evaluated and S, which will accumulate the sum $\{\sum_{\mathbf{h}} |F_{\mathbf{h}}|^2 G_{\mathbf{h},\mathbf{h}'}\}$, is set to zero.

Step 9. $\mathbf{h}_i$, the integral reciprocal lattice point in the first crystal nearest to the non-integral reciprocal lattice point $-\mathbf{h}'$ is found.

Steps 10 *and* 11. The n nearest neighbors around the point $\mathbf{h}_i$ are generated successively (this includes the point $\mathbf{h}_i$ itself). For the 27 nearest neighbors approximation, these points are given by

$$\mathbf{h} = \mathbf{h}_i + \mathbf{u},$$

where the components of u take on the values -1, 0, $+1$. $|\mathbf{H}|^2$, the square of the distance of the point $(\mathbf{h}+\mathbf{h}')$ from the origin of reciprocal space in the 'first' crystal can now be calculated.

Step 12. $|\mathbf{F}_{\mathbf{h}}|^2$ is found in the data table for each value of $\mathbf{h}$. $G_{\mathbf{h},\mathbf{h}'}$ is found from the table constructed in step 2.

Step 13. The sum S is incremented by $|F_{\mathbf{h}}|^2 G_{\mathbf{h},\mathbf{h}'}$.

Step 14. R is incremented by $|F_{\mathbf{p}}|^2 S$, as soon as S has been evaluated for all the n nearest neighbors of $\mathbf{h}_i$ for the given $\mathbf{p}$.

Step 15. The values of the rotation angles, the corresponding magnitude of the rotation function R, and the elements of the matrix [**C**] are printed out.

The fine mesh program

The fine mesh program is a modified version of the general program. Step 1′ is inserted between the points A_1 and A_2 (Fig. 2) in the flow diagram.

Step 1′. A table $G(I, \Delta h_1', \Delta h_2', \Delta h_3')$ is constructed of the values of $G_{\mathbf{h},\mathbf{h}'}$ for each of the 27 points $\mathbf{h}$ with respect to the mesh of non-integral points $\mathbf{h}'$. The latte is allowed to explore a three-dimensional grid $\Delta h_1'$, Δh $\Delta h_3'$ in steps of 0·2.

The innermost loops between the points B_1 and (Fig. 2) of the program are replaced by the part show in Fig. 2(*b*). The steps involved are:

Step 2′. The components $\Delta h_1'$, $\Delta h_2'$, $\Delta h_3'$ are calc lated.

Step 3′. h is determined from the current value of which is then used to find $|F_{\mathbf{h}}|^2$ from the array in th store.

Step 4′. The sum S is incremented by $|F_{\mathbf{h}}|^2 G_{\mathbf{h},\mathbf{h}'}(I, \Delta h$ $\Delta h_2'$, $\Delta h_3'$).

Step 5′. Steps 3′ and 4′ are repeated for all 27 valu of I.

5. Strategy in the application of the rotation functi

By using only the n nearest neighbors of $\mathbf{h}_i$ rather tha all the vectors $\mathbf{h}$ as the inner sum, a cut-off has bee applied to $G_{\mathbf{h},\mathbf{h}'}$. $G_{\mathbf{h},\mathbf{h}'}$ is the Fourier transform of function defined by

$$F(r) = 1 \text{ when } r \leq r_0 \quad ($$

or

$$F(r) = 0 \text{ otherwise,}$$

where $F(r)$ is defined in a space described by the sphe cal polar coordinates r, θ, φ. The Fourier transfor of $F(r)$ is $G(H)$. $F(r)$ can then be expressed as

$$F(r) = \int_0^\infty G(H) \frac{\sin 2\pi rH}{2\pi rH} \cdot H^2 \cdot dH \quad ($$

(Patterson, 1959). The table G, evaluated by the pr gram, was used to calculate the expression (4) betwe the limits 0 and H_0 (instead of infinity), in order

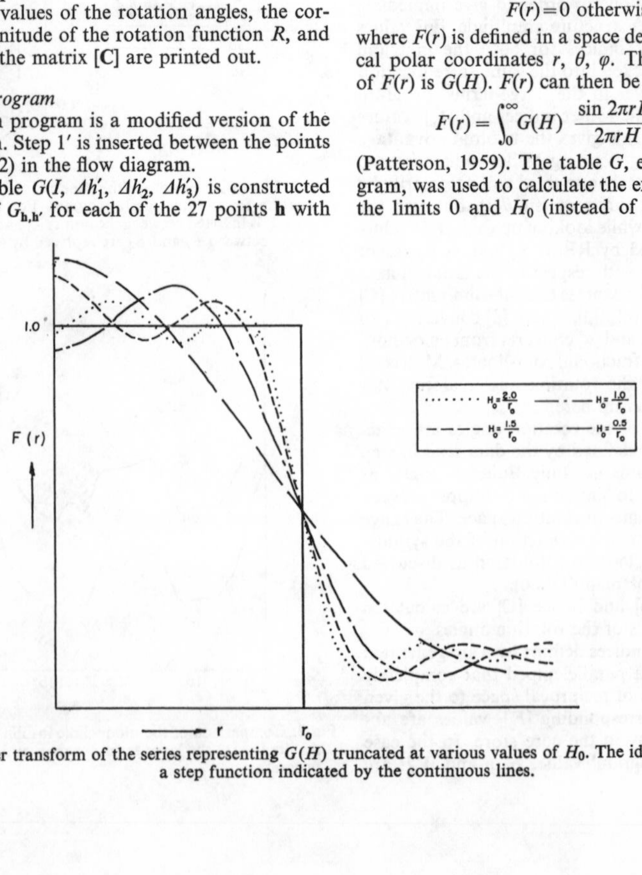

Fig. 4. The Fourier transform of the series representing $G(H)$ truncated at various values of H_0. The ideal shape of this curve a step function indicated by the continuous lines.

st the effect of applying a cut-off to $G(H)$. The results r different H_0 values are compared with the ideal here of (3) in Fig. 4. It is clear that the main effect to reduce the effective value of r_0. For values of $_0 < 1/r_0$, $F(r)$ is a poor representation of a sphere. It therefore important to consider carefully the choice the number of terms, n, in the inner loop, as this umber determines the effective value of H_0.

The effect of the termination of the series shows that is important to select with care which crystal shall P_1 and which P_2. The two criteria for this choice e rough equality of cell dimensions and lack of neral systematic absences. If possible, a crystal that ssesses both these properties should be chosen as P_1, else the number, n, of integration points **h** must be creased in at least one direction.

A further consideration arises in case (*b*) of §1. It is lpful to place the known rigid group in an arbitrary it cell of sufficient size to avoid overlap of the self-tterson vectors, that is leaving gaps between the oups equal to the diameter of the group. An even ger cell leads only to increase in computing time thout increase in clarity of the rotation function urnett, Tollin & Rossmann, to be published). The id group should also be placed in the unit cell in ch a way that its symmetry, if any, becomes a space oup operation. By so doing the Patterson function will have increased symmetry which will allow a luction in the time for the computations. If the sym-try element is not so chosen then a non-linear sym-try operation in the rotation function results and interpretation of the rotation function becomes mbersome (Tollin, Main & Rossmann, 1966).

APPENDIX

Errata in Rossmann & Blow (1962)

The expression for $\Omega_{\mathbf{hh}'}$ in (5) should be

$$-\pi \sum_{i=1}^{3} (h_i+h_i')(A_i^- + A_i^+) .$$

(*b*) The matrix **[C]** of equations (7) should be transposed.

(*c*) The footnote to page 26 is incorrect – the *same* convention was used by Patterson and hence

(*d*) The matrix **[ϱ]** in Table 1(*b*) should be transposed.

(*e*) Equations (11) define only the magnitudes of $\kappa\psi\varphi$. The quadrant in which they lie must be obtained by comparing corresponding entries in the two terms of **[ϱ]**.

(*f*) The expression defining $\cos\omega$ following equation (9) should read as $\cos\omega = (\cos\alpha_2 - \cos\alpha_1 \cos\alpha_3)/\sin\alpha_1 \sin\alpha_3$.

(*g*) The minimum permissible angular interval discussed in §6 can be more usefully considered in terms of the resolution of the reflection data. If only data with spacing greater than $d_{\min}$ are included in the calculations and if the radius of the sphere of Patterson comparison is r_0, then a reasonable angular interval is $\frac{1}{2}d_{\min}/r_0$. On this basis the Patterson function is moved through an angle which takes a point on the sphere through a distance equal to $\frac{1}{2}d_{\min}$.

We are grateful to Dr Peter Main for frequent helpful discussion, to Prof. D. Hodgkin for allowing us to use the monoclinic insulin data to test our programs, and to Mrs Julia Parsons and Mrs Jennie Roberts for technical assistance. This work was supported by NIH grant GM 10704-03 and NSF grant GB-02905.

References

PATTERSON, A. L. (1959). *International Tables for X-ray Crystallography*. Vol. II, p. 73. Birmingham: Kynoch Press.

ROSSMANN, M. G. & BLOW, D. M. (1962). *Acta Cryst.* **15**, 24.

TOLLIN, P., MAIN, P. & ROSSMANN, M. G. (1966). *Acta Cryst.* **20**, 404.

TOLLIN, P. & SCOULOUDI, H. (1966). To be published.

Acta Cryst. (1966). **20**, 404

The Symmetry of the Rotation Function

BY PATRICK TOLLIN*, PETER MAIN AND MICHAEL G. ROSSMANN
Department of Biological Sciences, Purdue University, Lafayette, Indiana, U.S.A.

The rotation function represents the sum of a point-by-point product of two different Patterson functions rotated with respect to one another. The magnitude of the rotation function can be plotted in a three-dimensional space where the three coordinates are measures of the three angular rotations. The space group of the rotation function expresses the relationship between equivalent rotations where identical magnitudes would be recorded. This symmetry depends upon the symmetry of the two original Patterson functions and the nature of the choice of the variables used to express the rotations. The rotation function need to be evaluated only over the asymmetric unit in rotation space. A simple method is described for obtaining the symmetry of the rotation functions in terms of Eulerian angles. The latter are shown to have considerable advantages over other choices of variables.

Introduction

The rotation function was derived by Rossmann & Blow (RB) in 1962. It has been used in determining the orientation of a known or unknown group with respect to another identical group either in the same or in a different crystal. The method bears much resemblance to the method used so successfully by Nordman & Nakatsu (1963), and much of the content of this paper will be equally true for their techniques. In both cases the amount of computing required is formidable. It is therefore essential to be able to calculate *a priori* the range of angles which needs to be explored before all independent rotation operations have been considered. A method for calculating the range of angles required is discussed in this paper. This method is general and easy to apply in contrast to the special and somewhat arbitrary procedure of RB.

The rotation space group

Let us rewrite the rotation function in the form

$$R=\int_U P_2(\mathbf{X}_2)P_1(\mathbf{X}_1)d\mathbf{X}_1 \qquad (1)$$

where we are comparing the Patterson function P_1 at $\mathbf{X}_1$ with the Patterson function P_2 at $\mathbf{X}_2$. The position vectors $\mathbf{X}_1$ and $\mathbf{X}_2$ are referred to a common orthogonal coordinate system in real space, and satisfy the relationship.

$$\mathbf{X}_2=[\varrho]\mathbf{X}_1 \qquad (2)$$

for all points within the volume U. The matrix $[\varrho]$ describes the rotation which transforms $\mathbf{X}_1$ into $\mathbf{X}_2$. The Patterson functions P_1 and P_2 may be the same functions, or may be different when derived from two different crystalline forms of the same molecular species.

* On leave of absence from Carnegie Laboratory of Physics University of St. Andrews, Queens College, Dundee, Scotland.

The symmetry of the two functions P_1 and P_2 within the volume U will fall into one of eleven Laue groups. In considering the symmetry of the rotation function, R, it is only necessary to consider the symmetry elements of the Laue group which describe proper rotations, that is, rotations without inversion. Thus, for each of P_2 and P_1 a 'proper rotation group' can be written down. A proper rotation group contains all the proper rotations present in the corresponding Laue group, of which it is a sub-group. For example, 222 is the proper rotation group of Laue group *mmm*.

If the symmetry operations of the proper rotation groups of P_1 and P_2 are described by the sets of matrices $[T_i]$ and $[T_j]$, respectively, then

$$R=\int_U P_2([T_j]\mathbf{X}_2)P_1([T_i]\mathbf{X}_1)d\mathbf{X}_1 \qquad (3)$$

will have the same value for all $[T_i]$ and $[T_j]$. Note that $[T_i]$ and $[T_j]$ are symmetry operations applied to the orthogonal coordinates as listed by Patterson (1959, p. 63). Hence from (2)

$$[T_j]\mathbf{X}_2=[\varrho][T_i]\mathbf{X}_1$$

or

$$\mathbf{X}_2=[T_j]^{-1}[\varrho][T_i]\mathbf{X}_1$$
$$=[T_j]^T[\varrho][T_i]\mathbf{X}_1 \qquad (4)$$

where $[T_j]^T$ is the transpose of $[T_j]$. Equation (4) implies that R will have the same value for each rotation which leaves $[T_j]^T[\varrho][T_i]$ unchanged for all values of i and j. The elements of the rotation matrix $[\varrho]$ are determined by the three angles of rotation $(\alpha_1\alpha_2\alpha_3)$. If we consider plotting the magnitude of the rotation function in a three-dimensional space defined by these three angles, then a unit-cell translation is performed whenever one of the angles is increased by 2π. If the sets of angles associated with $[\varrho']$ and $[\varrho]$ are $(\alpha_1'\ \alpha_2'\ \alpha_3')$ and $(\alpha_1\ \alpha_2\ \alpha_3)$, respectively, when $[\varrho']$ and $[\varrho]$ satisfy one of the sets of equations of the type

$$[\varrho']=[T_j]^T[\varrho][T_i]\,, \qquad (5)$$

then (α_1' α_2' α_3') and (α_1 α_2 α_3) are equivalent sets of rotation angles. They represent equivalent positions in the space defined above. The combination of all the symmetry operations of this type forms the rotation space group, an example of which is given by RB.

Let us define ${}_jS_i$ as the symmetry operation which results from satisfying one of the equations (5). Further let S_i be the symmetry operator when $[T_j]^T=[1]$, that is, when the Patterson function P_2 is of the Laue class $\bar{1}$ or proper rotation group 1. Similarly ${}_jS$ is the symmetry operator when P_1 is of the Laue class $\bar{1}$. Thus S_i represents the symmetry operation that satisfies the equation

$$[\varrho_i]=[\varrho][T_i]\,. \quad (6)$$

It follows that

$$[\varrho']=[T_j]^T[\varrho_i] \\ =[T_j]^T[\varrho][T_i]\,. \quad (7)$$

Now the symmetry operation ${}_jS$ satisfies (7). Thus the total symmetry operation which satisfies (4) is a 'product' of S_i and ${}_jS$, where multiplication implies successive application of S_i and ${}_jS$.

As there are only eleven proper rotation groups there will only be eleven different results for S_i and for ${}_jS$. In general, therefore, to determine the rotation space group for any desired rotation function we need only look up S_i and ${}_jS$ for the proper rotation groups of the Patterson functions P_1 and P_2 respectively. Multiplication, in the sense defined above, of these two sets of symmetry operations leads to the complete set ${}_jS_i$ which describe the equivalent general positions of the rotation space group.

The relationship between the symmetry operation ${}_jS_i$ and ${}_iS_j$

The order in which the Patterson functions are arranged in equation (1) is important. We may ask what angular relationships there are between equivalent points if the order is reversed.

Let

$$R_1=\int_U P_2(\mathbf{X}_2)P_1(\mathbf{X}_1)d\mathbf{X}_1$$

corresponding to the relationship

$$\mathbf{X}_2=[\varrho]\mathbf{X}_1$$

and rotation space group expressed by the symmetry operations ${}_jS_i$.

Let also

$$R_2=\int_U P_2(\mathbf{X}_1)P_1(\mathbf{X}_2)d\mathbf{X}_2$$

corresponding to the relationship

$$\mathbf{X}_1=[\varrho']\mathbf{X}_2$$

and rotation space group symmetry operations ${}_iS_j$. Then we may write $\mathbf{X}_2=[\varrho']^{-1}\mathbf{X}_1$ and it follows that

$$R_2=R_1 \text{ when} [\varrho]=[\varrho']^{-1}=[\varrho']^T\,. \quad (8)$$

Thus, reversal of the Patterson functions produces a different though related rotation function with a different rotation space group. All of the foregoing results can be applied to any set of angular variables used to describe the rotations. In the particular case of Eulerian variables, as defined by RB, inspection of the matrix $[\varrho]$ shows that the relationship between the two rotation functions is

$$R_1(\theta_1\theta_2\theta_3)=R_2(-\theta_3,\ -\theta_2,\ -\theta_1)\,. \quad (9)$$

For all proper rotation groups, other than the cubic groups, ${}_jS_i$ takes the form

$$R_1(\theta_1\theta_2\theta_3)=R_2(a_1+b_1\theta_1,\ a_2+b_2\theta_2,\ a_3+b_3\theta_3) \quad (10)$$

where the a's and b's are constants for a particular rotation group. Hence, from relationship (9), the ${}_iS_j$ have the form

$$R_2(\theta_1\theta_2\theta_3)=R_2(-a_3+b_3\theta_1,\ -a_2+b_2\theta_2,\ -a_1+b_1\theta_3)\,. \quad (11)$$

Thus, from (10) and (11) the ${}_iS_j$ can be derived from the ${}_jS_i$.

Tabulation of all possible symmetry operators ${}_jS$ and S_i

The Eulerian angles ($\theta_1\theta_2\theta_3$) are particularly useful for describing the symmetry operation S_i as they take a simple form for all but cubic groups. Apart from these cases the S_i can be described by symmetry planes and axes in the Eulerian variable space, and hence a rotation space group can be written down. The cubic groups lead to symmetry relationships of a different type and these are discussed in the next section.

Table 1 lists the eleven Laue groups, the corresponding proper rotation groups, the rotation axes with their directions relative to the Cartesian set **X**, and the Cartesian unique set of axes required to define the proper rotation groups. Table 2 lists the forms of ${}_jS$ and S_i for each of the symmetry elements which can occur in the proper rotation groups apart from cubic groups. An example of the derivation of S_i is the case of a twofold axis along [010]. In this case

$$[T_i]=\begin{pmatrix}-1 & 0 & 0\\ 0 & 1 & 0\\ 0 & 0 & -1\end{pmatrix}.$$

We are now required to find a set of Eulerian angles θ_1' θ_2' θ_3' which go to form the elements of the matrix $[\varrho']$ identical with the elements of the matrix product $[\varrho]$ $[T_i]$ (equation 6). Upon equating all nine elements of the Eulerian rotation matrix (RB) independently we see that these nine equations are satisfied only when

$$\theta'_1=\pi-\theta_1,\ \theta'_2=\pi+\theta_2,\ \theta'_3=\theta_3\,.$$

Let us now take, as an example, the determination of the rotation space groups in Eulerian variables when P_1 has symmetry $Pmmm$ and P_2 has symmetry $P2/m$. Table 1 shows that mmm corresponds to the proper rotation group 222 which has two unique axes, parall

Table 1. *Properties of proper rotation groups*

Laue group	Proper rotation group	Unique axes [001]	[010]	[100]	[111]
$\bar{1}$	1	1			
2/*m* (axis unique)	2		2		
2/*m* (axis unique)	2	2			
mmm	222	2	2		
4/*m*	4	4			
4/*mmm*	422	4	2		
$\bar{3}$	3	3			
$\bar{3}m$	321	3	2		
6/*m*	6	6			
6/*mmm*	622	6	2		
Cubic					
*m*3	23	2			3
*m*3*m*	432	4			3

b and c, say. We also see that 2/*m*, in the usual mono-
ic setting, has one twofold rotation axis parallel
b. Inspection of Table 2 then shows:
S_i, the symmetry operators on P_1, are:

$\theta_1\ \theta_2\ \theta_3 \rightarrow \pi+\theta_1,\ -\theta_2,\ \pi+\theta_3$ (onefold axis*)

$\theta_1\ \theta_2\ \theta_3 \rightarrow \pi-\theta_1,\ \pi+\theta_2\ \theta_3$ (twofold axis parallel to **b**)

$\theta_1\ \theta_2\ \theta_3 \rightarrow \pi+\theta_1,\ \theta_2,\ \theta_3$ (twofold axis parallel to **c**)

S, the symmetry operators on P_2 are

$\theta_1\ \theta_2\ \theta_3 \rightarrow \pi+\theta_1,\ -\theta_2,\ \pi+\theta_3$ (onefold axis)

$\theta_1\ \theta_2\ \theta_3 \rightarrow \theta_1,\ \pi+\theta_2,\ \pi-\theta_3$ (twofold axis parallel to **b**)

set of equivalent general positions obtained by
nbining these is

$\theta_1,$	$\theta_2,$	θ_3	
$\theta_1,$	$\pi+\theta_2,$	$\pi-\theta_3$	$({}_2S)$
$\theta_1,$	$-\theta_2,$	$\pi+\theta_3$	$(S_3 . S_1)$
$\theta_1,$	$\pi-\theta_2,$	$-\theta_3$	$(S_3 . {}_2S . S_1)$
$\pi+\theta_1,$	$\theta_2,$	θ_3	(S_3)
$\pi+\theta_1,$	$\pi+\theta_2,$	$\pi-\theta_3$	$({}_2S . S_3)$
$\pi+\theta_1,$	$-\theta_2,$	$\pi+\theta_3$	(S_1)
$\pi+\theta_1,$	$\pi-\theta_2,$	$-\theta_3$	$({}_2S . S_1)$
$-\theta_1,$	$-\theta_2,$	$-\theta_3$	$({}_2S . S_2 . S_1)$
$-\theta_1,$	$\pi-\theta_2,$	$\pi+\theta_3$	$(S_2 . S_1)$
$-\theta_1,$	$\theta_2,$	$\pi-\theta_3$	$(S_2 . {}_2S . S_3)$
$-\theta_1,$	$\pi+\theta_2,$	θ_3	$(S_3 . S_2)$
$\pi-\theta_1,$	$-\theta_2,$	$-\theta_3$	$(S_3 . {}_2S . S_2\ \ S_1)$
$\pi-\theta_1,$	$\pi-\theta_2,$	$\pi+\theta_3$	$(S_3 . S_2 . S_1)$
$\pi-\theta_1,$	$\theta_2,$	$\pi-\theta_3$	$({}_2S . S_2)$
$\pi-\theta_1,$	$\pi+\theta_2,$	θ_3	(S_2)

re the operations to obtain these positions are given
rackets after them. Multiplication implies the ap-
ation of the operators consecutively. Alternatively
space group can be found by recognizing that the

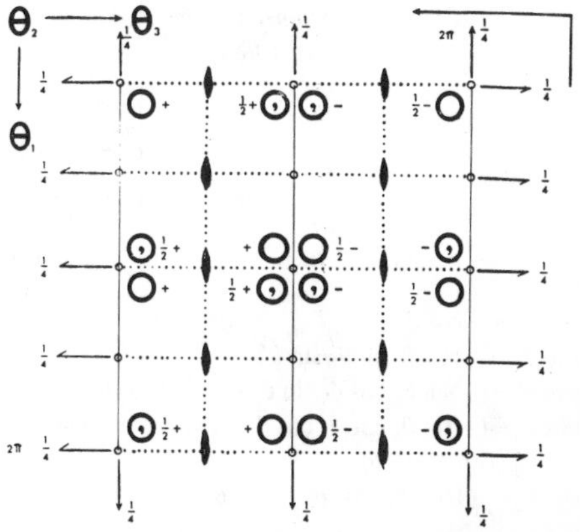

Fig. 1. Rotation space group diagram for rotation function of a *Pmmm* Patterson function (P_1) against a *P*2/*m* Patterson function (P_2). The Eulerian angles $\theta_1, \theta_2, \theta_3$ repeat themselves after an interval of 2π. Heights above the plane are given in fractions of a revolution.

symmetry operators S_1 and ${}_1S$ are *n*-glide planes in $\theta_1, \theta_2, \theta_3$ space perpendicular to θ_2, ${}_2S$ is a *b*-glide plane perpendicular to θ_3 and S_3 divides the total cell into two identical parts along θ_1. The latter combined with S_1 or ${}_1S$ leads to a *c*-glide plane perpendicular to θ_2. The combination of these operations gives two cells each of space group *Pbcb*, keeping the order $\theta_1\theta_2\theta_3$ (Fig. 1).

The non-linear symmetry relationships

If one attempts to develop the forms of S_i for the cubic groups in terms of $(\theta_1\theta_2\theta_3)$ or for other proper rotation groups in terms of other angles, for example, the angles $(\kappa\psi\varphi)$ defined by RB, one finds that the relationship between $(\alpha_1'\ \alpha_2'\ \alpha_3')$ and $(\alpha_1\ \alpha_2\ \alpha_3)$ cannot be written down as a linear transformation, and hence cannot be expressed as symmetry planes and axes in the appropriate variable space. An example of such non-linear symmetry operations is obtained when $[\varrho]$ is operated on by $[T_i]=\begin{pmatrix}0&1&0\\0&0&1\\1&0&0\end{pmatrix}$ which represents a threefold axis along 111. The relationship between $(\theta_1'\ \theta_2'\ \theta_3')$ and $(\theta_1\ \theta_2\ \theta_3)$ in this case is

* The necessity of considering this operation arises out of peculiar property of Eulerian angles, namely that there are ys two related sets of operations which produce the same ntation. Another peculiar property is that in the plane 0 all magnitudes for which $\theta_1+\theta_3$ is a constant are identi- This leads to a twofold axis in this plane.

Table 2. *Symmetry elements S_i and $_jS$ for all possible types of space group rotations*

Axis	Direction	S_i	$_jS$
1		$(\pi+\theta_1, -\theta_2, \pi+\theta_3)$	$(\pi+\theta_1, -\theta_2, \pi+\theta_3)$
2	[010]	$(\pi-\theta_1, \pi+\theta_2, \theta_3)$	$(\theta_1, \pi+\theta_2, \pi-\theta_3)$
2	[001]	$(\pi+\theta_1, \theta_2, \theta_3)$	$(\theta_1, \theta_2, \pi+\theta_3)$
4	[001]	$(-\pi/2+\theta_1, \theta_2, \theta_3)$	$(\theta_1, \theta_2, \pi/2+\theta_3)$
3	[001]	$(-2\pi/3+\theta_1, \theta_2, \theta_3)$	$(\theta_1, \theta_2, 2\pi/3+\theta_3)$
6	[001]	$(-\pi/3+\theta_1, \theta_2, \theta_3)$	$(\theta_1, \theta_2, \pi/3+\theta_3)$
*2	[110]	$(3\pi/2-\theta_1, \pi-\theta_2, \pi+\theta_3)$	$(\pi+\theta_1, \pi-\theta_2, -3\pi/2-\theta_3)$

* This axis is not unique (that is, it can always be generated by two other unique axes), but is included for completeness.

$$\cos\theta_1' = -\cos\theta_2'$$
$$\sin\theta_1' = -\cos\theta_1 \sin\theta_2/\sin\theta_2'$$
$$\sin\theta_3' = (-\sin\theta_1 \cos\theta_2 \sin\theta_3 + \cos\theta_1 \cos\theta_3)/\sin\theta_2'$$
$$\cos\theta_3' = (-\sin\theta_1 \cos\theta_2 \cos\theta_3 - \cos\theta_1 \sin\theta_3)/\sin\theta_2'$$
$$\cos\theta_2' = \sin\theta_1 \sin\theta_2$$
$$\sin\theta_2' = \pm[\sin^2\theta_1 \cos^2\theta_2 + \cos^2\theta_1]^{\frac{1}{2}} .$$

This is a threefold operation, in the sense that the application of this operation three times brings the original point back on itself. It is consistent with the infinite lattice in $(\theta_1\ \theta_2\ \theta_3)$ space and can combine with other linear or non-linear operations to form a group, although it cannot be described by one of the 230 spac groups.

This work was supported by NIH grant GM 10704 03 and NSF grant GB-02905.

We thank Mrs Julia Parsons for assistance in th preparation of the manuscript.

References

Nordman, C. E. & Nakatsu, K. (1963). *J. Amer. Chem Soc.* **85**, 353.

Patterson, A. L. (1959). In *International Tables for X-ra Crystallography*. Vol. II. Birmingham: Kynoch Press.

Rossmann, M. G. & Blow, D. M. (1962). *Acta Cryst.* **15**, 2

Reprinted from *Acta Crystallographica*, Vol. 17, Part 5, May 1964

Acta Cryst. (1964). **17**, 611

The differential rotation function. By YOSHIO SASADA*, *Medical Research Council Laboratory of Molecular Biology, Hills Road, Cambridge, England*

Rossmann & Blow (1962) proposed the rotation function in order to find the relative orientation between sub-units in one crystal or between molecules in different crystal forms. They applied this method to haemoglobin (Rossmann & Blow, 1962), insulin (Hodgkin, Harding, Rossmann & Blow, 1962) and α-chymotrypsin (Blow, Rossmann & Jeffrey, 1963) with successful results. However, this method takes a considerable length of time for computation. Rossmann & Blow estimated the computation time to be about 50 hours on EDSAC II for a crystal of horse haemoglobin if they explored the whole range of Eulerian angles with 20° intervals using 1000 reflexions. They cut down their computing time by using larger intervals with a limited number of reflexions to find the approximate peak positions, and then refined these with closer angular intervals and more reflexions.

In general, the background region of the rotation function has little physical significance. Hence, once the rough peak position has been determined, the major interest is to determine the accurate angular coordinates for which the rotation function has the maximum values. This situation suggests that a technique similar to the differential synthesis for the usual electron density distribution (Booth, 1946) can be applied to the present problem.

Let us assume that an approximate rotation between two identical units is known and is represented by angular coordinates θ_1, θ_2 and θ_3. Let $\Delta\theta_1$, $\Delta\theta_2$ and $\Delta\theta_3$ be the small angular displacements of this point from the true maximum of the rotation function. If they are small, then

$$\left(\frac{\partial^2 R}{\partial\theta_1^2}\right)\Delta\theta_1+\left(\frac{\partial^2 R}{\partial\theta_1\partial\theta_2}\right)\Delta\theta_2+\left(\frac{\partial^2 R}{\partial\theta_1\partial\theta_3}\right)\Delta\theta_3+\left(\frac{\partial R}{\partial\theta_1}\right)=0 \ \textit{etc.},$$

where $(\partial R/\partial\theta_1)$ and $(\partial^2 R/\partial\theta_1^2)$ *etc.* are the first and second derivatives of the rotation function at $(\theta_1, \theta_2, \theta_3)$.

The rotation function is defined as

$$R=\int^U \varrho(\mathbf{x})\varrho(\mathbf{x}')d\mathbf{x} \qquad (1)$$

or

$$R=\int^U \varrho(\mathbf{x})\varrho(\mathbf{x}')\exp\left[-a\mathbf{x}^2\right]d\mathbf{x} \qquad (2)$$

where $\mathbf{x}'$ and $\mathbf{x}$ are related by the rotation $[C]$ according to the relationship

$$\mathbf{x}'=[C]\mathbf{x}.$$

The function (2) has been called the 'shaded rotation function' (Rossmann, 1962). It was designed to increase the peak to background ratio. If U is taken as a sphere centred on the origin, then the rotation function can be written:

$$R=\sum_{\mathbf{h}}\sum_{\mathbf{p}}|F_{\mathbf{h}}|^2|F_{\mathbf{p}}|^2G_{\mathbf{hp}}\,.$$

Now G is the function of the distance, H, between the origin and the point $(\mathbf{h}+\mathbf{h}')$,

where

$$\mathbf{h}'=[\tilde{C}]\mathbf{p}\,,$$

and

$$G_{\mathbf{hp}}=\frac{3\,(\sin 2\pi Hr-2\pi Hr\cos 2\pi Hr)}{(2\pi Hr)^3}$$

for the usual rotation function or

$$G_{\mathbf{hp}}=\frac{1}{Hr}\int_0^1 r'\exp\left[-ar'^2\right]\sin 2\pi Hrr'dr'$$

for the shaded rotation function. The first derivative with respect to θ is then

$$\left(\frac{\partial R}{\partial\theta_1}\right)=\sum_{\mathbf{h}}\sum_{\mathbf{p}}|F_{\mathbf{h}}|^2|F_{\mathbf{p}}|^2\left(\frac{r}{2H}\right)\left\{\frac{3}{Hr}\left(\frac{\sin 2\pi Hr}{2\pi Hr}-G\right)\right\}\left(\frac{\partial H^2}{\partial\theta_1}\right)$$

for the usual rotation function, or

$$\left(\frac{\partial R}{\partial\theta_1}\right)=\sum_{\mathbf{h}}\sum_{\mathbf{p}}|F_{\mathbf{h}}|^2|F_{\mathbf{p}}|^2\left(\frac{r}{2H}\right)\left\{\frac{-A+2\pi HrB}{(Hr)^2}\right\}\left(\frac{\partial H^2}{\partial\theta_1}\right)$$

for the shaded rotation function, where

$$A=\int_0^1 r'\exp\left[-ar'^2\right]\sin 2\pi Hrr'dr'\,,$$

$$B=\int_0^1 r'^2\exp\left[-ar'^2\right]\cos 2\pi Hrr'dr'\,,$$

$$\left(\frac{\partial H^2}{\partial\theta_1}\right)=2\sum_{i=1}^{3}\left\{a_i^{*2}(h_i+h_i')+\sum_{i\neq j\neq k}^{3}\sum a_i^*a_j^*\cos\alpha_k^*(h_j+h_j')\right\}\left(\frac{\partial h_i'}{\partial\theta_1}\right),$$

$$\left(\frac{\partial h_i'}{\partial\theta_1}\right)=\sum_{j=1}^{3}\left(\frac{\partial C_{ji}}{\partial\theta_1}\right)p_j$$

and a_i^*, α_i^* $(i=1\sim 3)$ are the dimensions of the reciprocal unit cell. Similar expressions can be written for $(\partial R/\partial\theta_2)$ and $(\partial R/\partial\theta_3)$.

The second derivative is given by

$$\left(\frac{\partial^2 R}{\partial\theta_1\partial\theta_2}\right)=\sum_{\mathbf{h}}\sum_{\mathbf{p}}|F_{\mathbf{h}}|^2|F_{\mathbf{p}}|^2\left[\left(\frac{r}{2H}\right)\left\{\frac{3}{Hr}\left(\frac{\sin 2\pi Hr}{2\pi Hr}-G\right)\right\}\times\left(\frac{\partial^2 H^2}{\partial\theta_1\partial\theta_2}\right)+\left(\frac{r^2}{4H^2}\right)\left\{\frac{3}{(Hr)^2}\left(5G-6\frac{\sin 2\pi Hr}{2\pi Hr}+\cos 2\pi Hr\right)\right\}\times\left(\frac{\partial H^2}{\partial\theta_1}\right)\left(\frac{\partial H^2}{\partial\theta_2}\right)\right]$$

for the usual rotation function, or

$$\left(\frac{\partial^2 R}{\partial\theta_1\partial\theta_2}\right)=\sum_{\mathbf{h}}\sum_{\mathbf{p}}|F_{\mathbf{h}}|^2|F_{\mathbf{p}}|^2\left[\left(\frac{r}{2H}\right)\left\{\frac{-A+2\pi HrB}{(Hr)^2}\right\}\left(\frac{\partial^2 H^2}{\partial\theta_1\partial\theta_2}\right)+\left(\frac{r^2}{4H^2}\right)\left\{\frac{3A-6\pi HrB-4\pi^2(Hr)^2C}{(Hr)^3}\right\}\left(\frac{\partial H^2}{\partial\theta_1}\right)\left(\frac{\partial H^2}{\partial\theta_2}\right)\right]$$

for the shaded rotation function, where

* Present address: Institute for Protein Research, Osaka University, Kita-ku, Osaka, Japan.

$$C = \int_0^1 r'^3 \exp\,[-ar'^2] \sin 2\pi Hrr'dr' ,$$

$$\left(\frac{\partial^2 H^2}{\partial\theta_1\partial\theta_2}\right) = 2\sum_{i=1}^{3}\left[\left\{a_i^{*2}(h_i+h_i') + \sum_{i\neq j\neq k}^{3}\sum a_i^* a_j^* \cos\alpha_k^*(h_i+h_j')\right\}\right.$$
$$\times\left(\frac{\partial^2 h_i'}{\partial\theta_1\partial\theta_2}\right) + a_i^{*2}\left(\frac{\partial h_i'}{\partial\theta_1}\right)\left(\frac{\partial h_i'}{\partial\theta_2}\right)$$
$$\left. + a_j^* a_k^* \cos\alpha_i^*\left\{\left(\frac{\partial h_j'}{\partial\theta_1}\right)\left(\frac{\partial h_k'}{\partial\theta_2}\right) + \left(\frac{\partial h_k'}{\partial\theta_1}\right)\left(\frac{\partial h_j'}{\partial\theta_2}\right)\right\}\right]$$

and

$$\left(\frac{\partial^2 h_i'}{\partial\theta_1\partial\theta_2}\right) = \sum_{j=1}^{3}\left(\frac{\partial^2 C_{ji}}{\partial\theta_1\partial\theta_2}\right) p_j .$$

It is necessary to examine the nature of the first and second derivatives of the rotation function. As $(\partial H^2/\partial\theta)$ is a function of $(\mathbf{h}+\mathbf{h}')$ and $\mathbf{p}$, $|F_{\mathbf{p}}|^2(r/H)(\partial H^2/\partial\theta)$ as a whole does not change so drastically with H and $\mathbf{p}$. Therefore, it is concluded that the change of $(\partial R/\partial\theta)$ with Hr is controlled mainly by the factor

$$\frac{3}{Hr}\left(\frac{\sin 2\pi Hr}{2\pi Hr} - G\right)$$

for the usual rotation function or

$$\frac{-A + 2\pi HrB}{(Hr)^2}$$

for the shaded rotation function. These two factors are plotted against Hr in Fig. 1 by full and dotted lines, respectively. We now see that the values of the first derivatives do not exceed about 5% of their maximum value if Hr is larger than 1·8. Similar consideration for the second derivatives showed that they are controlled by the factor

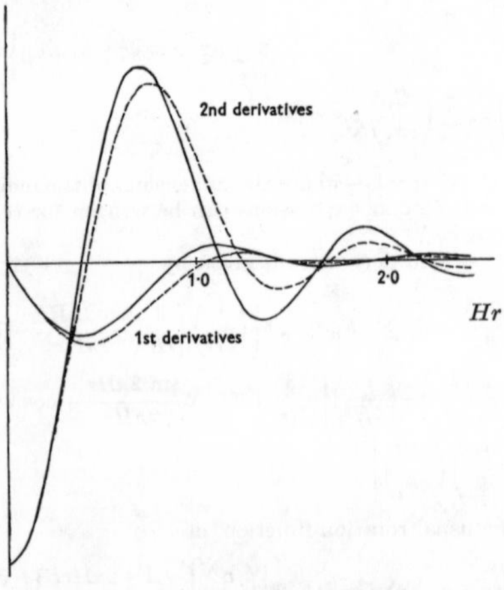

Fig. 1. Variation of the first and second derivatives of the rotation function with Hr. Full lines for the usual and dotted for the shaded rotation function, on a correctly normalized scale.

$$\frac{3}{(Hr)^2}\left(4G - 5\frac{\sin 2\pi Hr}{2\pi Hr} + \cos 2\pi Hr\right)$$

for the usual rotation function or

$$\frac{2A - 4\pi HrB - 4\pi^2(Hr)^2C}{(Hr)^3}$$

for the shaded rotation function. These are also shown in Fig. 1. The values for the second derivatives do not exceed 5% of their maximum values when Hr is greater than 2·0. These properties of the derivatives suggest that they may be evaluated by considering only a few of the terms in the summation over $\mathbf{p}$, as is also true for the calculation of the rotation function itself. It is obvious from Fig. 1 that the shaded rotation function is more favourable than the usual one with respect to this point.

A program for the differential rotation function was written for the IBM 7090 computer. It was tested on the 10Å chymostrypin data, in order to determine the accurate angular relationship between the two independent crystallographic molecules in the asymmetric unit of the $P2_1$ lattice. The progress of a typical refinement is given in Table 1. The time for one cycle using about 280

Table 1. *An example of progress of a refinement by the differential rotation function, using* 10Å *α-chymotrypsin data*

The shaded rotation function was used with a radius of 30 Å and $a=2·0$. The total refinement required 7·76 minutes

Cycle number	$\varkappa$	ψ	φ	R
0	175·0	85·0	85·0	—
1	179·4	86·5	88·2	$0·5478\times 10^9$
2	179·7	88·0	88·7	$0·5709\times 10^9$
3	180·1	89·9	89·4	$0·5856\times 10^9$
4	180·0	90·0	89·3	$0·5984\times 10^9$

(The exploration suggests the maximum at $\varkappa=180·0$, $\psi=90·0$, $\varphi=89·0$).

independent reflexions and 27 terms in the summation over $\mathbf{p}$ was about 1·75 minutes. An exploration of the peak area by the evaluating the rotation function at say 30 points might have taken half an hour.

I wish to express my sincere thanks to Dr M. F. Perutz for his encouragement, to Dr M. G. Rossmann for suggestion of this problem and for his help and discussions throughout this investigation, and to Drs D. M. Blow & M. G. Rossmann for permission to use the α-chymotrypsin data. This study, made in Cambridge, was made possible by a grant from the Rockefeller Foundation.

References

Blow, D. M., Rossmann, M. G. & Jeffrey, B. A. (1963). *J. Mol. Biol.* Submitted for publication.

Booth, A. D. (1946). *Trans. Faraday Soc.* **43**, 444.

Hodgkin, D. Harding, M., Rossmann, M. G. & Blow, D. M. (1962). Symposium, Munich, 28–31, July, 1962.

Rossmann, M. G. (1962). Private communication.

Rossmann, M. G. & Blow, D. M. (1962). *Acta Cryst.* **15**, 24.

Reprinted from TRANSACTIONS OF THE AMERICAN CRYSTALLOGRAPHIC ASSOCIATION, Vol. 2, 1966

VECTOR SPACE SEARCH AND REFINEMENT PROCEDURES*

C. E. Nordman
University of Michigan, Ann Arbor, Michigan

In this talk I should like to discuss some of our efforts to use a priori molecular structure information to get a start at interpreting Patterson functions.

Figure 1 shows the approach in a nutshell. Suppose that we know that our molecule

Search mode	Independent vectors	Example (N=3)
Rotation of group	N(N-1)/2	
Translation of groups in fixed orientation, subject to symmetry	N(N+1)/2	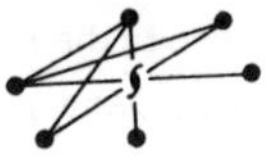
Translation of external point, i.e. 2N-fold Patterson superposition	2N	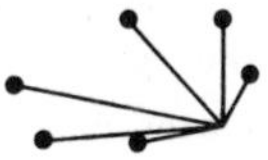

FIG. 1. Summary of rigid group search and superposition

contains a rigid group, perhaps a benzene ring, or whatever might be symbolically represented by the triangular group in the figure. Then the orientation of such a fragment might be established or, more realistically, a large number of possible orientations might be established, by looking for fits of the vectors within such a group to the Patterson function as the group is rotated through all pertinent orientations. If we find the orientation correctly, we can make a meaningful translational search of the Patterson function using the interatomic vectors between two or more such groups related by one or more symmetry elements. And provided we succeed in finding a fit, we will have a partial structure composed of two or more fragments or groups in the unit cell, that is, one per asymmetric unit. We then do a multiple superposition of the Patterson function to find the rest of the atoms. In the bottom part of the figure this superposition is shown as a roving point which looks for fits of vectors from itself to the presumed atoms.

Figure 2 shows an overall flow sheet of the procedures we are using, as they stand at the present time. We start at the top with the preparation of the Patterson function, and of the "rotation search vectors," i.e. a suitable input of the geometrical structure information. There follows a rotation search, as we just suggested, and then a translation search, a refinement stage, superposition, and then, hopefully, least squares refinement. I would like to use this flow sheet as a table of contents for the next 15 or 20 minutes, and go on to discuss several parts of the diagram in somewhat more detail. I should say that some parts of the scheme are

*Supported by the National Institutes of Health under Grant HE-08612.

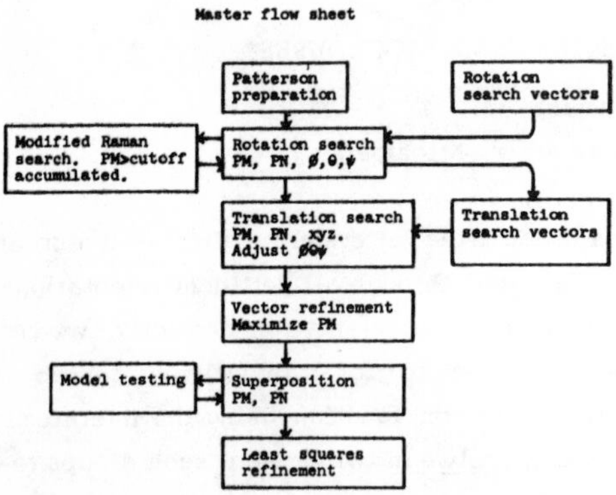

FIG. 2. Overall flow diagram for vector space search and refinement. PM (PN) represents the average of the M (N) lowest Patterson values.

a bit experimental at the moment, and I cannot say that we have experience enough even to recommend them, but the indications are that at least some of the parts are useful.

PATTERSON PREPARATION

Table I summarizes the steps in the preparation of the Patterson function. Using values of the scale factor k and thermal parameter B from a conventional Wilson treatment, a set of initial Patterson coefficients (PATC) are computed. These are in the form of a product of a "point atom" coefficient (Origin peak removed), and a damping factor $\exp(-D\sin^2\theta/\lambda^2)$, where D is a suitable chosen damping parameter. Using these initial coefficients a synthesis of the origin region of

TABLE I

Preparation of the Patterson function

$$\text{PATC} = [kF_o^2(\Sigma Z_i^2/\Sigma f_i^2)\exp(2B\sin^2\theta/\lambda^2) - \Sigma Z_i^2]\ \exp(-D\sin^2\theta/\lambda^2)$$

Synthesis of origin region of Patterson

$$\Delta(\text{PATC}) = \alpha\Sigma P(\underline{r}_i)\cos 2\pi\underline{h}\cdot\underline{r}_i \qquad |\underline{r}_i| < 0.6 - 0.8\ \text{Å}$$

Synthesis using revised PATC. Punch negatives.

$$\text{PATC} = \beta \sum_{neg} P(\underline{r}_j)\cos 2\pi\underline{h}\cdot\underline{r}_j \qquad \underline{h}\ \text{unrecorded.}$$

Final Patterson synthesis D = 0 - 5. Packed words on binary cards and/or tape.

the Patterson is carried out. The parameter D is probably best chosen as zero in this synthesis. We assume that the excursions from zero in the near-origin region are due to artifacts, and proceed to calculate a set of corrections to the PATC's by means of a Fourier inversion of the near-origin region of the Patterson. This calculation is approximate by a sum over the near-origin grid points, an the resulting corrections, (PATC), are scale so as to give a least squares fit to zero c the corrected Patterson in the origin region Since the origin region is small, the resultin (PATC)'s will be a relatively slowly varyin function in reciprocal space. One can thin of this origin-flattening treatment as a correc tion for such effects as an overall therma anisotropy, unequal temperature factors in th structure, and other effects which would pr duce a non-zero origin region in the conven tional scaling and origin peak removal pr cedure.

The next step is a Patterson synthesis using the revised coefficients. One now has the option of "extending the data" by generating PATC values for unrecorded reflections by means of a Fourier analysis of the negative regions in the Patterson function. Our inspiration to write this program came largely from Raman's paper at the Gatlinburg meeting, and also from an earlier paper by Karle and Hauptman (1964). We have had very little experience with this procedure as yet, and are not in a position to recommend it or otherwise. It would be very desirable to put it to a realistic test using a known structure, for which the ability of the data extension procedure to retrieve the missing data could be quantitatively assessed. It is clear that the calculation is going to be rather demanding as far as computer time is concerned.

PREPARATION OF STRUCTURAL INFORMATION INPUT

A suitable input for the rotation search consists of a set of vectors which comprises any or all of the interatomic vectors within the search group. Each input vector is characterized by its weight, or relative expected peak height, and its three components in a crystal-fixed Cartesian coordinate system. This information can easily be calculated by hand, if the group is small. If it is large, it becomes more convenient to do the calculation by computer. Doing it by computer also makes is possible to assign the weights of the vectors more judiciously than would be feasible by hand.

TABLE II

Rotation search vectors

Cartesian input $(x_i y_i z_i)$, and Z_i. $i = 1, \ldots, N$

$N(N-1)/2$ sets of vector components. Weights = $Z_i Z_j$

Identify pairs of vectors differing by less than R_{min}. Combine and add weights.

Identify pairs of vectors differing by less than R_{max}. Increase weights by overlap.

Final weight = $Z_i Z_j + \Sigma Z_m Z_n G(R)$, where $R < R_{max}$. $G(R)$ depends on D and $(\sin\Theta/\lambda)_{max}$.

Eliminate less discriminating vectors: Nearest neighbor, low weight, etc.

The steps involved in such a program are shown in Table II. The vector weights are initially taken as the products of the two atomic numbers Z. Any vectors which are coincident or nearly coincident - say, within R_{min} = 0.05 to 0.10 A - are combined, and their weights added.

Next, the weights of all vectors are incremented by the overlap from any neighbors lying within the expected peak radius, R_{max}, typically 0.5 to 0.6 A. Each member (mn) of a pair of vector peaks separated by R R_{max} will add to the expected peak height of the other member a fraction G(R) of its own initial weight $Z_m Z_n$. The function G(R) is expressible as a power series in R^2. The coefficients in this series depend on the damping parameter D, and on the amount of experimental data, approximately expressible in terms of $(\sin\Theta/\lambda)_{max}$.

Having now computed all the vector components and the expected total Patterson values at the vector points, one has the option of deleting part of the vectors from the set. This would be done to save computing time in the subsequent rotation search. For example, vectors of low weight might be deleted, if the total number of vectors is large. Also, vectors representing nearest neighbor atoms tend to fall on a shell of very high vector density in the Patterson function. Such vectors tend to be less discriminating and could be deleted.

PATTERSON SEARCHES

Figure 3 shows the crystal-fixed Cartesian coordinate system (xyz), to which the input values of the search vector components are referred. The familiar definition of the Euler angles Ø, θ and ψ is also shown. Table III is a condensed flow diagram for the rotation search.

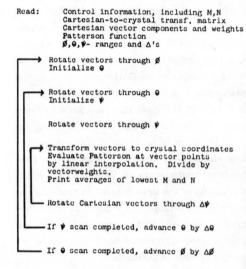

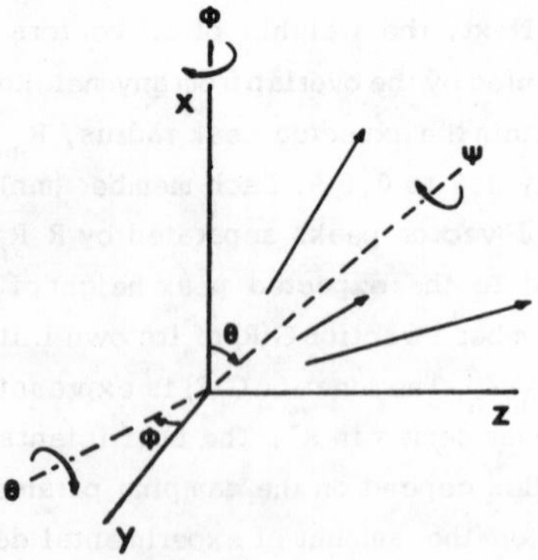

FIG. 3. Rotation search: Cartesian input and Euler angle coordinate systems.

TABLE III

Rotation Search

```
Read:   Control information, including M,N
        Cartesian-to-crystal transf. matrix
        Cartesian vector components and weights
        Patterson function
        Ø,θ,ψ- ranges and Δ's

→ Rotate vectors through Ø
  Initialize θ

  → Rotate vectors through θ
    Initialize ψ

    Rotate vectors through ψ

    → Transform vectors to crystal coordinates
      Evaluate Patterson at vector points
      by linear interpolation. Divide by
      vectorweights.
      Print averages of lowest M and N

    Rotate Cartesian vectors through Δψ

  If ψ scan completed, advance θ by Δθ

If θ scan completed, advance Ø by ΔØ
```

The rotation search is accomplished by systematically stepping through the appropriate ranges of the three Euler angles. The rotations are carried out on the Cartesian coordinates of the vector points. The transformation matrix for rotation through a given angle about an axis of specified direction cosines is given in the International Tables for x-ray Crystallography. (Vol. II, p. 63 Clearly, the elements of this matrix depend on the particular rotation in question. For example, the elements of the matrix used to step through ψ are evaluated using the current values of θ and Ø as well as Δψ.

It can be seen from Figure 3 that the ψ range can be reduced if the search group as an axis of symmetry. If the set of input ectors has an n-fold axis along the Cartesian -axis, the necessary search range in ψ is nly one nth of a turn.

For each $\phi\,\theta\,\psi$ setting a table is gen-rated, internally, which contains the values f the Patterson function at all the vector oints.

The stored Patterson function con-ists of all the values corresponding to a rid, say, in 60ths of the unit cell edges, overing one asymmetric unit. On the IBM 090 it is necessary to pack the grid point alues three to a word in order to accom-odate a monoclinic Patterson function.

The Patterson values of the vector oints are calculated by linear interpolation etween four neighboring grid point values. lternatively, the grid point value nearest e vector point may be used.

The Patterson values of the vector oints are then divided by their respective ector weights, i.e. expected peak heights. his gives a set of reduced Patterson values, hich are more valid indicators of fit or mis-t of the vectors to the Patterson function.

Finally we print out the averages of e M lowest and of the N lowest reduced atterson values in the set. M and N are pecified as input parameters. If M equals , the output is the minimum function, in ffect. If it equals the total number of ectors, we get the sum function. It has een our experience that the average of the Patterson values of the lowest 10 - 20 per-cent of the vectors is a more reliable cri-terion of fit than the minimum function. It is also less noisy.

A complete rotation search tends to be rather time consuming. Obviously, the time depends on the number of vectors, the sym-metry of the Patterson function and of the search group, and on the values chosen for $\Delta\phi$, $\Delta\theta$ and $\Delta\psi$. The optimum values of the Δ's depend on the size and shape of the group. The rotation searches for the struc-tures mentioned below required 20 - 60 minutes on the IBM 7090, using Δ's in the range of about 4 to 8 degrees.

Next comes the translation search, which is outlined in Figure 4. The input con-sists of control and search range information, the original Cartesian atomic coordinates of

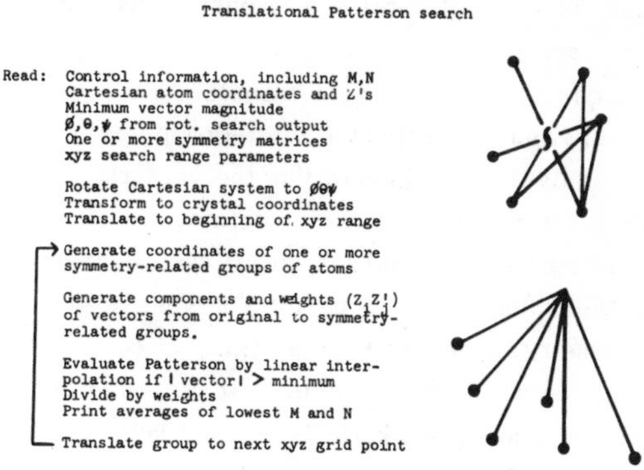
Translational Patterson search
Read: Control information, including M,N
Cartesian atom coordinates and Z's
Minimum vector magnitude
ø,θ,ψ from rot. search output
One or more symmetry matrices
xyz search range parameters
Rotate Cartesian system to øθψ
Transform to crystal coordinates
Translate to beginning of xyz range
Generate coordinates of one or more symmetry-related groups of atoms
Generate components and weights (Z_i Z_j') of vectors from original to symmetry-related groups.
Evaluate Patterson by linear interpolation if | vector | > minimum
Divide by weights
Print averages of lowest M and N
Translate group to next xyz grid point

FIG. 4. Condensed flow diagram for translational Patterson search, and two equivalent formulations of search vectors.

the search group, one or more sets of promising $\phi\theta\psi$ values from the rotation search, and one or more symmetry operation matrices. These matrices are used to generate the atomic coordinates of symmetry related groups in the structure.

A provision for ignoring all vectors which are shorter than a specified magnitude is also included in this program. The thought behind this provision is that the near-origin region of the Patterson is likely to contain errors and artifacts, and that vector points falling within, say, 2 A from the origin might best be disregarded.

The rest of the flow diagram in Figure 4 is similar to the rotation search, or otherwise self-explanatory.

There is an alternative approach to the translation search in cases where one pair of symmetry-related groups, that is, one symmetry operation, is involved. As one can see from Figure 4, translating the twc groups and generating the inter-group vectors is equivalent to generating the vectors and then translating the vector points. In each case the translational search will be one, two, or three dimensional depending on whether the symmetry element is a plane, axis, or center. The second formulation is that proposed by Hoppe and co-workers (Hoppe, 1957) and recently automated and applied to three-dimensional problems (Huber, 1965; Huber and Hoppe, 1965). Its advantages are somewhat faster computing, and the ease with which vector weights can be employed. This vector and weight calculation is shown a an alternative path in Figure 2.

In space groups with several symmetr elements, computing time consideration usually favor doing the initial, full range translation searches separately, for one symmetry element at a time. This means that th advantage afforded by the atom-coordinat input version is not as great as one migh think, although in fine searches of promisin regions it is often convenient to be able t handle several symmetry elements simultaneously.

VECTOR SPACE REFINEMENT

Following the rotation and translatic searches we have a partial structure compose of one rigid group per asymmetric unit. Or w may in practice have several tentative partia structures of this kind. It is desirable to b able to refine such structures, both in ord to optimize the input to the subsequent superposition, and in order to choose among severa alternative partial structures.

A condensed flow sheet for a refinement procedure for a partial structure is show in Figure 5. The principle is to optimize th fit of the interatomic vectors in the parti structure to the Patterson function. All interatomic vectors in the partial structure a calculated, and those less than some prese minimum, say 2 A, optionally disregarde Of the remaining vectors the one having th lowest Patterson value is identified. Th atoms involved in this vector are moved i

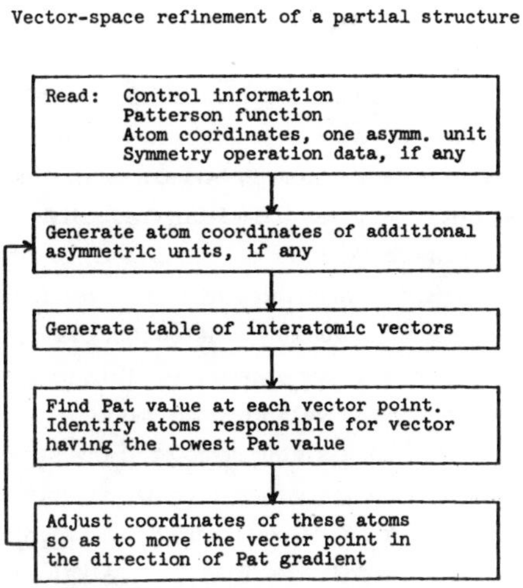

FIG. 5. Condensed flow diagram for vector-space refinement of a partial structure.

such a way as to make the vector point move in the direction of the gradient of the Patterson function. Next, the components of all vectors involving one or both of the shifted atoms are recomputed, the lowest Patterson value identified, and so forth. The average of the lowest M Patterson values is monitored, and when this average ceases to improve, the refinement is discontinued.

The vector refinement is followed by a more or less conventional multiple superposition. Here, too, we have found it useful to apply the proximity, test, i.e., to ignore vectors less than about 2 A. Also, we have found that the averages of several of the lowest Patterson values tend to give more reliable superposition maps than the straight minimum function. Generally speaking, the use of the averaging procedure, as opposed to the minimum, makes it practical to use a more highly sharpened Patterson, including D=0 (Table I).

EXTENSIONS AND APPLICATIONS

To the left of Figure 2 there are shown two proposed extensions of these procedures. We have had very little actual experience with them as yet, and we must consider them rather experimental.

The first is a modified minimum-accumulation function calculation essentially as proposed by Raman and Lipscomb (1961).

Let us consider a rigid group of atoms in a proposed orientation, and let the group be translated through Patterson space with its orientation maintained. If the orientation is correct, all of the atoms will fall on peaks whenever the Patterson origin occupies the position of some atom in the structure. If the orientation is incorrect, the chances that all atoms in the group simultaneously fall on peaks will be less. Consequently, a function calculated as the accumulation of all values of the lowest Patterson value, or of the average of a few lowest, as the group is stepwise translated through part or all of the Patterson cell could be used as an aid in deciding among proposed orientations. Better discrimination appears to result if minimum (or average) values are included in the accumulation only when their values exceed a certain threshold value, say, a value slightly less than the expected single vector peak value.

The computing time would appear to rule out any use of this calculation to search all orientations, but it appears promising as an added device to find the correct orientation among several possible ones.

The second extension is an automatic procedure for successively augmenting a given **partial** structure by testing proposed additional atoms, such as superposition peaks, for compatibility with it. This program was designed and written by Jesse Schilling (1965) of our laboratory. A greatly simplified flow diagram is given in Figure 6. Starting with a partial structure and a set of tentative additional atoms, the partial structure is gradually built up. Prior to adding an atom to an existing n atom structure all possible n + 1 atom structures are subjected to vector refinement. At each cycle one atom is added, unless more than one atom gives essentially equally good fit. In the latter case all are added, and the ones least compatible with the resulting structure subsequently deleted. On the basis of our limited experience with it this program appears to be of very definite value.

We have so far completed the structure determination of four unknown structures in our laboratory, using the procedures which I have outlined. The first two, alkaloid C from Alstonia muelleriana (Nordman and Nakatsu (1963), and an isoxazoline derivative of pyrethrosin (Gabe and Nordman, to be published) were completely straightforward. The third structure, a dimeric indole alkaloid, villalstonine (Nordman and Kumra, 1965), was a bit more troublesome in the sense that the correct partial structure could not be unambigu-

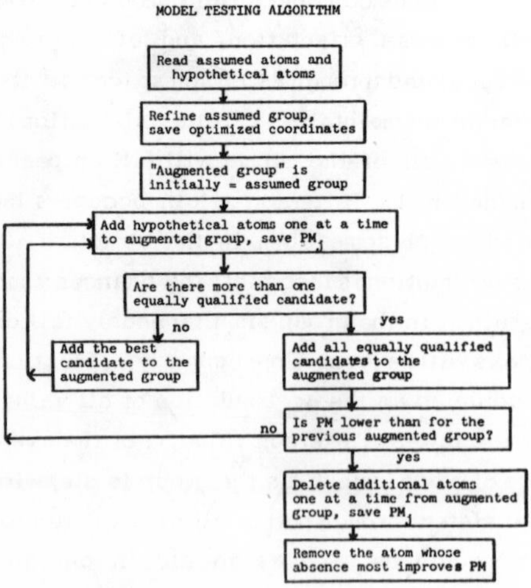

FIG. 6. Condensed flow diagram for successively adding atoms to a partial structure.

TABLE IV

Compound	Space group	Atoms per cell	Assumed
Alstonia alkaloid C $C_{20}H_{22}O_3N_2$	$P2_1$	50	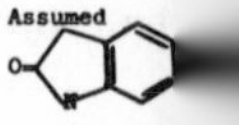
Pyrethrosin deriv. $C_{24}H_{26}O_6NCl$	$P2_1$	64	
Villalstonine $C_{41}H_{48}O_4N_4 + CH_3OH$	$P2_1$	102	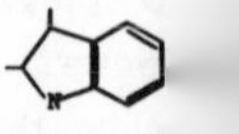
Benzyne adduct $C_{18}H_{14}$	$P2_12_12_1$	72	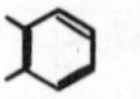

ously recognized until the vector refinement stage. The same was to some extent true of the fourth problem, a benzyne adduct hydrocarbon (Schilling and Nordman, to be published), where the number of distinct vectors contained in the assumed group was relatively small. Data for these compounds including the parts of the molecules used as known groups are given in Table IV. As we modified and improved the procedures in the course of these structure analyses, I think we can say that in the end they all appeared quite straightforward. I think one can claim a reasonable level of promise for this approach to determining structures of the complexity of those listed, and with these rather modest amounts of a priori information available.

REFERENCES

W. Hoppe (1957). Acta Cryst. 10, 750; Z. Elektrochem. 61, 1076.

R. Huber (1965). Acta Cryst. 19, 353.

R. Huber and W. Hoppe (1965). Chem. Ber. 98, 2403.

J. Karle and H. Hauptman (1964). Acta Cryst. 17, 392.

C. E. Nordman and K. Nakatsu (1963). J. Am. Chem. Soc. 85, 353.

C. E. Nordman and S. K. Kumra (1965). J. Am. Chem. Soc. 87, 2059

S. Raman and W. N. Lipscomb (1961). Z. Krist. 116, 314.

J. W. Schilling (1966). Ph.D. Thesis, University of Michigan, in preparation.

DISCUSSION

P. W. R. Corfield, Northwestern University

When you are trying to refine and you are trying to move up the gradient, how do you do it? Do you move one atom one way and the other another way?

C. E. Nordman

Yes, move one one way and the other the other way. We specify an initial shift, which is some small fraction of the unit cell, and whenever we start moving up a gradient we move each atom by this amount. Then, on the next cycle, if the role of worst fitting vector has been taken over by another vector, we apply those same shifts to those two atoms. If on two consecutive cycles the same vector has the role of worst fitting vector, you keep shifting until you come to the peak. But sooner or later you are going to have a situation where you worsen your agreement. Then you back up, halve the shift and try again. If it still worsens, you halve again. This way you phase out.

J. A. Ibers, Northwestern University

Am I correct in assuming that with today's computer, at least, the method you describe would not be useful if you had more than one molecule in the asymmetric unit?

Because you would have to rotate in some complicated way, each of them separately?

C. E. Nordman

No. I am working on a structure with two molecules in the asymmetric unit. What I would hope to find is two peaks in the rotation search, and you would proceed with either one, or both. In fact, a slight generalization could be used, where you do a translation search with two fragments, in general unequal, but in this case perhaps equal, which are not related by symmetry. I think, since you gave me the chance, that this would be the extension of this approach. Look for whatever molecular fragments you have, in general several in the same molecule. Then do an intramolecular translation search, at which stage you can apply some more chemical criteria of fit, which I think would be very desirable. That runs into a good deal of computing, and we can't claim that we are doing that now.

B. THE TRANSLATION PROBLEM

Reprinted from *Acta Crystallographica*, Vol. 17, Part 4, April 1964

ta Cryst. (1964). **17**, 338

The Relative Positions of Independent Molecules Within the Same Asymmetric Unit

By Michael G. Rossmann and D. M. Blow
M. R. C. Laboratory of Molecular Biology, Hills Road, Cambridge, England
and Marjorie M. Harding* and Eleanor Coller
Chemical Crystallography Laboratory, South Parks Road, Oxford, England

If x and x′ are position vectors of equivalent points in identical molecules in different parts of the crystallographic asymmetric unit, then the linear relationship between these points may be written as x′ = [C]x + d, when [C] is a rotation matrix and d a translation vector. A function is derived for determining d, given [C], when no knowledge of the phases is available.

onsider a crystal structure which contains two or ore molecules, or other identical distributions of ectron density, within the crystallographic asym- etric unit. Such distributions of density will be ferred to as sub-units. In a previous paper we have own how the angular relationship between the b-units may be derived from the Patterson function ossmann & Blow, 1962). This depended on the idea at the Patterson vectors within one sub-unit ne 'self-vectors') formed a similar distribution for ch sub-unit; so that a rotation can be found which ings the self-vectors from one sub-unit into coin- dence with those from the other.

* Present address: Department of Chemistry, University Edinburgh, West Mains Road, Edinburgh 9, Scotland.

In this paper we shall consider how the 'cross-vectors', or Patterson vectors from one sub-unit to another, can be used to determine the translation required to bring one sub-unit into coincidence with the other, after suitable rotation about a given axis. In other papers (Hodgkin, Harding, Coller & Rossmann, 1964; Blow, Rossmann & Jeffery, 1964) we describe the application of this method to the proteins insulin and chymotrypsin. In a further paper (Rossmann & Blow, 1963) we have suggested how the condition that the sub-units must be identical, once their relative orientation and position are known, may be used to determine phases, thus leading to a solution of the structure.

Although the result of a rotation and translation in three dimensions depends on the position of the rotation axis, the component of translation in a direction parallel to the axis of rotation is independent

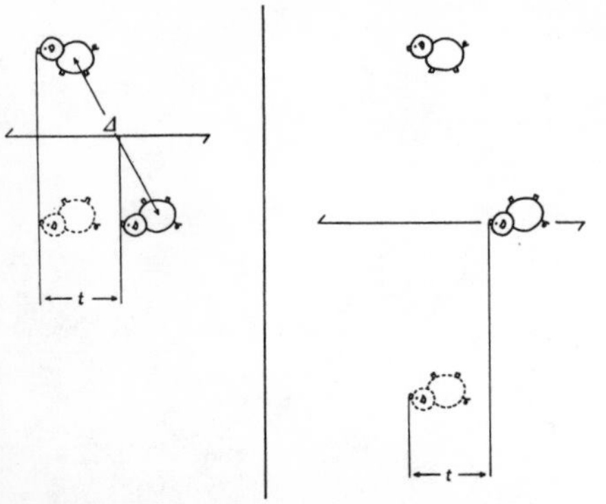

Fig. 1. The position of the twofold rotation axis which relates the two piglets is completely arbitrary. The diagram on the left shows the situation when the translation is parallel to the rotation axis. The diagram on the right has an additional component of translation perpendicular to the rotation axis, but the component parallel to the axis remains unchanged.

of this position (Fig. 1). It is this quantity which can be derived accurately by the method described below. The effect of space group symmetry is to allow a number of such translations to be determined, corresponding to choosing different pairs of sub-units related by the same rotation. Finally the localization in the Patterson projection of cross-vectors related by a particular rotation gives a less accurate indication of the positions of the sub-units in the unit cell.

Relationship between cross-vectors

The relation between two identical arrays of atoms, A and B, may be expressed by a matrix [C] corresponding to a rotation about the origin of coordinates, and a translation vector **d**, where

$$\mathbf{x}_i^B = [\mathbf{C}]\mathbf{x}_i^A + \mathbf{d} \qquad (1)$$

for the arrays of N atoms, $i=1, \ldots, N$. In a crystal, if [C] does not correspond to a crystallographic rotation, the relation (1) can only apply to a localized group of atoms in the crystal. We define a *sub-unit* A as the array of N atoms at positions $\mathbf{x}_i^A$ which are related to identical atoms at $\mathbf{x}_i^B$ by (1).

It is convenient to choose a reference point **S** near the centre of each sub-unit, as an origin of a local system of coordinates **X**, so that

$$\mathbf{X}_i^A = \mathbf{x}_i^A - \mathbf{S}^A \qquad (2)$$

and

$$|\mathbf{X}_i^A| < r \quad (i=1, \ldots, N)\,.$$

(The purpose of choosing **S** near the centre of the sub-unit is that r shall be as small as possible.) Th reference points are to be equivalent, so that

$$\mathbf{S}^B = [\mathbf{C}]\mathbf{S}^A + \mathbf{d}\,. \qquad ($$

It is convenient to define a translation indepe dently of the choice of origin. This requirement fulfilled by the vector

$$\Delta^{AB} = \mathbf{S}^B - \mathbf{S}^A. \qquad ($$

This is related to **d** by

$$\Delta^{AB} = ([\mathbf{C}] - [\mathbf{I}])\mathbf{S}^A + \mathbf{d}\,.$$

where **I** is the identity matrix.

We shall now consider vectors between one su unit and another, which may be called 'cross-vector and we shall assume that [C] is known (Rossma & Blow, 1962). Every vector **v** from $\mathbf{x}_i^A$ to $\mathbf{x}_j^B$ related to a vector **v′** from $\mathbf{x}_i^B$ to $\mathbf{x}_j^A$. To the exte that we can demonstrate a relation between the independent of $\mathbf{X}_i$ and $\mathbf{X}_j$, the existence of any cros vector **v** implies the existence of another cross-vect **v′**, determined only by [C] and Δ^{AB}. We propose determine the translation Δ^{AB} by searching t Patterson distribution for appropriately related arra of vectors.

Let

$$\mathbf{v} = \mathbf{x}_j^B - \mathbf{x}_i^A = [\mathbf{C}]\mathbf{x}_j^A + \mathbf{d} - \mathbf{x}_i^A = [\mathbf{C}]\mathbf{X}_j^A + \Delta^{AB} - \mathbf{X}_i^A$$

by (1) and (2), and similarly let

$$\mathbf{v}' = \mathbf{x}_j^A - \mathbf{x}_i^B = \mathbf{x}_j^A - [\mathbf{C}]\mathbf{x}_i^A - \mathbf{d} = \mathbf{X}_j^A - [\mathbf{C}]\mathbf{X}_i^A - \Delta^{AB}.$$

Then, eliminating $\mathbf{X}_i^A$ between the expressions f **v** and **v′**

$$\mathbf{v}' = [\mathbf{C}]\mathbf{v} - ([\mathbf{I}] + [\mathbf{C}])\Delta^{AB} - ([\mathbf{C}]^2 - [\mathbf{I}])\mathbf{X}_j^A. \qquad ($$

Rotation of 180°

In three cases already studied we have found a rotati of 180° relating protein sub-units (Rossmann & Blo 1962; Hodgkin *et al.*, 1964; Blow *et al.*, 1964). Sin this appears to be a common mode of association sub-units, it is an important special case.

If [C] represents a rotation of 180°, $[\mathbf{C}]^2 = [\mathbf{I}]$ ar (5) becomes

$$\mathbf{v}' = [\mathbf{C}]\mathbf{v} - ([\mathbf{I}] + [\mathbf{C}])\Delta^{AB} \qquad ($$

which is independent of the atomic positions X This means the cross-vector **v** can always be supe imposed on **v′** by the rotation and translation give by (6). It is possible to define a function $T(\Delta)$ whic will have a large value only if Δ has the value give by (6).

$$T(\Delta) = \int_{|\mathbf{v}-\Delta|<2r} P(\mathbf{v})\,.\,P(\mathbf{v}')\,d\mathbf{v}. \qquad ($$

Here $P(\mathbf{v})$ represents the Patterson function, and and **v′** are related by (6). The volume of integratio

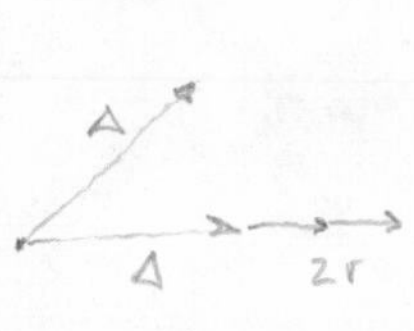

ill include all cross-vectors related by (6). (The tegration (7) is over a sphere; if more detailed formation about molecular shape were available y other suitable shape could be used.)

The expression (7) can readily be expanded in a rm suitable for direct calculation from the observed tensities. Putting $\mathbf{u}=\mathbf{v}-\Delta$, one finds

$$T(\Delta)=\int_{|\mathbf{u}|<2r} P(\mathbf{u}+\Delta)P([\mathrm{C}]\mathbf{u}-\Delta)\,d\mathbf{u}\,.$$

his form shows that the translation function depends comparing a region of the rotated Patterson funcon around $-\Delta$ with a region of the unrotated atterson function around $+\Delta$. Expanding in Fourier ries

$$T(\Delta)=\int_{|\mathbf{u}|<2r}[\sum_{\mathbf{h}} F_{\mathbf{h}}^2 \exp\{2\pi i(\mathbf{h}.\mathbf{u}+\Delta)\}]$$
$$\times[\sum_{\mathbf{p}} F_{\mathbf{p}}^2 \exp\{2\pi i\mathbf{p}([\mathrm{C}]\mathbf{u}-\Delta)\}]\,d\mathbf{u}$$
$$=\sum_{\mathbf{h}}\sum_{\mathbf{p}} F_{\mathbf{h}}^2 F_{\mathbf{p}}^2 \exp\{2\pi i(\mathbf{h}-\mathbf{p}).\Delta\}$$
$$\times\int_{|\mathbf{u}|<2r}\exp\{(\mathbf{h}+\mathbf{p}[\mathrm{C}]).\mathbf{u}\}\,d\mathbf{u}\,.$$

he integral has been discussed by Rossmann & Blow 962), where it is written as $(U/V)G_{\mathbf{hp}}\exp(i\Omega_{\mathbf{hp}})$. the present case $\Omega_{\mathbf{hp}}=0$, as the volume of inteation is symmetrical about $\mathbf{u}=0$. Using the Friedel lationships this gives

$$T(\Delta)=(U/V)\sum_{\mathbf{h}}\sum_{\mathbf{p}} F_{\mathbf{h}}^2 F_{\mathbf{p}}^2 G_{\mathbf{hp}}\cos 2\pi(\mathbf{h}-\mathbf{p}).\Delta\,. \quad (8)$$

his may be recognized as a centrosymmetric Fourier mmation with coefficients

$$\{\sum_{\mathbf{p}} F_{\mathbf{H}-\mathbf{p}}^2 F_{\mathbf{p}}^2 G_{\mathbf{H}-\mathbf{p},\mathbf{p}}\}$$

r the term with indices $\mathbf{H}=\mathbf{h}-\mathbf{p}$.

Precise and imprecise parameters

hereas $\mathbf{d}$ in equation (1) has a value as precise as e values of atomic coordinates, the 'centre' of a b-unit is a much less precise concept. As shown in g. 1, Δ^{AB} has a precise component, $\mathbf{t}$, parallel to e rotation axis and an imprecise one perpendicular it; the component $\mathbf{t}$ is always the same, no matter here the rotation axis is placed. The vector]+[C])Δ^{AB} in equation (6) is parallel to the rotation is, and is equal to $2\mathbf{t}$. Thus the vector $\mathbf{v}'$ is superposed on $\mathbf{v}$ by rotation of the Patterson, followed translation along the axial direction. The only fect of the component of Δ perpendicular to the tation axis is to vary the region of the Patterson er which the integral (7) is taken. $T(\Delta)$ will be latively insensitive to such variation, since the perposable vectors lie in a region $2r$ in diameter. It is therefore convenient to consider two components of Δ. Any peak in the translation function $T(\Delta)$ precisely determines one parameter, $\mathbf{t}$, representing the translation parallel to the rotation axis between two sub-units. At the same time it determines in a relatively imprecise way the perpendicular (or sideways) component, $\mathbf{s}$, of the vector separating the sub-units. This is illustrated in two dimensions in Figs. 2, 3 and 4. Fig. 2 shows a postulated structure; Fig. 3 its Patterson function and Figs. 4(a), (b) and (c) show various attempts at matching up the cross

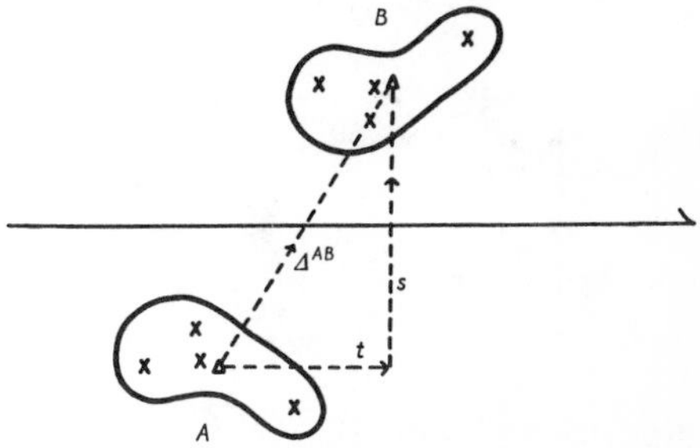

Fig. 2. The crosses represent atoms in a two-dimensional model structure. The triangles are the points chosen as approximate centres of molecules A and B. Δ^{AB} has components $\mathbf{t}$ and $\mathbf{s}$ parallel and perpendicular to the screw rotation axis, respectively.

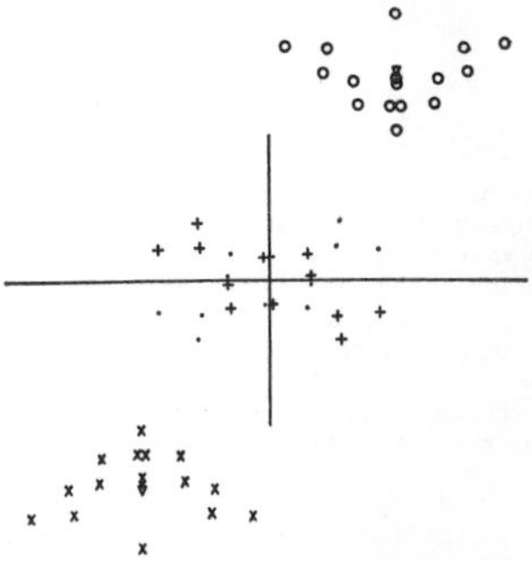

Fig. 3. The vectors arising from the structure in Fig. 2. The self-vectors of molecules A and B are represented by + and · ; the cross-vectors from molecules A to B and B to A by × and ○. Triangles mark the position of $+\Delta^{AB}$ and $-\Delta^{AB}$.

Patterson vectors. In Fig. 4(a) the Patterson within the circle centred at $-\Delta^{AB}$ has been rotated about the known rotation axis through the origin and translated by $2\mathbf{t}$ parallel to this axis. This gives the best match within the circle. A translation other than $2\mathbf{t}$ produces no overlap at all (Fig. 4(b)). If the circle is placed at a centre Δ with the same component $\mathbf{t}$ parallel to the rotation axis, but an altered perpendicular component, not all the vector coincidences

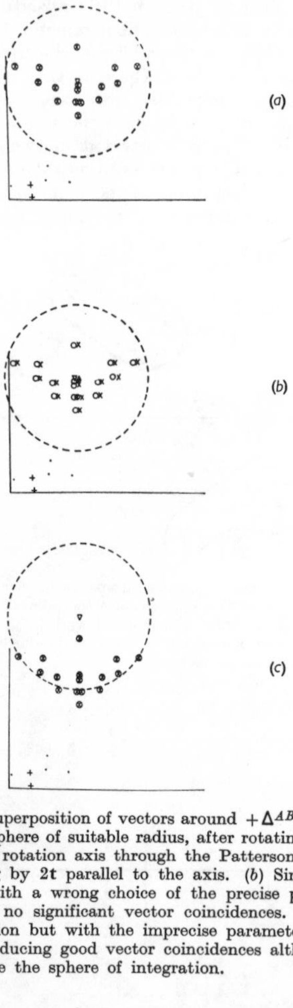

Fig. 4. (*a*) Superposition of vectors around $+\Delta^{AB}$ and $-\Delta^{AB}$ within a sphere of suitable radius, after rotating the latter about the rotation axis through the Patterson origin and translating by $2\mathbf{t}$ parallel to the axis. (*b*) Similar superposition with a wrong choice of the precise parameter $\mathbf{t}$ producing no significant vector coincidences. (*c*) Similar superposition but with the imprecise parameter $\mathbf{s}$ chosen badly, producing good vector coincidences although some fall outside the sphere of integration.

will lie within the circle, and a reduced value of $T(\Delta)$ will result (Fig. 4(*c*)).

General rotation

In the case of a 180° rotation $([\mathbf{C}]^2-[\mathbf{1}])=0$, which gives (5) a simple form. A similar simplification may be made in the case of n sub-units related by rotations of $2\pi/n$, by considering three of these sub-units A, B, C, and letting $\mathbf{v}=\mathbf{x}_j^B-\mathbf{x}_i^A$ while $\mathbf{v}'=\mathbf{x}_i^B-\mathbf{x}_j^C$. For a completely general rotation there is no way of eliminating $\mathbf{X}_j^A$ from (5). This means that no rotation and translation of the Patterson function can lead to exact superposition of all cross-vectors between the two sub-units. Nevertheless, especially when a pair of sub-units is related by rotation through an ang near to 0° or 180°, all cross-vectors can be brough close to superposition.

If $[\mathbf{C}]$ represents a rotation $\varkappa$ about some axi $[\mathbf{C}]^2$ represents a rotation $2\varkappa$ about the same axis an $([\mathbf{C}]^2-[\mathbf{1}])\mathbf{X}_j$ is bound to lie in a plane perpendicul to the axis of rotation. Bearing in mind that $|\mathbf{X}_j^A|<$ it follows that $([\mathbf{C}]^2-[\mathbf{1}])\mathbf{X}_j^A$ must lie on a dis centred at the origin of coordinates, perpendicul to the axis of rotation, of radius $|2r\sin\varkappa|$. Equatio (5) thus indicates a rotation and translation of th vector $\mathbf{v}'$ which will cause the vector between it an $\mathbf{v}$ to lie on such a disc. In this case the 'translatio function' must evaluate the correlation between th Patterson density at $\mathbf{v}$ and that in the disc of possib positions for $\mathbf{v}'$:

$$T(\Delta)=\int_{|\mathbf{u}|<2r}P(\mathbf{v})\left\{\int\!\!\int_{|\mathbf{X}_j|<r}P(\mathbf{v}')d\mathbf{X}_j\right\}d\mathbf{u}\;,$$

where $\mathbf{v}'$ is related to $\mathbf{v}$ and X_j by (5), and $\mathbf{u}=\mathbf{v}-$ as before. Making these substitutions

$$T(\Delta)=\int_{|\mathbf{u}|<2r}P(\mathbf{u}+\Delta)\times\left\{\int\!\!\int_{|\mathbf{X}|<r}P[\mathbf{C}]\mathbf{u}-\Delta-([\mathbf{C}]^2-[\mathbf{1}])\mathbf{X})d\mathbf{X}\right\}d\mathbf{u}\;.$$

The expansion in Fourier series yields

$$T(\Delta)=\sum_{\mathbf{h}}\sum_{\mathbf{p}}F_{\mathbf{h}}^2F_{\mathbf{p}}^2G_{\mathbf{hp}}w_{\mathbf{p}}\cos 2\pi(\mathbf{h}-\mathbf{p})\,.\,\Delta\;,\quad(9)$$

where

$$w_{\mathbf{p}}=\int_{|\mathbf{X}|<r}\exp\{-2\pi i\mathbf{p}\,.\,([\mathbf{C}]^2-[\mathbf{1}])\mathbf{X}\}\,d\mathbf{X}$$

is a weighting function which gives full weight reflexions for which the vector $\mathbf{p}$ lies along the rotati axis, and reduced weight elsewhere. It is, in fac the Fourier transform of a weighted disc, orientat with its normal along the axis of $[\mathbf{C}]$, and is simil to the function $(1/2\pi rR)J_1(2\pi rR)$ which is the tran form of a uniform disc.

The summation (9) is seen to be a centrosymmetr Fourier summation with coefficients

$$\{\sum_{\mathbf{p}}F_{\mathbf{H}-\mathbf{p}}^2F_{\mathbf{p}}^2w_{\mathbf{p}}G_{\mathbf{H}-\mathbf{p},\mathbf{p}}\}$$

for the term with indices $\mathbf{H}=\mathbf{h}-\mathbf{p}$.

Effect of space group symmetry

So far, only an isolated pair of sub-units has bee considered. In space group $P1$ the choice of orig is entirely arbitrary, and may be taken as the positi of $\mathbf{S}^A$, so that $\mathbf{S}^A=0$, $\mathbf{S}^B=\Delta^{AB}$.

In all cases of higher symmetry, the positions crystallographic symmetry elements provide referen points in the unit cell from which the positions sub-units must be measured. In these cases there a a number of distinct ways of choosing pairs of su nits, so that each of these pairs will be associated ith a different translation vector Δ. The relation etween these values of Δ will usually allow the ositions of the sub-units to be related to those of the ymmetry elements.

A special difficulty arises in some cases where the on-crystallographic rotation [**C**] is about an axis erpendicular to a crystallographic symmetry axis, ecause the sub-unit as defined may become infinite ı its extent in the direction parallel to the crystallo-raphic axis. These points are illustrated in detail ı other papers (Hodgkin *et al.*, 1964; Blow *et l.*, 1964), which describe application of the trans-tion function to space groups $R3$ and $P2_1$.

Removal of self-vectors

; is important to remember that the self-vectors can e made to superimpose by the rotation [**C**], with ny lattice translation (including zero) giving rise to rge origin peaks in $T(\Delta)$. These peaks can easily wamp a peak due to superposition of cross-vectors, pecially when the translation Δ is small. It is ıerefore important to remove the self-vectors.

We have attempted to do this by modifying the atterson coefficients so as to produce a region of ero density within a volume U' around each origin. he modifying function

$$M(\mathbf{u}) = \sum_{\mathbf{p}} m_{\mathbf{p}} \exp\{2\pi i \mathbf{p}.\mathbf{u}\} = 0 \text{ if } \mathbf{u} \text{ is within } U'$$
$$= 1 \text{ if } \mathbf{u} \text{ is outside } U'.$$

hen the modified Patterson function

$$P'(\mathbf{u}) = P(\mathbf{u}).M(\mathbf{u}) = \sum_{\mathbf{h}} Q_{\mathbf{h}} \exp\{2\pi i \mathbf{h}.\mathbf{x}\}$$

here

$$Q_{\mathbf{h}} = \sum_{\mathbf{p}} F^2_{\mathbf{h}-\mathbf{p}} m_{\mathbf{p}}$$

y the convolution theorem. From the definition of $I(\mathbf{u})$ it follows that

$$m_{\mathbf{p}} = \frac{1}{V}\left[\int_V \exp\{-2\pi i \mathbf{p}.\mathbf{u}\}d\mathbf{u} - \int_{U'} \exp\{-2\pi i \mathbf{p}.\mathbf{u}\}d\mathbf{u}\right],$$

where V is the volume of the unit cell. Hence

$$m_0 = 1 - U'/V$$

and

$$m_{\mathbf{p}} = -(U/V)G_{\mathbf{p},0} \quad (\text{where } \mathbf{p} \neq 0),$$

$G_{\mathbf{p},0}$ having the same significance as before. Hence the modified coefficients are

$$Q_{\mathbf{h}} = F^2_{\mathbf{h}}\left(1 - \frac{U'}{V}\right) - \frac{U'}{V} \sum_{\mathbf{p}\neq\mathbf{h}} F^2_{\mathbf{h}-\mathbf{p}} G_{\mathbf{p},0}. \qquad (10)$$

If there is overlap between the volumes U' centred on neighbouring origins, the effective value of U'/V in (10) is altered. In this case an empirical value was calculated by ensuring that the modified Patterson density is zero at the origin. If k is the effective value of U'/V

$$(1-k)\sum_{\mathbf{h}} F^2_{\mathbf{h}} - k \sum_{\mathbf{h}} \sum_{\mathbf{p}\neq\mathbf{h}} F^2_{\mathbf{h}-\mathbf{p}} G_{\mathbf{p},0} = 0.$$

k seldom differed by more than 5% from U'/V, once all mistakes concerning the multiplicities had been eliminated from the program.

We thank Prof. Dorothy Hodgkin for constant guidance. We are indebted to the University of Cambridge Mathematical Laboratory for their assistance in running our work on the EDSAC 2 computer, and to IBM United Kingdom Ltd. for a gift of free time on the IBM 7090. We also wish to thank Miss Jill Collard and Miss Angela Campbell for assistance in all stages of the work. The program ERFR2 by W. G. Sly, D. P. Shoemaker & J. H. Van den Hende was used for some of the Fourier syntheses.

References

Blow, D. M., Rossmann, M. G. & Jeffery, B. A. (1964). *J. Mol. Biol.* **8**, 65.

Hodgkin, D., Harding, M., Coller, E. & Rossmann, M. G. (1964). In preparation.

Rossmann, M. G. & Blow, D. M. (1962). *Acta Cryst.* **15**, 24.

Rossmann, M. G. & Blow, D. M. (1963). *Acta Cryst.* **16**, 39.

Reprinted from *Acta Crystallographica*, Vol. 21, Part 4, October 1966

cta Cryst. (1966). **21**, 613

)n the determination of molecular location. By PATRICK TOLLIN, *Carnegie Laboratory of Physics, University of St. Andrews, Queen's College, Dundee, Scotland*

. number of techniques have been described recently for etermining the positions $\mathbf{r}_j$ of a known group of atoms in molecular crystal with respect to an arbitrarily chosen rigin. Once the positions $\mathbf{r}_j$ are known, it remains to etermine the position $\mathbf{r}_0$ of their arbitrary origin with espect to the origin of the chosen unit cell. Methods for etermining $\mathbf{r}_0$ have been described by Nordmann & Iakatsu (1963), Vand & Pepinsky (1952), and Tollin & :ochran (1964) (the last will be called TC hereafter). All f these methods require the computation of a three-imensional function of the three coordinates of $\mathbf{r}_0$.

The slightly modified derivation of the function $Q(\mathbf{r}_0)$ TC) given here shows that a separate function $Q(\mathbf{r}_0)$ is not equired for each space group. It is now apparent that eparate one- and two-dimensional functions can be obained which determine the position of the arbitrary origin elative to individual symmetry elements. These simpler)-functions are fewer in number, faster to compute and asier to interpret than the three-dimensional $Q(\mathbf{r}_0)$ of TC. . similar separation into one- and two-dimensional funcons has been observed by Hoppe in the application of the onvolution molecule method (Hoppe, 1957).

The new Q-functions are obtained by considering each ymmetry element of the space group separately.

If there are n atoms in the known group the sum function 3uerger, 1959) obtained by setting down the origin of the atterson function at the ends of the n vectors $\mathbf{r}_j$ is

$$S_n(\mathbf{r})=\sum_{\mathbf{h}}|F(\mathbf{h})|^2\sum_{j=1}^{n}\cos 2\pi\mathbf{h}\,.\,(\mathbf{r}_j-\mathbf{r})\,. \qquad (1)$$

Concentrating on one particular symmetry operation, , in the space group and defining $\mathbf{R}_0$ as the position of the rbitrary origin with respect to the symmetry operation nder consideration, the sum function should have peaks the positions $\mathbf{r}=T(\mathbf{r}_j+\mathbf{R}_0)-\mathbf{R}_0$. Substituting for $\mathbf{r}$ in (1) nd summing over all the sites gives a new Q-function,

$$Q(\mathbf{R}_0)=\sum_{\mathbf{h}}|F(\mathbf{h})|^2\sum_{j,j'=1}^{n}\cos 2\pi\mathbf{h}\,.\,[\mathbf{r}_j+\mathbf{R}_0-T(\mathbf{r}_{j'}+\mathbf{R}_0)]\,. \qquad (2)$$

he explicit forms of the Q-functions required for twofold xes and planes of symmetry are given as an example.

If T represents a twofold axis parallel to $\mathbf{b}$,

$$T(xyz)=-x,\ y+\delta y,\ -z$$

here $\delta y=0$ if the axis is a rotation axis and $\delta y=\frac{1}{2}$ if it is screw axis. This can be substituted in (2). If we define

$$C=\sum_{j=1}^{n}\cos 2\pi(hx_j+ky_j+lz_j)$$

$$C'=\sum_{j=1}^{n}\cos 2\pi(hx_j-ky_j+lz_j)$$

nd S and S' the corresponding sine functions, then quation (2) can be rearranged in the most convenient form or computation as

$$Q(X_0Z_0)=\sum_{hl}U(hl)\cos 4\pi(hX_0+lZ_0)-V(hl)\sin 4\pi(hX_0+lZ_0)$$

where

$$U(hl)=\sum_k(-1)^q|F(hkl)|^2(CC'-SS')$$

and

$$V(hl)=\sum_k(-1)^q|F(hkl)|^2(CS'+SC')$$

where

$$q=2k\delta y\,.$$

Similarly if T represents a plane of symmetry it will be of the form $T(xyz)=x+\delta x,\ -y,\ z+\delta z$

and substitution in (2) gives

$$Q(Y_0)=\sum_k U(k)\cos 4\pi kY_0-V(k)\sin 4\pi kY_0$$

where

$$U(k)=\sum_{hl}(-1)^q|F(hkl)|^2(CC'+SS')$$

and

$$V(k)=\sum_{hl}(-1)^q|F(hkl)|^2(SC'-CS')$$

where

$$q=2(h\delta x+l\delta z)\,.$$

Once the U's and V's have been calculated, the Q-functions can be calculated with the use of standard Fourier programs.

Examination of equation (2) shows that a large peak will occur in the Q-function whenever there are two atoms in the known group having relative coordinates $\mathbf{r}_1$ and $\mathbf{r}_2$ such that the relationship

$$T(\mathbf{r}_1+\mathbf{R}_0)-(\mathbf{r}_2+\mathbf{R}_0)=0 \qquad (3)$$

holds for some value of $\mathbf{R}_0$. At this value of $\mathbf{R}_0$ the magnitude of $Q(\mathbf{R}_0)$ is of the order of $\sum_{\mathbf{h}}|F(\mathbf{h})|^2$. It can be shown that the relationship (3) will be satisfied whenever there is a pair of atoms in the known group which would give rise to a non-Harker peak in the appropriate Harker section (Lipson & Cochran, 1953, p.159). For example, in a structure containing a 2_1 axis and having two atoms with relative fractional coordinates (x_1,y_1,z_1) and $(x_2,\frac{1}{2}+y_1,z_2)$ a 'false' peak will occur in the Q-function at

$$X_0=-\tfrac{1}{2}(x_1+x_2)\quad Z_0=-\tfrac{1}{2}(z_1+z_2)\,.$$

The false peaks will have the same order of magnitude as the peak which defined the true position of the known group. The false peaks can be removed from the Q-function by modifying the $|F|^2$ values to remove the origin peak from the Patterson function (Lipson & Cochran 1953, p.174). However, this is not necessary since their positions can be accurately predicted before the Q-function is calculated. Since, in the final summation, the trigonometric functions have arguments of the form $4\pi(\mathbf{h}\,.\,\mathbf{r})$ the peaks in the Q-functions are very sharp. It follows therefore that the false peaks cannot cause confusion by overlapping the origin-locating peaks. Because of the sharpness of the peaks in the Q-functions it is important to evaluate them over sufficiently closely spaced intervals.

In all the examples which follow, 'sharpened' $|F|^2$ values were used in the calculation of the Q-functions. $Q(X_0Z_0)$ was calculated using the relative coordinates of the eleven atoms in the plane of the purine residue in deoxyadenosine. The relative coordinates were those obtained from the determination of the molecular orientation (Watson, Sutor & Tollin, 1965). The space group is $P2_1$. The map obtained is shown in Fig. 1(a). The expected positions of peaks due to atoms separated by $b/2$ are marked in the map. The largest remaining peak is that which determines the position of the origin. The map of $Q(X_0Z_0)$ obtained using the relative coordinates for the atoms of the sugar residue in deoxyadenosine is shown in Fig. 1(b). In this case only eight out of a total of twenty heavy atoms in the molecules were used. The coordinates used were the final coordinates from the refined structure with an arbitrary change of origin to $x=0{\cdot}2$, $z=0{\cdot}3$. In this case there are no atoms separated by half in their fractional y coordinates.

The function $Q(Y_0)$ was calculated from relative coordinates for pyrimidine obtained by taking the final published coordinates (Wheatley, 1960) and giving them an arbitrary shift of origin to $x=-0{\cdot}15$, $y=-0{\cdot}3$. The space group is $Pna2_1$. $Q(Y_0)$ was used to define the position of the molecule relative to the a-glide plane. Only the fifty largest 'sharpened' $|F|^2$ values were used. The resulting map is shown in Fig. 2 with the origin shifted to $y=-\frac{1}{4}$ to allow for the fact that the a-glide occurs at $y=\frac{1}{4}$. The dotted vertical line represented the correct answer of $y=-0{\cdot}3$. The results show that even with this small amount of data the origin position is well defined. It can also be seen that the determination of the y coordinate is independent of the fact that at this stage the x coordinate of the arbitrary origin is not known. In all these examples the error in determining the origin position was less than 0·05 Å.

These Q-functions have also been used to determine the structure of 4-acetyl-2′-fluorobiphenyl (Tollin, Young & Sutherland, 1965).

The author wishes to thank Professor W. Cochran, F.R.S., Dr M. G. Rossmann and Dr P. Main for their advice and criticism.

References

BUERGER, M. J. (1959). *Vector Space*. New York: John Wiley.

HOPPE, W. (1957). *Z. Elektrochem.* **61**, 1076.

LIPSON, H. & COCHRAN, W. (1953). *The Determination* *Crystal Structures*. London: Bell.

NORDMAN, C. E. & NAKATSU, K. (1963). *J. Amer. Chen* *Soc.* **85**, 353.

TOLLIN, P. & COCHRAN, W. (1964). *Acta Cryst.* **17**, 132.

TOLLIN, P., YOUNG, D. W. & SUTHERLAND, H. (1965). Pape presented at A.C.A. meeting Gattlinburg, Tennessee.

VAND, V. & PEPINSKY, R. (1956). *Z. Kristallogr.* **108**, 1.

WATSON, D. G., SUTOR, D. J. & TOLLIN, P. (1965). *Ac* *Cryst.* **19**, 111.

WHEATLEY, P. G. (1960). *Acta Cryst.* **13**, 80.

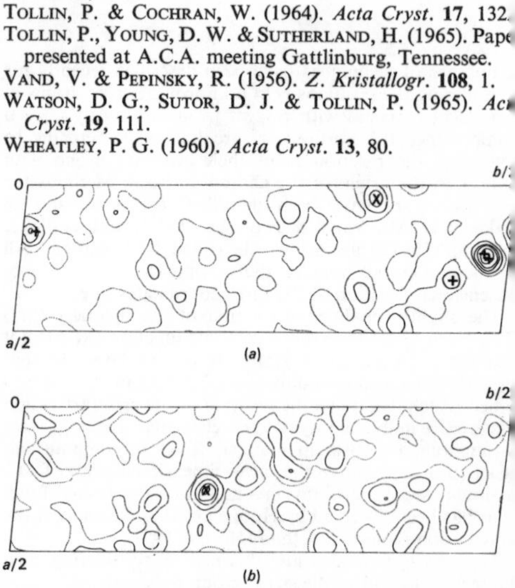

Fig. 1. $Q(X_0Z_0)$ for deoxyadenosine (a) using purine relativ coordinates (b) using sugar relative coordinates. + indi cates false peaks. × indicates expected positions.

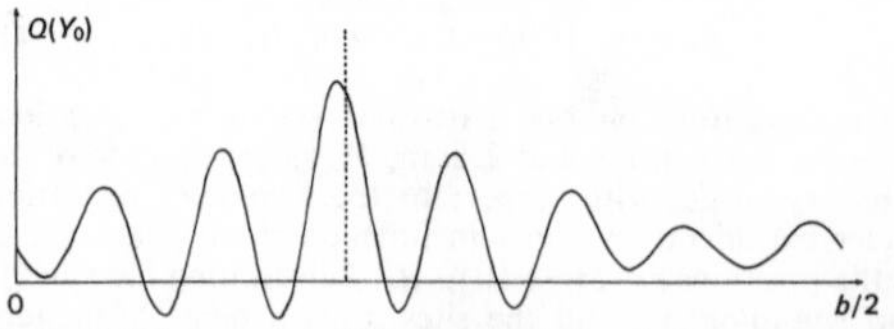

Fig. 2. $Q(Y_0)$ for pyrimidine. Dotted line indicates expecte peak position.

Reprinted from *Acta Crystallographica,* Vol. 23, Part 4, October 1967

cta Cryst. (1967). **23**, 544

A Method of Positioning a Known Molecule in an Unknown Crystal Structure

By R. A. Crowther and D. M. Blow
Medical Research Council Laboratory of Molecular Biology, Hills Road, Cambridge, England

A function is proposed for determining the position of a known molecule of known orientation relative to a crystallographic symmetry element in an unknown crystal structure. A Fourier-series summation with appropriate coefficients is used to express the correlation between the observed Patterson function of the crystal and the set of cross-Patterson vectors of a model structure. The point of maximum correlation gives the value of the intermolecular vector between molecules related by the chosen symmetry element. The function has been tested on sperm whale myoglobin.

Introduction

number of methods exist for determining the orientation of a known molecule in an unknown crystal structure (Rossmann & Blow, 1962; Nordman & Nakatsu, 1963; Tollin & Cochran, 1964). Several methods have also been used to solve the subsequent translational problem of positioning the molecule relative to the chosen origin of the crystal (Nordman & Nakatsu, 1963; Tollin & Cochran, 1964; Tollin, 1966). We wish to present a new method of solving the translational problem. The proposed function is simple to compute and, we believe, particularly well suited to the analysis of complex molecules. We expect to be able to apply it to the study of crystalline proteins in cases where a closely related protein structure is known (Scouloudi, 1960).

Consider the problem of positioning a known molecule relative to a particular crystallographic symmetry element. The term 'known molecule' here implies that not only do we know the atomic coordinates relative to some local origin O, fixed in the molecule, but also that the molecule is in the same orientation as one of the molecules in the unknown crystal structure. We wish to determine the position of the local origin O with respect to the chosen crystallographic symmetry element. If the known molecule is placed at an arbitrary position in the unit cell, the position of the symmetry related molecule is then fixed and it is possible to calculate the set of Patterson vectors from the known molecule to the symmetry related molecule. As the position of the known molecule varies, the relative configuration of this set of Patterson vectors is unchanged but the set moves bodily to a position characterized by the vector joining the local origins of the known molecule and the symmetry related molecule. This set of vectors will be referred to as the cross-Patterson of the model structure and is to be regarded as a function of two variables, namely position in Patterson space and also position of the local origin of the known molecule in the model structure.

A well known method of finding the position of the local origin O is to move this set of cross-Patterson vectors over the observed Patterson function of the crystal, using a minimum function or similar measure of fit to determine the correct solution (see Buerger, 1959). This method is most powerful when there are few atoms in the molecule. If there are very many atoms it would be natural to sum up the observed Patterson density at every point corresponding to an expected cross-Patterson peak and to use this total as a measure of fit for a particular position of O. This is equivalent to the convolution of the observed Patterson function with the group of cross-Patterson vectors of the model structure. This convolution may be achieved by multiplying the Fourier coefficients of the two functions, and performing a Fourier summation with the coefficients so obtained. The resulting function should have a prominent peak corresponding to the vector between the two origins. In the next section we give a formal derivation.

Derivation of the translation function

If an atom in the reference molecule has crystallographic coordinates $\mathbf{x}$, then let the corresponding atom in the symmetry related molecule have crystallographic coordinates $(\mathbf{Ax}+\mathbf{d})$ (Fig. 1). The set of cross-Patte son vectors from the reference molecule to the sy metry related molecule may be written as

$$P_{01}(\mathbf{u})=\int_V \varrho_0(\mathbf{x})\varrho_1(\mathbf{x}+\mathbf{u})d\mathbf{x} \quad ($$

where ϱ_0, ϱ_1 represent the electron densities within t reference molecule and the symmetry related molecu respectively, and the integral is taken over the who unit cell volume, V. If the local origin of the know molecule is at $\mathbf{s}$, we may express (1) in terms of t electron density, ϱ_M, of the known molecule relati to the local origin O.

$$P_{01}(\mathbf{u},\mathbf{s})=\int_V \varrho_M(\mathbf{x}-\mathbf{s})\varrho_M[\mathbf{A}^{-1}(\mathbf{x}+\mathbf{u}-\mathbf{As}-\mathbf{d})]d\mathbf{x}\,.$$

Expanding ϱ_M as a Fourier series in terms of the stru ture factors, F_M, of the known molecule calculat relative to the local origin O, we have

$$\begin{aligned}P_{01}(\mathbf{u},\mathbf{s})&=\int_V \sum_{\mathbf{h}} F_M(\mathbf{h})\exp[-2\pi i\mathbf{h}.(\mathbf{x}-\mathbf{s})]\\&\quad\times\sum_{\mathbf{p}} F_M(\mathbf{p})\exp[-2\pi i\mathbf{p}\mathbf{A}^{-1}(\mathbf{x}+\mathbf{u}-\mathbf{As}-\mathbf{d})]d\mathbf{x}\\&=\sum_{\mathbf{h}}\sum_{\mathbf{p}} F_M(\mathbf{h})F_M(\mathbf{p})\exp[2\pi i(\mathbf{h}.\mathbf{s}+\mathbf{p}\mathbf{A}^{-1}(\mathbf{As}+\mathbf{d}))]\\&\quad\exp(-2\pi i\mathbf{p}\mathbf{A}^{-1}\mathbf{u})\int_V\exp[-2\pi i(\mathbf{h}+\mathbf{p}\mathbf{A}^{-1})\mathbf{x}]d\mathbf{x}\,.\end{aligned}$$

Since $\mathbf{A}$ is a crystallographic symmetry operator t integral vanishes unless $\mathbf{h}+\mathbf{p}\mathbf{A}^{-1}=0$, when it takes t value unity. Therefore,

$$P_{01}(\mathbf{u},\mathbf{s})=\sum_{\mathbf{h}} F_M(\mathbf{h})F_M(-\mathbf{hA})\exp[2\pi i\mathbf{h}.(\mathbf{s}-\mathbf{As}-\mathbf{d})]\exp(2\pi i\mathbf{h}.\mathbf{u})\,.$$

Writing the intermolecular vector $\mathbf{t}=-\mathbf{s}+\mathbf{As}+\mathbf{d}$ (Fi 1) and using the Friedel relation, this becomes

$$P_{01}(\mathbf{u},\mathbf{t})=\sum_{\mathbf{h}} F_M(\mathbf{h})F_M^*(\mathbf{hA})\exp(-2\pi i\mathbf{h}.\mathbf{t})\exp(2\pi i\mathbf{h}.\mathbf{u})\,. \quad ($$

We now define the translation function $T(\mathbf{t})$ by t convolution

$$T(\mathbf{t})=\int_V P_{01}(\mathbf{u},\mathbf{t})P(\mathbf{u})d\mathbf{u}\,, \quad ($$

where $P(\mathbf{u})$ represents the observed Patterson functi of the crystal. When $\mathbf{t}$ becomes equal to the 'tru intermolecular vector $\mathbf{t}_0$, the computed cross-Patters vectors P_{01} fit correctly to the observed Patterson fun tion P, and $T(\mathbf{t}_0)$ will have a large positive value.

Expanding the observed Patterson function $P(\mathbf{u})$ a Fourier series and using the expression (2) we m write (3) as

$$T(\mathbf{t})=\int_V \sum_{\mathbf{h}} F_M(\mathbf{h})F_M^*(\mathbf{hA})\exp(-2\pi i\mathbf{h}.\mathbf{t})\exp(2\pi i\mathbf{h}.\mathbf{u})\sum_{\mathbf{p}}|F_{\rm obs}(\mathbf{p})|^2\exp(-2\pi i\mathbf{p}.\mathbf{u})d\mathbf{u}\,.$$

ıe integral vanishes unless $\mathbf{h}-\mathbf{p}=0$, so that we have ally

$$T(\mathbf{t})=\sum_{\mathbf{h}} |F_{\text{obs}}(\mathbf{h})|^2 F_M(\mathbf{h})F^*_M(\mathbf{hA}) \exp(-2\pi i\mathbf{h}.\mathbf{t})\,.$$

'e have thus expressed the correlation between a set cross-Patterson vectors for a model structure and e observed Patterson function in terms of a Fourier ries with coefficients which are simple to compute. ie translation function can then be evaluated by eans of a standard Fourier summation program.

Modified translation functions

ıe observed Patterson function of the crystal contains th intramolecular and intermolecular Patterson vec-rs. Since we are interested in fitting the intermolecular ctors, the intramolecular vectors only serve to in-ease the background noise in the summation. How-er, since the molecular structure is known, it is pos-le to remove the intramolecular vectors from the served Patterson function, provided the observed tensities can be put on an appropriate scale. Suppose at there are n molecules in the unit cell and that the molecule is related to the known molecule by a mmetry operator whose rotational part is represented matrix $\mathbf{A}_i$, where $\mathbf{A}_0$, the matrix relating the known olecule to itself, is the identity matrix. Then the odified translation function, which fits the set of termolecular vectors between the known molecule d the chosen symmetry related molecule to the com-ete set of intermolecular vectors in the observed Pat-son function is given by

$$T_1(\mathbf{t})=\sum_{\mathbf{h}} \left(|F_{\text{obs}}(\mathbf{h})|^2 - \sum_{i=0}^{n-1} |F_M(\mathbf{hA}_i)|^2\right) \times F_M(\mathbf{h})F^*_M(\mathbf{hA}) \exp(-2\pi i\mathbf{h}\,.\,\mathbf{t})\,,$$

where F_{obs} and F_M are assumed to be on an absolute scale.

Unless the molecule has a symmetry of its own, $F_M(\mathbf{h})$ has no symmetry, and in general the functions $T(\mathbf{t}), T_1(\mathbf{t})$ will have only $P1$ symmetry. However, because of Friedel's Law, some special cases arise. Let us write

$$F_M(\mathbf{h})F^*_M(\mathbf{hA})=F_M(\mathbf{h})F_M(-\mathbf{hA})\,.$$

If $\mathbf{A}$ is a twofold rotation, $-\mathbf{A}$ is a reflexion in a perpendicular mirror plane, and since Friedel's Law also enforces this symmetry on $|F_{\text{obs}}(\mathbf{h})|$, the translation functions have Pm symmetry. Conversely if $\mathbf{A}$ is a mirror operation, the translation functions have $P2$ symmetry. In each of these cases, the translation vector $\mathbf{t}_0$ must always lie in a special position in a plane or on an axis.

The expressions given so far represent the fitting of one particular set of cross-Patterson vectors of a model structure containing two molecules to the complete set of intermolecular vectors in the observed Patterson function. Which intermolecular vector is found depends on which two molecules were used in the model structure. It is possible, however, to modify the expression for the translation function in such a way that it has higher symmetry and contains peaks corresponding to all possible intermolecular vectors in the unknown structure.

To do this we must use a model structure which contains the same number of molecules as the unknown structure. Using the above notation the set of cross-Patterson vectors from molecule i to molecule j may be written, by comparison with equation (1) above, as

$$P_{ij}(\mathbf{u},\mathbf{t}_{ij})=\sum_{\mathbf{h}} F_M(\mathbf{hA}_i)F^*_M(\mathbf{hA}_j) \exp(-2\pi i\mathbf{h}\,.\,\mathbf{t}_{ij}) \exp(2\pi i\mathbf{h}\,.\,\mathbf{u})\,,$$

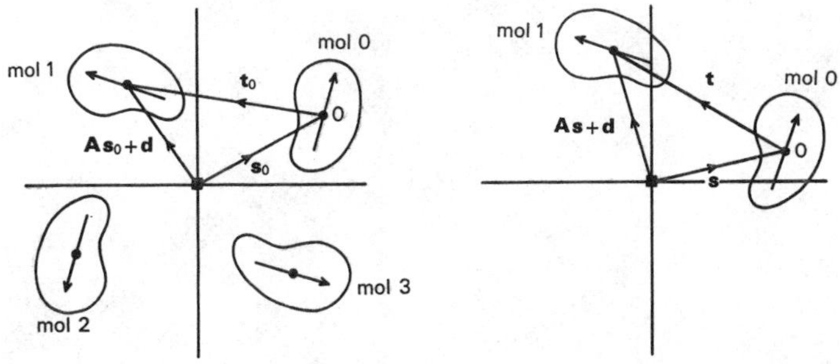

(a) (b)

ɜ.1. (a) Unknown structure containing four molecules in space group $P4$. In this case $\mathbf{A}=\begin{pmatrix}0 & -1 & 0\\ 1 & 0 & 0\\ 0 & 0 & 1\end{pmatrix}$ $\mathbf{d}=(0,0,0)$. (b) Model structure containing two molecules in correct orientation relative to the unknown structure and related by a fourfold axis, but at an otherwise arbitrary position in the unit cell. As vector $\mathbf{s}$ varies, the correlation between the set of Patterson vectors from molecule 0 to molecule 1 in the model structure and the observed Patterson function of the unknown structure takes its largest value when $\mathbf{s}=\mathbf{s}_0$. The peak in the translation function representing the required intermolecular vector occurs at the point $\mathbf{t}_0$.

where $\mathbf{t}_{ij}$ is now the intermolecular vector between molecule i and molecule j. If we sum over all possible pairs (i,j) and convolute the resulting expression with the observed Patterson function we obtain

$$\sum_{\mathbf{h}} |F_{\text{obs}}(\mathbf{h})|^2 [\sum_{i=0}^{n-1} \sum_{\substack{j=0 \\ i\neq j}}^{n-1} F_M(\mathbf{h}\mathbf{A}_i) F^*_M(\mathbf{h}\mathbf{A}_j) \exp(-2\pi i \mathbf{h}.\mathbf{t}_{ij})] \ .$$

Since the exponent appears within the inner summations, this function cannot be computed by a single Fourier summation. However, a Fourier summation of the form

$$T_2(\mathbf{t}) = \sum_{\mathbf{h}} |F_{\text{obs}}(\mathbf{h})|^2 [\sum_{i=0}^{n-1} \sum_{\substack{j=0 \\ i\neq j}}^{n-1} F_M(\mathbf{h}\mathbf{A}_i) F^*_M(\mathbf{h}\mathbf{A}_j)] \exp(-2\pi i \mathbf{h}.\mathbf{t})$$

will have peaks for all possible intermolecular vect in the unknown structure. The spatial arrangement a relative weights of the peaks will be the same as peaks in the Patterson function of the point group the molecules within the unit cell of the unkno structure, but with the origin peak removed. As befo the intramolecular vectors may be removed from observed Patterson function before convoluting it w

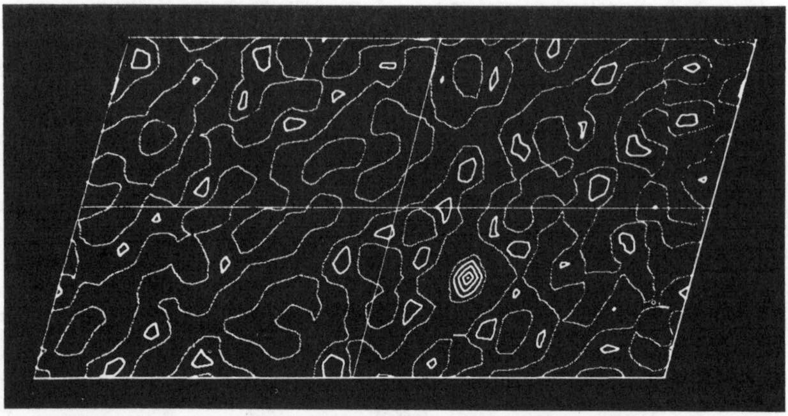

(a)

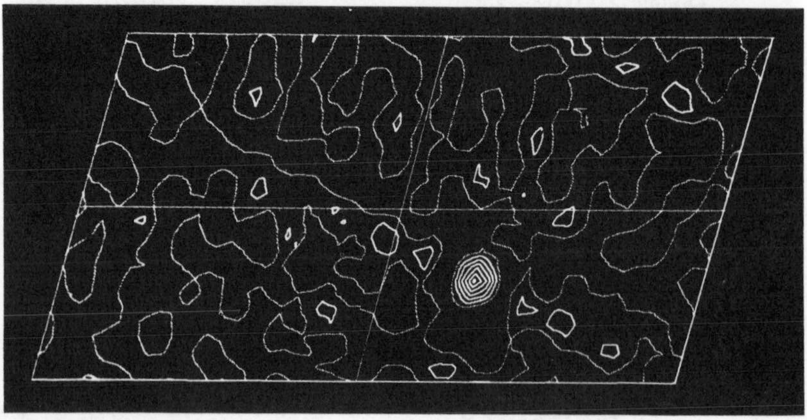

(b)

Fig. 2. (a) Two-dimensional translation function $T_1(t_x,t_z)$ for sperm whale myoglobin (case 2, Table 1). (b) Section $y=\frac{1}{2}$ fr three-dimensional translation function $T_1(t_x,\frac{1}{2},t_z)$ for sperm whale myoglobin (case 3, Table 1). In each case t_x is horizon Negative contours have been suppressed and the zero contour has been plotted half-weight. The expected peak, for particular choice of local origin made, should occur at (0·645, 0·708).

model Patterson function. This function $T_2(\mathbf{t})$ is no ter than $T(\mathbf{t})$ from the point of view of the ratio peak and background, though because of its higher nmetry it may be easier to compute.

Application

e method has been tested by applying it to sperm ale myoglobin. This protein has a molecular weight approximately 17000 and crystallizes in space group $_1$ with two molecules in the unit cell. The expressions the translation function in this case become

$$T(t_x,t_y,t_z)=\sum_h\sum_k\sum_l |F_{\text{obs}}(hkl)|^2 F_M(hkl)F_M(h\bar{k}l)\exp[-2\pi i(ht_x+kt_y+lt_z)]$$

$$T_1(t_x,t_y,t_z)=\sum_h\sum_k\sum_l (|F_{\text{obs}}(hkl)|^2-|F_M(hkl)|^2-|F_M(h\bar{k}l)|^2)F_M(hkl)F_M(h\bar{k}l)\exp[-2\pi i(ht_x+kt_y+lt_z)]\,.$$

ce the relative y coordinate of the two molecules known to be $\frac{1}{2}$, it is only necessary to compute the tion $y=\frac{1}{2}$ in the Fourier summation. Alternatively hould be possible to determine the relative x and z ordinates by means of a two-dimensional summation. e translation function in projection becomes:

$$T(t_x,t_z)=\sum_h\sum_l |F_{\text{obs}}(h0l)|^2 F_M^2(h0l)\exp[-2\pi i(ht_x+lt_z)]$$

$$T_1(t_x,t_z)=\sum_h\sum_l (|F_{\text{obs}}(h0l)|^2-2|F_M(h0l)|^2)F_M^2(h0l)\exp[-2\pi i(ht_x+lt_z)]\,.$$

The molecular structure factors were calculated from mic coordinates kindly supplied by Dr H. C. Watson d Dr J. C. Kendrew. For the particular choice of local gin used in calculating the molecular structure facs, the required peak should occur at $t_x=0{\cdot}645$, $=0{\cdot}708$. The results are summarized in Table 1. Cases and 2 relate to calculations in projection including ly $h0l$ reflexions with spacings between 8 and 4 Å pproximately 180 terms). Case 3 relates to section $=\frac{1}{2}$ from a three-dimensional summation, again inding reflexions between 8 and 4 Å (approximately 1000 terms). Fig. 2 shows the translation function as calculated in cases 2 and 3.

Table 1. *Summary of results for sperm whale myoglobin*

Case	Function	Ratio of expected to next highest peak
1	T (projection)	1·60
2	T_1 (projection)	2·14
3	T_1 (section)	3·28

Table 1 shows that the results are improved by using the function T_1 rather than T. Reflexions corresponding to spacings greater than 8 Å were omitted, because the observed structure amplitudes include large contributions to low order terms from the mother liquor, which fills the spaces between the protein molecules in the crystal. The shapes of these regions do not obey the required translation relations.

It is extremely encouraging that the method gives such clear cut results even when working in projection, when the number of terms included in the summation is comparatively small. The number of terms cannot be reduced much further: when the summation is restricted to $h0l$ reflexions between 8 and 5 Å (approximately 100 terms), no significant peak is obtained.

We are grateful to Dr H. C. Watson and Dr J. C. Kendrew for providing atomic coordinates for sperm whale myoglobin. We thank Professor Gill and the Manager of the Computer Centre, Imperial College of Science and Technology, for making computing facilities available. A contour-plotting program written by Mr T. H. Gossling was used in preparing Fig. 2. One of us (R.A.C.) is a holder of a Medical Research Council scholarship.

References

BUERGER, M. J. (1959). *Vector Space*, chapters 10 and 11. New York: John Wiley.

NORDMAN, C. E. & NAKATSU, K. (1963). *J. Amer. Chem. Soc.* **85**, 353.

ROSSMANN, M. G. & BLOW, D. M. (1962). *Acta Cryst.* **15**, 24.

SCOULOUDI, H. (1960). *Proc. Roy. Soc.* A, **258**, 181.

TOLLIN, P. (1966). *Acta Cryst.* **21**, 613.

TOLLIN, P. & COCHRAN, W. (1964). *Acta Cryst.* **17**, 1322.

Acta Cryst. (1969). A**25**, 376

A Comparison of the *Q*-Functions and the Translation Function of Crowther and Blow

BY PATRICK TOLLIN

Carnegie Laboratory of Physics, University of Dundee, Dundee, Scotland

An attempt is made to show that the *Q*-functions [Tollin, *Acta Cryst.* (1966) **21**, 613] and the translation function [Crowther & Blow, *Acta Cryst.* (1967) **23**, 544] are virtually identical, and the modifications to the translation function proposed by Crowther & Blow are discussed.

The translation problem is the problem of determining he position in the unit cell of a known molecule, or :nown part of a molecule, once its orientation with espect to the crystal axes has been determined. A umber of solutions to this problem have been proosed (Nordman & Nakatsu, 1963; Vand & Pepinsky, 956; Hoppe, 1957; Huber, 1965 and others). In paricular Tollin & Cochran (1964) (hereafter TC) proosed a set of functions, which they called *Q*-funcions, which made use of the properties of the sum unction (Buerger, 1959). Later Tollin (1966*a*) (hereefter PT) proposed a modification of these *Q*-functions hich allowed the determination of the position of the nown group with respect to the individual symmetry ements of the space group of the crystal, in turn. ubsequently Crowther & Blow (1967) (hereafter CB) roposed a new solution to the translation function. he object of this note is to show that the *Q*-functions nd the translation function of CB are virtually idencal. That the close similarity between these two funcons is not immediately obvious is a result firstly of the fferent notations used by the authors and secondly f the fact that in PT the *Q*-functions have been exessed in terms of the sum function while the transtion function of CB is explained in terms of the Patrson function.

The translation function $T(\mathbf{t})$, which has its largest lue when $\mathbf{t}$ is the vector between two molecules reted by a symmetry element, is defined in CB by the uation:

$$T(\mathbf{t})=\sum_{\mathbf{h}}|F(\mathbf{h})|^2F_m(\mathbf{h})F_m^*(\mathbf{h}\,.\,\mathbf{A})\exp(-2\pi i\mathbf{h}\,.\,\mathbf{t})\,.$$

(h)| are the observed structure amplitudes and $F_m(\mathbf{h})$ the structure factors of the known group with pect to the local origin. The particular symmetry eration of the space group relates the point defined the vector $\mathbf{x}$ to the point $\mathbf{A}\,.\,\mathbf{x}+\mathbf{d}$. If there are n ms in the known group having coordinates $\mathbf{r}_j$ with pect to the arbitrary origin, whose position in the it cell is $\mathbf{s}_0$, then

$$F_m(\mathbf{h})=\sum_{j=1}^{n}f_j\exp(+2\pi i\mathbf{h}\,.\,\mathbf{r}_j)=C+iS\,.$$

for the present, we ignore the scattering factors f_j, n the translation function can be written

$$T(\mathbf{t})=\sum_{\mathbf{h}}|F(\mathbf{h})|^2\sum_{j=1}^{n}\sum_{j'=1}^{n}\cos[2\pi\mathbf{h}\,.\,(\mathbf{r}_j-\mathbf{A}\,.\,\mathbf{r}_{j'}-\mathbf{t})]\,.$$

In PT the vector $\mathbf{R}_0$ is defined as the vector which fixes the arbitrary origin with respect to the symmetry element and not the origin of the unit cell, it is convenient therefore at present to ignore the vector $\mathbf{d}$. Since, in the notation of CB

$$\mathbf{t}=\mathbf{A}\,.\,\mathbf{s}-\mathbf{s}$$

(CB Fig. 1), the above equation for $T(\mathbf{t})$ can be written

$$T(\mathbf{s})=\sum_{\mathbf{h}}|F(\mathbf{h})|^2\sum_{j,j'=1}^{n}\cos\{2\pi\mathbf{h}\,.\,[\mathbf{r}_j+\mathbf{s}-\mathbf{A}\,.\,(\mathbf{r}_{j'}+\mathbf{s})]\}\,,$$

which is identical with the expression for $Q(\mathbf{R}_0)$ given in equation (2) of PT. Introducing the vector $\mathbf{d}$ merely shifts the origin of the function and corresponds to defining the vector $\mathbf{R}_0$ as the vector from the origin of the unit cell to the local origin as in TC. Introducing the scattering factors f_j corresponds to replacing the sum function, equation (1) of PT, by the alpha-synthesis (Ramachandran & Raman, 1959) and, as they show, this gives peaks in the same positions as the sum function, and, unless atoms of the structure have markedly different scattering powers, does not make a great difference to the function.

The identity of the two methods is also seen by considering the section of $T(t_xt_yt_z)$ at $t_y=\frac{1}{2}$ in the last paragraph of CB. Then,

$$\begin{aligned}T(t_x,\tfrac{1}{2},t_z)=&\sum_h\sum_k\sum_l(-1)^k|F(hkl)|^2\\&\times\{[C(hkl)C(h\bar{k}l)-S(hkl)S(h\bar{k}l)]\cos 2\pi(ht_x+lt_z)\\&-[C(hkl)S(h\bar{k}l)+C(h\bar{k}l)S(hkl)]\sin 2\pi(ht_x+lt_z)\}\,,\end{aligned}$$

which is identical with the expression for $Q(X_0Z_0)$ of PT.

Two modified translation functions are proposed by CB. The expression which they suggest for $T_2(\mathbf{t})$, which is the translation function obtained by considering all the symmetry operations simultaneously, bears a close resemblance to the original $Q(\mathbf{r}_0)$ defined in TC, where the point is made that 'when $\mathbf{r}_0$ has its correct value, the value of $Q(\mathbf{r}_0)$ is simply the sum of the values of the Patterson function at positions which correspond to vectors between atoms in different groups.' The function $T_1(\mathbf{t})$ defined in CB makes use of the Patterson function after the origin peak and the intramolecular vectors have been removed. This corresponds to an extension of the point made in PT that the origin peak may lead to false peaks in the Q-function, but can be removed.

The expression for $T(\mathbf{t})$ obtained by CB represents in one respect a more general form of the Q-functions than that given by PT. Since $T(\mathbf{t})$ is expressed in terms of $F_m(\mathbf{h})$, the transform of the individual molecule, it need not be calculated, as suggested by the expressions given above, in terms of a set of discrete atoms. If, for example, a molecule of a protein has been obtained at less than atomic resolution, its transform may still be calculated by numerical methods from the electron density. The possibility of such an extension has been suggested previously (Tollin, 1966*b*) in terms of the Q-functions. In this case the quantities CC' and SS' in the notation of PT must be obtained by such numerical integration. At what resolution such a function will prove useful is a matter for experiment.

The Q-functions have now been successfully applied to the determination of the structure of a number of molecular crystals (for example, Young, Tollin & Sutherland, 1968; Tollin, Young & Wilson, 1968). Recently the author has applied the Q-function to the determination of the position in the unit cell of the seal myoglobin molecule (Scouloudi, 1960) once its orientation had been determined. The orientation was found using the rotation function (Rossmann & Blow, 1962) to compare the 5·8 Å resolution data for seal and sperm whale myoglobin (Tollin, 1966*b*). A report of the details of this determination is in preparation. However, it is worth noting here that since the protein molecule is so large that many atoms are in positions which would give rise to non-Harker peaks in the Harker section, it is essential in this case to remove the origin peak from the Patterson.

It should be noted that, as Hoppe & Paulus (1967) mention in a footnote, 'it is possible to translate operations with convolution molecules into reciprocal space...' The Q-functions are closely similar to the reciprocal space equivalent of the convolution molecule method where the sum of the convolution molecule and the Patterson structure is used as the criterion of fit.

The author is grateful to Professor W. Cochran, for his views on the comparison given here.

References

BUERGER, M. J. (1959). *Vector Space*. New York: Wiley.

CROWTHER, R. A. & BLOW, D. M. (1967). *Acta Cryst.* **23**, 544.

HOPPE, W. (1957). *Z. Elektrochem.* **61**, 1076.

HOPPE, W. & PAULUS, E. F. (1967). *Acta Cryst.* **23**, 339.

HUBER, R. (1965). *Acta Cryst.* **19**, 353.

NORDMAN, C. E. & NAKATSU, K. (1963). *J. Amer. Chem. Soc.* **85**, 353.

RAMACHANDRAN, G. N. & RAMAN, S. (1959). *Acta Cryst.* **12**, 957.

ROSSMANN, M. G. & BLOW, D. M. (1962). *Acta Cryst.* **15**, 24.

SCOULOUDI, H. (1960). *Proc. Roy. Soc.* A**258**, 181.

TOLLIN, P. & COCHRAN, W. (1964). *Acta Cryst.* **17**, 1322.

TOLLIN, P. (1966*a*). *Acta Cryst.* **21**, 613.

TOLLIN, P. (1966*b*). *Acta Cryst.* **21**, A 165.

TOLLIN, P., YOUNG, D. W. & WILSON, H. R. (1968). *Nature, Lond.* **217**, 1148.

VAND, V. & PEPINSKY, R. (1956). *Z. Kristallogr.* **108**, 1.

YOUNG, D. W., TOLLIN, P. & SUTHERLAND, H. (1968). *Acta Cryst.* B**24**, 161.

C. THE MOLECULAR REPLACEMENT EQUATIONS AND THEIR SOLUTION

Reprinted from *Acta Crystallographica*, Vol. 16, Part 1, January 1963

Cryst. (1963). **16**, 39

etermination of Phases by the Conditions of Non-Crystallographic symmetry

Michael G. Rossmann and D. M. Blow

M.R.C. Laboratory of Molecular Biology, University Postgraduate Medical School, Hills Road, Cambridge, England

If a molecule is either repeated more than once within the same crystallographic asymmetric unit, or if more than one crystal form is available, then the phase problem can be reduced to finding the set of unknown phases (α's) which gives the largest value of R in the expression

$$R = \sum_i \sum_j A_{ij} \cos(\alpha_i + \alpha_j + \varphi_{ij})$$

The coefficients A_{ij} and angles φ_{ij} are simple functions of the structure amplitudes and overall dimensions of the molecule relative to a chosen origin. The matrix $[A_{ij}]$ is populated mainly along its diagonal. A general technique for finding the phases from the expression R is given. It is applied to a two-dimensional case where there are two identical five-atom molecules in plane group $p1$.

1. Introduction

re (1952) has given the crystallographic inter- ;ation of a theorem of Shannon (1949), which been considered from a more general standpoint Brillouin (1956). The theorem indicates that if the nsities $|F|^2$ could be measured at points corre- nding to the reciprocal lattice of the doubled cell, ct structure determination could be accomplished. ituation approaching this arises when two identical ecules (or 'sub-units') are contained in the crys- ographic asymmetric unit; and a similar situation es when the identical structure may be crystallized two different unit cells. In each case, for the ermination of a structure of given volume, the nber of observable intensities is doubled.

n an earlier paper (Rossmann & Blow, 1962, rred to as R. & B.) we have described how the tive angular orientations of the sub-units may be ermined. We now wish to show how the condition t the sub-units shall have identical structure vides information about the phases. The method be illustrated by a two-dimensional example in ch two sub-units of five atoms exist in a unit cell plane group $p1$ (Fig. 1).

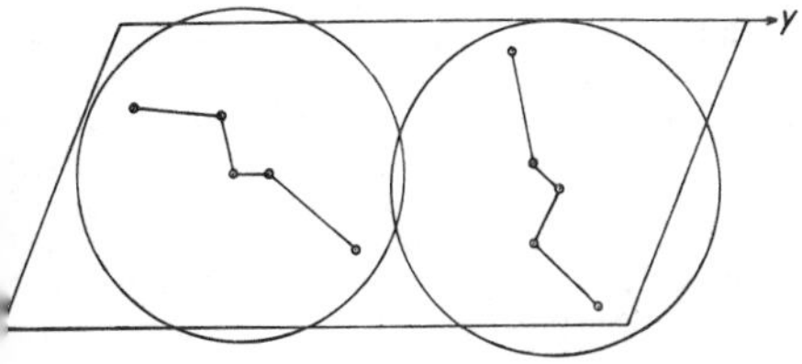

. 1. Ten atom structure showing two identical five atom nolecules contained within the 11 Å radius circles and elated by a rotation of −140°.

In order to solve this problem, it is necessary to be able to define the operation which, by rotation and translation, brings one sub-unit into coincidence with the other, and to have a rough idea of how the sub-units are arranged in the unit cell. The rotational parameters can be derived by the methods of R. & B. In some cases the translational parameters can then be found by comparing the original and rotated Patterson functions, (this has been done successfully for insulin, unpublished), while, for instance, in plane group $p1$ the translation is trivial, since the origin may be chosen to lie on the rotation axis. Whether the arrangement of sub-units is then uniquely determined will depend on the physical information available about their size and shape. For the purposes of this communication, we shall assume that this problem can be solved.

The 'rotation function' described in R. & B. was applied to a model structure, with the result shown

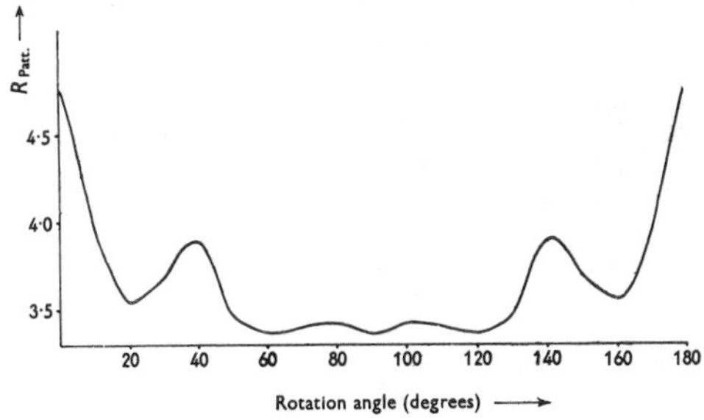

Fig. 2. Rotation function (2 Å resolution), $R_{Patt.}$, which measures the different overlap of the Patterson with a rotated version of itself. The relative orientation of the two five atom molecules is shown to be −140°, −40°, +40° or +140°. (The calculation was done by Mr D. Davies, to whom we are indebted.)

in Fig. 2. The effect of the ambiguity between rotations of $\pm 40°$ and $\pm 140°$ will be discussed later.

The next step is to specify two areas U, U', which are related by the correct rotation and translation parameters, and which contain the two molecules. Their precise shape is of no great importance, and in the model structure circular areas were chosen, as indicated in Fig. 1, which together cover an area $2U = 90\%$ the area V of the unit cell.

2. Equalization of sub-units

We now wish to apply the condition that the electron density at any point within one circle shall equal the electron density at an appropriately related point in the other circle. This condition is to be used to obtain information about the phases.

Let

$$E = \int_U [\varrho(\mathbf{x}) - \varrho(\mathbf{x}')]^2 d\mathbf{x}\,, \qquad (1)$$

where

$$\mathbf{x}' = [\mathrm{C}]\mathbf{x} + \mathbf{d}\,. \qquad (2)$$

$\mathbf{x}'$ is the point in U' which is to be identified with $\mathbf{x}$ in U, by the rotation [C] and the translation $\mathbf{d}$. E will become a minimum, tending to zero, when electron densities of the two sub-units are equalized. Then

$$E = \int_U [\varrho^2(\mathbf{x}) + \varrho^2(\mathbf{x}')]d\mathbf{x} - 2\int_U \varrho(\mathbf{x})\,.\,\varrho'\mathbf{x}')d\mathbf{x}\,. \qquad (3)$$

If we make the assumption that *all* the density of the cell lies in either U or U', then the first integral becomes equal to

$$(1/V^2)\sum_h F^2(\mathbf{h})\,,$$

while the second integral has already been defined (in R. & B.) as the 'rotation function' of the electron density. If some density lies outside U and U' the value of the first integral is changed, but it is readily shown (by considering a structure which is identical to the real structure within U, but has no density outside) that the condition for minimizing E is to a good approximation the same as for maximizing the second integral R. We shall now consider the variation of R as a function of the phase angles.

It is shown in R. & B. that if

$$R = \int_U \varrho(\mathbf{x})\,.\,\varrho(\mathbf{x}')d\mathbf{x}$$

then

$$R = (U/V^3)\sum_h\sum_p |F_h||F_p|G_{hp} \times \cos(\alpha_h + \alpha_p + \Omega_{hp} - 2\pi\mathbf{p}\,.\,\mathbf{d})\,. \qquad (4)$$

In this equation $|F_h|$ and α_h are the magnitude and phase of the structure factor associated with $\mathbf{h}$; $\mathbf{d}$ is the translation vector in equation (2) and G_{hp} and Ω_{hp} are the magnitude and phase of the diffraction function of the volume U for the reciprocal lat vector $\mathbf{h} + [\tilde{\mathrm{C}}]\mathbf{p}$:

$$G_{hp}\exp[i\Omega_{hp}] = (V/U)\int_U \exp\{-2\pi i(\mathbf{h} + [\tilde{\mathrm{C}}]\mathbf{p})\,.\,\mathbf{x}\}$$

G_{hp} has large values only if the reciprocal s vector $\mathbf{h}$ is brought close to $-\mathbf{p}$ by the rota expressed by [C] in equation (2), and Ω_{hp} is zer the volume U is centrosymmetric about the or The expression (4) has the disadvantage that i in general not symmetrical about the two varia $\mathbf{h}$ and $\mathbf{p}$; it can be cast into a symmetrical form writing

$$R = \sum_i\sum_j A_{ij}\cos(\alpha_i + \alpha_j + \phi_{ij})$$

where

$$\begin{aligned} A_{ij}\exp[i\phi_{ij}] &= (U/2V^3)[|F_i||F_j|G_{ij} \\ &\quad \times \exp\{i(-2\pi\mathbf{j}\,.\,\mathbf{d} + \Omega_{i,j})\} \\ &\quad + |F_j||F_i|G_{ji}\exp\{i(-2\pi\mathbf{i}\,.\,\mathbf{d} + \Omega_{j,i})\}] \\ &= A_{ji}\exp[i\phi_{ji}]\,. \end{aligned}$$

The significance of the two contributions in with respect to proper and improper rotations discussed in Appendix I.

In order to equalize the sub-units, E must be m zero, which means finding a set of phases α_i w gives R its largest possible value. This clearly im that for many of the terms with large A_{ij} the a $(\alpha_i + \alpha_j + \phi_{ij})$ must be close to 0 (or $2n\pi$). Since ϕ_{ij} can be calculated from the known paramet each term of the summation thus represents a prob *phase relationship* between α_i and α_j, whose portance depends on the magnitude of A_{ij}. Sinc is a maximum,

$$\partial R/\partial\alpha_i = -2\sum_j A_{ij}\sin(\alpha_i + \alpha_j + \phi_{ij}) = 0\,.$$

This condition, satisfied by the same phase relati ships, is necessary but not sufficient, since R w plotted as a function of the α's has many maxi most of which are small.

3. Some properties of the equations (7)

The set of equations (7) may conveniently be thou of as a matrix with elements A_{ij}, each with an attac phase $(\alpha_i + \alpha_j + \phi_{ij})$. Any one equation (7) is re sented by one row of the matrix, and by (6) the mat is symmetrical. This matrix does not have the nificance of a matrix in the usual linear algeb equations (7) are non-linear, and form a set of sir taneous transcendental equations, for which no *di* method of solution exists. Before describing approach to solution which has been adopted, shall consider some features of this matrix.

(i) *Matrix populated along the diagonal*

It is convenient to assign a number i to each struct factor in order of increasing Bragg angle. Associa each reflexion i is its reciprocal-lattice vector $\mathbf{s}_i$. ;an only be large if $\mathbf{s}_i$ and $-\mathbf{s}_j$ (or $\mathbf{s}_j$ and $-\mathbf{s}_i$) uch that one is brought close to the other by given rotation [C]. Whatever the rotation, this only happen if the terms have a similar Bragg . Thus if the terms are set in order of increasing g angle, all large A_{ij} are near the diagonal of the ix.

All phases may be changed by π

e may note that

$$\text{s}\,[\alpha_i+\alpha_j+\phi_{ij}] = \cos\,[(\alpha_i+\pi)+(\alpha_j+\pi)+\phi_{ij}]\,,$$

at if a set of phases α_i satisfies (7) or maximizes he set $(\alpha_i+\pi)$ will do so equally well. The effect n electron density map of changing all phases is to reverse the sign of the electron density. e is one phase, α_0 (for the (000) reflexion), which physically unreasonable to reverse. (There is a analogy to Babinet's principle in Fraunhofer action.) This allows us to distinguish between the possible sets.

Terms on the diagonal

cases of higher symmetry, or with a rotation 80°, it may happen that a vector $\mathbf{s}_i$ is rotated $-\mathbf{s}_i$ or to a symmetry-related position. Under conditions the relevant term in (7),

$$A_{ii}\sin\,(\alpha_i+\alpha_i+\phi_{ii})\,,$$

dominate in the ith row, indicating the phase ionship $2\alpha_i \simeq 2n\pi-\phi_{ii}$.

we define α_i by the limits $0 \leq \alpha_i < 2\pi$, then $(\pi-\frac{1}{2}\phi_{ii})$ or $(2\pi-\frac{1}{2}\phi_{ii})$. We now have, instead e usual type of phase relationship, an indication hase, with an ambiguity. This ambiguity will be ved by the effect of the off-diagonal terms in row.

Relationship with the 'shrinkage stage' methods of agg & Perutz (1952)

s previously indicated, important phase relations will only arise when $\mathbf{s}_i$ and $\mathbf{s}_j$ both correspond similar Bragg angle. Bragg & Perutz (1952) exied a series of haemoglobin crystals in which the cell lengths a, b, and $c\sin\beta$ were scarcely altered, β varied between 84° and 143°. The corresponding reciprocal-lattice points were all arranged along of constant h, but the different shrinkage stages wed these lines to be sampled at many more ts than would be possible with a single-crystal . By comparing intensities at adjacent points, were able to determine where the sign of the ecular transform changed, applying the principle it could not change too rapidly. This is exactly ogous to the procedure by which (5) and (7) cate phase relationships between points with sim- Bragg angles. The chief differences are

(*a*) that the criterion of equalizing sub-units (1) is more stringent than the 'principle of minimum wavelength' (Bragg and Perutz, 1952);

(*b*) that by considering a rotation of the three-dimensional reciprocal lattice, phase relationships are generated through the lattice in a more general way.

4. Solution of the phase requirements

It is shown in Appendix II that the ith row of the matrix has a magnitude

$$S_i \equiv \sum_j A_{ij}\cos\,(\alpha_i+\alpha_j+\phi_{ij}) = F_i^2/V^2\,. \tag{8}$$

For convenience, define $\Theta_{ij}=\alpha_i+\alpha_j+\phi_{ij}$. If it is assumed that the angles Θ_{ij} are independent of each other, each term in the summation over j is like one step of a random walk, with the limitation that the sum of steps in a row is S_i.

Let us fix our attention on one term, A_{ij}. If it is assumed that all the other steps in the ith row, $A_{ik}(k\neq j)$, are in random directions, the probability that their resultant lies between Q and Q$+d$Q can be calculated by the Markoff method (see Chandrasekhar, 1943). The length of each step, A_{ik}, is known, but the probability function is unsuitable for rapid calculation. A much simpler form is obtained by assuming that the length of each step is governed by a Gaussian probability distribution whose mean-square length is A_{ik}. We then have

$$P(\mathrm{Q})d\mathrm{Q} \propto \exp\,\{-|\mathrm{Q}|^2/\sum_{k\neq j} A_{ik}^2\}\,d\mathrm{Q}\,.$$

However, we know that on taking the final step of length A_{ij} in a direction Θ_{ij} with S_i, we must reach the end of the vector $\mathbf{S}_i$. Hence

$$|\mathrm{Q}|^2 = A_{ij}^2+S_i^2-2A_{ij}S_i\cos\Theta_{ij}\,,$$

and thus it can be shown that

$$P_{ij}(\Theta)d\Theta \propto \exp\,\{-(4A_{ij}S_i/\sum_{k\neq j} A_{ik}^2)\sin^2\tfrac{1}{2}\Theta\}\,d\Theta\,. \tag{9}$$

Let us first consider the case when $j=i$ for the term under consideration, A_{ii}. Expression (9) gives the probability distribution for Θ_{ii} based on this diagonal term. Here $\Theta_{ii}=2\alpha_i+\phi_{ii}$. Thus if $p_{ij}(\alpha)d\alpha$ is the probability, according to the jth term of the ith row, that α_i lies between α and $\alpha+d\alpha$, then

$$p_{ii}(\alpha) \propto \exp\,\{-(4A_{ii}S_i/\sum_{k\neq i} A_{ik}^2)\sin^2(\alpha-\tfrac{1}{2}\phi_{ii})\}\,. \tag{10}$$

In the general case, $i\neq j$, expression (9) gives us the probability distribution for $\alpha_i+\alpha_j=\Theta_{ij}-\phi_{ij}$. Thus if some probability function $P_j(\alpha)$ is available for phase angle j, then this ij term indicates a probability distribution for α_i as follows:

$$p_{ij}(\alpha) = \int_{\Theta=0}^{2\pi} P_{ij}(\Theta)P_j(\Theta-\alpha-\phi_{ij})\,d\Theta\,. \tag{11}$$

The integration over Θ is introduced as all values of Θ have a finite probability. Thus

$$p_{ij}(\alpha) \propto \int_0^{2\pi} P_j(\Theta-\alpha-\phi_{ij}) \exp\{(-4A_{ij}S_i / \sum_{k\neq j} A^2_{ik}) \sin^2 \Theta/2\} d\Theta. \tag{12}$$

In practice there are several significant terms A_{ij}, affecting α_i, each giving a different distribution $p_{ij}(\alpha)$. It is to be expected that these distributions will be similar, or, if they are different, then it is hoped that only those distributions with small A_{ij} will differ grossly. Nevertheless it is important to take into account all terms in a single row. We may consider the final distribution for $P_i(\alpha)$ as the joint distribution of all separate distributions from each term in an equation.

$$\therefore P_i(\alpha) = \prod_m \{\prod_j p_{ij}(\alpha)\}$$

or, from (11)

$$P_i(\alpha) = \prod_m \left\{\prod_j \left[\int_0^{2\pi} P_{ij}(\Theta) P_j(\Theta-\alpha-\phi_{ij}) d\Theta\right]\right\}. \tag{13†}$$

Let us now consider the total process of determining the phase probability distributions, starting only with a knowledge of the coefficients A_{ij} and phases ϕ_{ij}. We may write down immediately that $\alpha_0 = 0$ with a probability of unity. We as yet know nothing at all about any other phase, and express our present ignorance by setting the probabilities of all values of phase α_i as equal. We then apply (10) to the diagonal term of each row ($j=i$) and take $p_{ii}(\alpha)$ as our first estimate of $P_i(\alpha)$. This form of $P_i(\alpha)$ can now be used in (12) with all ij terms, which are then combined by (13) to give improved versions of $P_i(\alpha)$. Because of the ambiguity of $p_{ii}(\alpha)$, indicating two phases 180° apart as equally probable, all these probability distributions will have two peaks 180° apart, except where an interaction with α_0 exists. Where such an interaction does exist, a preliminary indication of phase will be given.

The new joint probability distributions $P_i(\alpha)$ are used in a second cycle of refinement, and the initial distributions are discarded. In the second cycle, phase indications will be obtained for those phases which interact with equations whose phases were previously determined because of their strong A_{io} terms. The iterative process can be repeated until the phases so determined give values of E (equation (3)) approaching zero, the phase indications spreading further from the origin of reciprocal space with each cycle of refinement.

Consider now the case of an equation with a dominant diagonal term A_{ii}. The value of R (equation (4)) will be little changed whether $\alpha_i = \pi - \frac{1}{2}\phi_{ii}$ or $2\pi - \frac{1}{2}\phi_{ii}$, that is to say the probabilities $P_i(\alpha = \pi - \frac{1}{2}\phi_{ii})$ $P_i(\alpha = 2\pi - \frac{1}{2}\phi_{ii})$ are almost equal. The simplest proach would be to use the phase with the gre probability, but should that not be correct, the e introduced into the Fourier summation would be la Blow & Crick (1959) and Dickerson, Kendrew Strandberg (1961) show that the best approach the formally identical problem of combining information from different isomorphous replacem derivatives is to use the centroid of the phase p ability distribution as Fourier coefficients, ξ, in electron-density calculation.

That is

$$\xi_i = |F_i| \int_0^{2\pi} P_i(\alpha) \exp[i\alpha] d\alpha \Big/ \int_0^{2\pi} P_i(\alpha) d\alpha .$$

† The phase probability distribution of all m symmetry related phases can be multiplied together, provided one takes care of their relative phases as required by any particular space group.

5. A worked example

A two-dimensional structure (Fig. 1), in plane gr $p1$, in a cell with $a = 21{\cdot}6$, $b = 42{\cdot}0$ Å, $\gamma = 11$ containing two independent, but identical molec each with five equal atoms was chosen as a trial the proposed method. In order to limit the amo of computation, calculations were restricted to 35 reflexions of lowest Bragg angle. The calcula structure amplitudes for these reflexions, correspo ing to 6·2 Å resolution, were used as 'observed' from which to deduce the phase angles. A Fou synthesis using these structure amplitudes with 'correct' calculated phases is shown in Fig. 3.

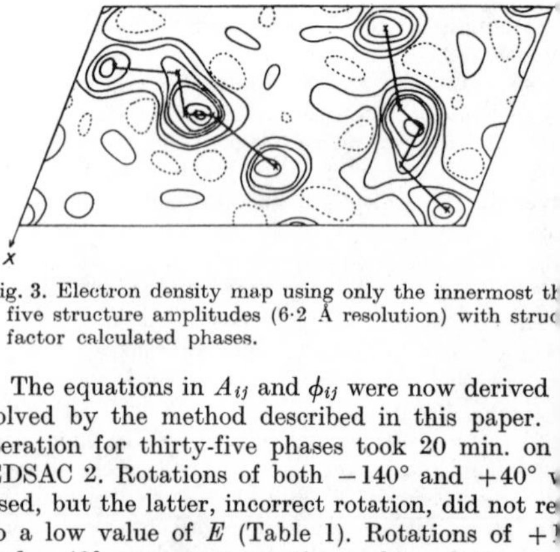

Fig. 3. Electron density map using only the innermost th five structure amplitudes (6·2 Å resolution) with struc factor calculated phases.

The equations in A_{ij} and ϕ_{ij} were now derived solved by the method described in this paper. iteration for thirty-five phases took 20 min. on EDSAC 2. Rotations of both −140° and +40° used, but the latter, incorrect rotation, did not re to a low value of E (Table 1). Rotations of + and −40°, represent enantiomorphic solutions.

The first refinement (seven cycles) using the cor rotation of −140° led to a recognizable struc (Fig. 4). The phases are given in Table 2. The sec refinement process used $|G_{hp}|$ instead of G_{hp} in calculation of the coefficients A_{ij}. This can be sh to be rather like the physical criterion of minimi

$$E' = \int_U [\varrho^2(\mathbf{x}) - \varrho^2(\mathbf{x}')]^2 d\mathbf{x} ,$$

or maximizing

$$R' = \int_U \varrho^2(\mathbf{x}) \cdot \varrho^2(\mathbf{x}')\, d\mathbf{x}\,. \qquad (15)$$

Table 1. *Values of the functions E and R*

Rotation	Structure	$2R\times10^4$	$E\times10^4$
+40°	'correct' phases	1·41	1·51
	deduced phases 1	1·99	0·93
−140°	'correct' phases	2·69	0·23
	deduced phases 2	2·62	0·30
	deduced phases 3	2·76	0·16

The 'correct' phases refer to the phases given by conventional structure factor calculations, from the assumed atomic positions.
Deduced phases 1 were found by refining the G criterion (maximization of R, equation (4)) using the rotation of +40°, which represents an extraneous solution of the rotation function.
Deduced phases 2 were found by refining the G criterion (maximization of R, equation (4)) using rotation of −140°, which represents the correct solution of the rotation function.
Deduced phases 3 were found by refining the $|G|$ criterion (maximization of R', equation (15)) using rotation of −140°.

Table 2. *Comparison of 'correct' structure factor calculated phases and those found on refinement of the G and |G| criteria, corresponding to the 'deduced 2' and 'deduced 3' phase angles*

i	Indices (h, k)		α_i^0 (correct)	α_i^0 (deduced 2)	α_i^0 (deduced 3)	$\lvert F_i\rvert$
0	0	0	0	0	0	60
1	0	1	300	304	308	6
2	−1	1	321	287	306	21
3	1	0	181	178	182	17
4	0	2	195	222	213	17
5	−1	2	22	21	22	41
6	1	1	192	305	214	11
7	−1	3	288	316	286	22
8	0	3	233	153	148	3
9	1	2	39	226	32	10
0	−2	1	152	88	156	13
1	−2	2	221	195	209	18
2	−1	4	217	7	229	26
3	2	0	350	57	1	7
4	−2	3	345	243	339	23
5	0	4	51	271	64	20
6	1	3	36	177	347	6
7	2	1	310	28	7	14
8	−2	4	52	221	50	8
9	−1	5	13	71	83	12
	0	5	20	298	255	1
	2	2	228	240	212	24
	1	4	262	170	237	28
	−2	5	290	5	326	14
	−3	2	36	339	357	22
	−3	3	186	85	161	8
	−3	1	95	39	33	20
	−1	6	48	193	95	15
	−3	4	274	173	189	15
	2	3	342	263	271	16
	−2	6	254	308	286	32
	3	0	167	282	212	8
	1	5	174	237	272	14
	0	6	275	241	246	11
	−3	5	51	26	24	8
	3	1	320	242	202	25

This criterion led to a structure more nearly like the correct structure (Fig. 5). The phases given by the sixth cycle of refinement, are shown in Table 2.

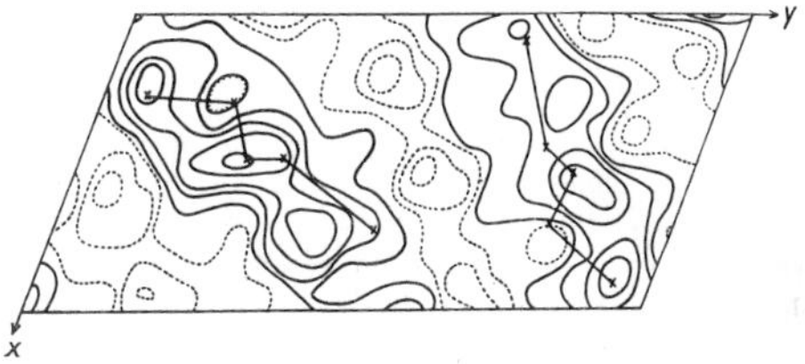

Fig. 4. Electron density map using the innermost thirty five structure amplitudes with phases deduced by maximizing R (equation (4)).

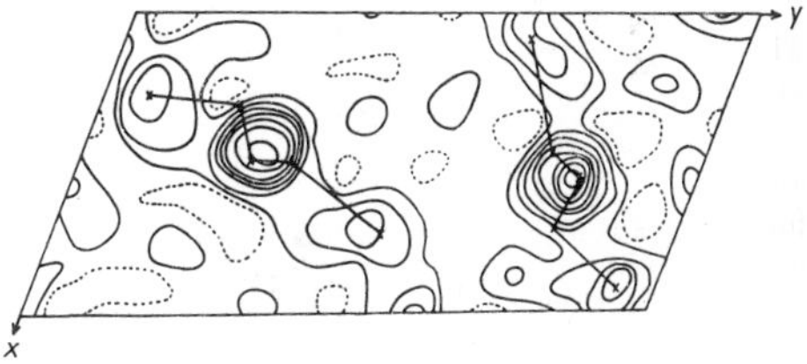

Fig. 5. Electron density map using the same structure amplitude but phases deduced on the basis of maximizing R', (equation (15)).

It may be noted from Table 2 that the phase determination deteriorates with increasing i. Indeed an electron-density map including only those terms for which $i \le 23$ is substantially better than that shown in Fig. 5. In these phase probability calculations only the interactions between the 35 innermost reflections were considered. As the largest A_{ij} elements must lie on or near the diagonal of the matrix, the effect of neglecting A_{ij} terms with $j > 35$ becomes more serious as i increases. In our example a significant number of terms have been neglected in a large proportion of the equations and the effect is serious. It becomes less important as the number of unknown phases becomes larger. A measure of the seriousness of the effect is the ratio of the surface area to volume of the 'sphere of reflection' used to terminate the data.

APPENDIX I

The effect of proper rotations

Let

$$\phi_{hp} = [-2\pi\mathbf{p}\,.\,\mathbf{d} + \Omega_{hp}]$$
$$= -2\pi[\mathbf{p}\,.\,\mathbf{d} + (\mathbf{h}+\mathbf{h}')\,.\,\mathbf{S}]$$

(see R. & B.)

where $\mathbf{h}' = [\tilde{\mathbf{C}}]\,.\,\mathbf{p}$, and $\mathbf{S}$ is the position vector of the centre of the volume U over which the integration was performed, and for which $G_{hp}\exp[i\Omega_{hp}]$ represents the diffraction function.

$$\begin{aligned}\therefore \phi_{hp} &= -2\pi[\mathbf{p}.\mathbf{d}+\mathbf{h}.\mathbf{S}+\{[\tilde{\mathbf{C}}].\mathbf{p}\}.\mathbf{S}]\\ &= -2\pi[\mathbf{h}.\mathbf{S}+\mathbf{p}\{[\mathbf{C}].\mathbf{S}+\mathbf{d}\}]\\ &= -2\pi[\mathbf{h}.\mathbf{S}+\mathbf{p}.\mathbf{S}']\end{aligned}$$

where $\mathbf{S}'$ is the position vector of the centre of the volume U'. That is $\mathbf{S}'=[\mathbf{C}].\mathbf{S}+\mathbf{d}$.

Now if the rotation is proper we may take $\mathbf{S}=\mathbf{S}'$ and integrate over the volume of both sub-units, for it is irrelevant where the boundary between these is drawn. Thus for a proper rotation

$$\phi_{hp} = -2\pi[(\mathbf{h}+\mathbf{p}).\mathbf{S}] = \phi_{ph}\,,$$

but for an improper rotation

$$\phi_{hp} = -2\pi[\mathbf{h}.\mathbf{S}+\mathbf{p}.\mathbf{S}'] \neq \phi_{ph}\,.$$

APPENDIX II

The magnitude, S_i, of the sum of the terms in a row of the matrix $A_{ij}\cos(\alpha_i+\alpha_j+\phi_{ij})$

By definition of a structure factor

$$|F(h)|\exp[-i\alpha_h] = V\int_V \varrho(\mathbf{x})\exp[-2\pi i\mathbf{h}.\mathbf{x}]d\mathbf{x}$$

where V is the volume of the unit cell. If there is no density outside the volumes U and U', and within V, then it follows that

$$\begin{aligned}|F(\mathbf{h})|\exp[-i\alpha_h] &= V\left\{\int_U \varrho(\mathbf{x})\exp[-2\pi i\mathbf{h}.\mathbf{x}]d\mathbf{x} + \int_{U'}\varrho(\mathbf{x})\exp[-2\pi i\mathbf{h}.\mathbf{x}]d\mathbf{x}\right\},\\ &= V\left\{\int_U \varrho(\mathbf{x})\exp[-2\pi i\mathbf{h}.\mathbf{x}]d\mathbf{x} + \int_U \varrho(\mathbf{x}')\exp[-2\pi i\mathbf{h}.\mathbf{x}']d\mathbf{x}\right\},\end{aligned}$$

since whenever $\mathbf{x}$ is in U, $\mathbf{x}'$ (given by equation (2)) is within U'. But since $\varrho(\mathbf{x})=\varrho(\mathbf{x}')$:

$$|F(\mathbf{h})|\exp[-i\alpha_h] = V\left\{\int_U \varrho(\mathbf{x}')\exp[-2\pi i\mathbf{h}.\mathbf{x}]d\mathbf{x} + \int_U \varrho(\mathbf{x})\exp[-2\pi i\mathbf{h}.\mathbf{x}']d\mathbf{x}\right\}.$$

Substituting a Fourier summation for $\varrho(\mathbf{x})$; that is, writing

$$\varrho(\mathbf{x}) = (1/V)\sum_p |F_p|\exp[i(\alpha_p-2\pi\mathbf{p}.\mathbf{x})]\,,$$

we have

$$\begin{aligned}|F(\mathbf{h})|\exp[-i\alpha_h] &= \int_U\left\{\sum_p |F(\mathbf{p})|\exp[i(\alpha_p-2\pi\mathbf{p}.\mathbf{x}')]\right\}\exp[-2i\mathbf{h}.\mathbf{x}]d\mathbf{x}\\ &\quad+\int_U\left\{\sum_p |F(\mathbf{p})|\exp[i(\alpha_p-2\pi\mathbf{p}.\mathbf{x})]\right\}\\ &\quad\times\exp[-2\pi\mathbf{h}.\mathbf{x}']d\mathbf{x}\,.\end{aligned}$$

Making use of (2) to write $\mathbf{x}'$ in terms of $\mathbf{x}$

$$\begin{aligned}|F(\mathbf{h})| &= \sum_p |F(\mathbf{p})|\exp[i(\alpha_p+\alpha_h)]\\ &\times\left\{\exp[-2\pi i\mathbf{p}.\mathbf{d}]\int_U \exp[-2\pi i(\mathbf{h}.\mathbf{x}+\mathbf{p}.[\mathbf{C}].\mathbf{x})]d\mathbf{x}\right.\\ &\left.+\exp[-2\pi i\mathbf{h}.\mathbf{d}]\int_U \exp[-2\pi i(\mathbf{p}.\mathbf{x}+\mathbf{h}.[\mathbf{C}].\mathbf{x})]d\mathbf{x}\right\}\end{aligned}$$

Since $\mathbf{p}.[\mathbf{C}].\mathbf{x}=[\tilde{\mathbf{C}}]\mathbf{p}.\mathbf{x}$, the first integral becomes

$$\int_U \exp[-2\pi i(\mathbf{h}+[\tilde{\mathbf{C}}]\mathbf{p})\mathbf{x}]d\mathbf{x} = (U/V)G_{hp}\exp[i\Omega_{hp}]$$

by definition.

Making a similar substitution for the second integra[l] leads to

$$\begin{aligned}|F(\mathbf{h})| &= (U/V)\sum_p |F(\mathbf{p})|\exp[i(\alpha_p+\alpha_h)]\\ &\quad\times\{\exp[-2\pi i\mathbf{p}.\mathbf{d}]G_{hp}\exp[i\Omega_{hp}]\\ &\quad+\exp[-2\pi i\mathbf{h}.\mathbf{d}]G_{ph}\exp[i\Omega_{ph}\}\\ |F(\mathbf{h})|^2 &= (U/V)\sum_p |F(\mathbf{p})||F(\mathbf{h})|\exp[i(\alpha_p+\alpha_h)]\\ &\quad\times\{\exp[-2\pi i\mathbf{p}.\mathbf{d}]G_{hp}\exp[i\Omega_{hp}]\\ &\quad+\exp[-2\pi i\mathbf{h}.\mathbf{d}]G_{ph}\exp[i\Omega_{ph}]\}\,.\end{aligned}$$

This may be compared with (6), $\mathbf{h}$ being replaced [b] $\mathbf{i}$ and $\mathbf{p}$ by $\mathbf{j}$. It is evident that

$$|F(\mathbf{i})|^2 = 2V^2\sum_j A_{ij}\exp[i(\alpha_i+\alpha_j+\phi_{ij})]\,.$$

Using Friedel's Law

$$|F(\mathbf{i})|^2 = 2V^2\sum_j A_{ij}\cos(\alpha_i+\alpha_j+\phi_{ij}) = 2VUS_i\,.$$

So that

$$S_i = (1/2V^2)|F(\mathbf{i})|^2.$$

We wish to thank Mr David Davies who w[as] responsible for some of the programming for t[he] EDSAC 2 computer, made available to us by t[he] University of Cambridge Mathematical Laborato[ry]. We are also grateful to Dr E. L. McGandy w[ho] designed the two-dimensional structure and, toget[her] with Mr G. King helped to design the rotati[on] function program. Finally we wish to thank M[r] G. Collard, Mrs D. Thomas and Mrs J. Blows, w[ho] gave assistance throughout.

References

CHANDRASEKHAR, S. (1943). *Rev. Mod. Phys.* **15**, 1.
BLOW, D. M. & CRICK, F. H. C. (1959). *Acta Cryst.* 794.

BRAGG, W. L. & PERUTZ, M. F. (1952). *Proc. Roy. Soc.* A, **213**, 425.
BRILLOUIN, L. (1956). *Science and Information Theory*, p. 93. New York: Academic Press.
DICKERSON, R. E., KENDREW, J. C. & STRANDBERG, B. E. (1961). *Acta Cryst.* **14**, 1188.
ROSSMANN, M. G. & BLOW, D. M. (1962). *Acta Cryst.* **15**, 24.
SAYRE, D. (1952). *Acta Cryst.* **5**, 843.
SHANNON, C. E. (1949). *Proc. Inst. Radio Engrs. New York*, **37**, 10.

Reprinted from *Acta Crystallographica*, Vol. 17, Part 11, November 1964

Acta Cryst. (1964). **17**, 1474

Solution of the phase equations representing non-crystallographic symmetry. By MICHAEL G. ROSSMANN, *Department of Biological Sciences, Purdue University, Lafayette. Indiana, U.S.A.* and D. M. BLOW, *M.R.C. Laboratory of Molecular Biology. Hills Road. Cambridge, England*

A set of phase relationships must be satisfied whenever the asymmetric unit contains some non-crystallographic symmetry. For instance if there are two molecules or subunits in the asymmetric unit which are related by a local twofold axis, as is the case for α-chymotrypsin (Blow, Rossmann & Jeffery, 1964), there are conditions which the phase angles must fulfill if the electron density distributions of the two subunits are to be equal. The derivation of the necessary conditions has been given by Rossmann & Blow (1963) (equations (7) and (8)). These two equations may be combined to give an equation of the form

$$\sum_j A_{ij} \exp\,[i(\alpha_i+\alpha_j+\varphi_{ij})] = S_i \qquad (1)$$

for each reflection. Here i and j identify the individual reflections, and the quantities A_{ij}, S_i and φ_{ij} can be calculated from a knowledge of the structure amplitudes and the rotational and translational relationship between the two independent molecules. α_i and α_j are the phases of the ith and jth structure factor. In any one equation there are few terms with significantly large magnitudes A_{ij}.

Since writing the previous paper (Rossmann & Blow, 1963) we have found an alternative procedure leading towards a solution of these equations which we believe to be superior, as it considers the interdependence of each of the terms in a single equation instead of treating them independently. Also, the amount of computation involved is greatly reduced.

Let us write (1) as

$$\exp\,(i\alpha_i) \sum_j A_{ij} \exp\,[i(\alpha_j+\varphi_{ij})] = S_i \qquad (2)$$

or

$$T_i \exp\,[i(\alpha_i+\Phi_i)] + A_{ii} \exp i(2\alpha_i+\varphi_{ii}) = S_i \qquad (3)$$

where

$$T_i \exp\,(i\Phi_i) = \sum_{j\neq i} A_{ij} \exp\,[i(\alpha_j+\varphi_{ij})]\,. \qquad (4)$$

At any stage of the refinement we have an estimate of the phase angle α_i from previous results. The precision of this estimate can be expressed in terms of a figure of merit m_j (Dickerson, Kendrew & Strandberg, 1961) which varies from unity for complete certainty about the phase angle to zero when there is no phase information. We propose to replace (4) by the following expression for actual calculation:

$$T_i^c \exp(i\Phi_i^c) = \sum_{j \neq i} A_{ij} m_j \exp[i(\alpha_j^c + \varphi_{ij})] \, . \qquad (5)$$

The right hand side of equation (4) represents a series of steps each of length A_{ij} in a direction making an angle $(\alpha_j + \varphi_{ij})$ with the real axis on an Argand diagram. In summation (5) each step has been shortened by a factor m_j. Because α_j is not accurately known, a probability distribution exists for $\exp(i\alpha_j)$. $m_j \exp(i\alpha_j^c)$ is the centroid of this distribution. Similarly, the summation (5) represents the centroid of the probability distribution for $T_i \exp(\alpha_i + \Phi_i)$.

The values T_i^c and Φ_i^c calculated from (5) may now be substituted back in (3) in place of T_i and Φ_i. Because of the error which we know exists, we do not seek an explicit value of α_i, but determine how closely (3) is satisfied as a function of α_i. The 'lack of closure' error (Fig. 1)

$$\varepsilon(\alpha_i) = |(T_i^c \exp[i(\alpha_i + \Phi_i^c)] + A_{ii} \exp[i(2\alpha_i + \varphi_{ii})] - S_i)| \qquad (6)$$

may be compared with an expected root mean square error E.

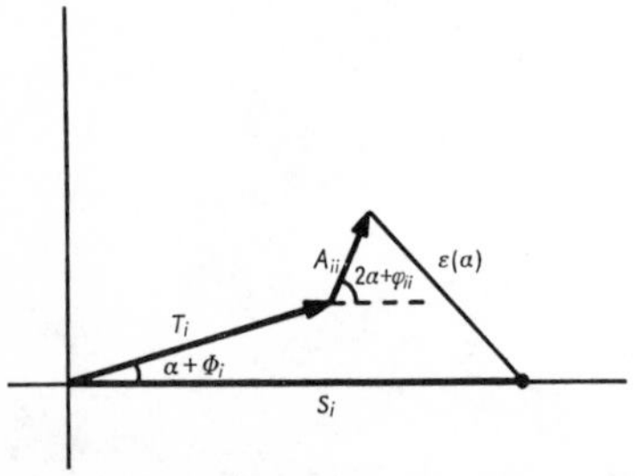

Fig. 1. Any one equation can be represented by the sum of two vectors, T_i^c and A_{ii} rotating at a speed of α and 2α respectively. The distance $\varepsilon(\alpha)$ between the end of the sum of three vectors and the point S_i on the real axis represents the lack of closure of that equation for any angle α.

By assuming a normal distribution of error, we may now set up a probability function for the phase angle α_i:

$$P_i(\alpha) = \exp[-\varepsilon^2(\alpha)/2E^2] \, . \qquad (7)$$

To form an estimate of E we have to recognize, first, that the quantities A_{ij}, φ_{ij}, S_i which are assumed known, will contain errors due to inaccuracy in measured F's, errors in the rotational and translational parameters, and errors in choosing an envelope for each independent subunit. The mean square contribution to ε of all these errors may be taken as some constant, e^2. A much more significant source of error is that whenever $\exp(i\alpha_j)$ occurs in (2), we employ the approximation $m_j \exp(i\alpha_j^c)$. It may be shown that $\langle(\exp i\alpha_j - n_j \exp i\alpha_j^c)^2\rangle = 1 - m_j^2$ (see Dickerson, Kendrew & Strandberg, 1961), where the symbol $\langle\ \rangle$ represents the averaging with appropriate weights over all the possibilities. Although the distribution of error for a single term will have a marked dependence on phase angle, it seems a sufficient approximation to use the sum of the squares of the magnitudes of the errors as a measure of the mean square error in the summation (5) thus:

$$E^2 = e^2 + \sum_{j \neq i} A_{ij}^2 (1 - m_j^2) \, . \qquad (8)$$

The probabilities defined by (7) can now be calculated by using (6) and (8). They may then be used to find a new phase angle and figure of merit in just the same way that this is done for the isomorphous replacement technique (Blow & Crick, 1959; Dickerson, Kendrew & Strandberg, 1961)

$$m_i \exp(i\alpha_i^c) = \frac{\int_0^{2\pi} P(\alpha) \exp(i\alpha) d\alpha}{\int_0^{2\pi} P(\alpha) d\alpha} \qquad (9)$$

When new values have been calculated for all the values of m_i, α_i by (9), a further round of refinement may be begun.

It is evident that this type of procedure will cause (1) to be better satisfied when some critical estimates of the α_i exist. If the procedure is commenced with no phase information except that α_0, the phase of the $F(000)$ term, is zero, so that $m_0 = 1$, and all other m_i are zero, then the early stages of the procedure run closely parallel to the method described previously (Rossmann & Blow, 1963). However, the interdependence of significant terms is considered from the beginning. The method can also be used when phase information is available which would not in itself be sufficient to allow the structure to be solved, such as that obtained from a single isomorphous pair of non-centrosymmetric crystal structures. In such a case one might expect that the bimodal phase probability curves obtained from the single isomorphous replacement method would become unimodal as refinement proceeds, selecting one of the two alternative phase angles as correct.

If the arrangement of subunit centres is centrosymmetric, the necessary conditions expressed by (1) will be equally well fulfilled by the enantiomorphic as by the true structure. Once, however, any one phase has been selected in favor of one enantiomorph, the solutions of the remaining phases must then all satisfy this enantiomorph. However, this last condition is difficult to achieve in practice, for no phase is known with certainty, and less still do we know in advance which phase will unequivocally distinguish between the two enantiomorphs. Thus, unless some other information is available, as for instance X-ray data for the same subunit from another crystal form, we may find our solution to be a combination of the two enantiomorphic forms.

The approach described in this paper was developed while we were both on the staff of the Medical Research Council Laboratory of Molecular Biology, Hills Rd., Cambridge, England, and was tested by using computational facilities provided by the Medical Research Council.

References

Blow, D. M. & Crick, F. H. C. (1959). *Acta Cryst.* **12**, 794.

Blow, D. M., Rossmann, M. G. & Jeffery, B. A. (1964). *J. Mol. Biol.* **8**, 65.

Dickerson, R. E., Kendrew, J. C. & Strandberg, B. E. (1961). *Acta Cryst.* **14**, 1188.

Rossmann, M. G. & Blow, D. M. (1963). *Acta Cryst.* **16**, 39.

Reprinted from *Acta Crystallographica*, Vol. 21, Part 1, July 1966

Acta Cryst. (1966). **21**, 67

Relationships among Structure Factors due to Identical Molecules in Different Crystallographic Environments

PETER MAIN AND MICHAEL G. ROSSMANN

Department of Biological Sciences, Purdue University, Lafayette, Indiana, U.S.A.

Restraints on phases are imposed when a molecule crystallizes in different crystal forms or occurs more than once per asymmetric unit. These restrictions are expressed by the equations

$$|F_p| \exp \{i\alpha_p\} = \frac{U}{V} \sum_{h=-\infty}^{+\infty} |F_h| \exp \{i\alpha_h \sum_{n=1}^{N} G_{hpn} \exp \{i\varphi_{hpn}\}.$$

Here $|F_p|$, α_p, $|F_h|$, and α_h are the structure factors and their phases at the reciprocal lattice points **p** and **h** in either the same or different crystals. G_{hpn} and φ_{hpn} are simple functions of the rotation and translation parameters relating the molecules in the structures concerned. These equations have been tested in both one and three dimensions. In the one-dimensional case the same arbitrary electron density distribution was repeated several times at irregular intervals within the unit cell. All chosen distributions led to equations that could be solved correctly, suggesting that in general there is a unique solution. Refinement of initial approximate translation parameters during phase solution was also successful.

Introduction

When there are chemically identical molecules in different crystallographic environments, the phase problem may be approached in three distinct stages. The first stage involves determining the three rotation parameters that relate any two molecules. The rotation function (Rossmann & Blow, 1962; Sasada, 1964) has proved successful for this purpose in a number of cases (Blow, Rossmann & Jeffery, 1964; Prothero & Rossmann, 1964; Dodsen, Harding, Hodgkin & Rossmann, 1966; Palmer, Palmer & Dickerson, 1964). The second stage involves determining the translation parameters that relate these molecules. A method of determining these parameters has been worked out in a special situation when the independent molecules are within the same crystal, related by a non-crystallographic two-fold rotation axis (Rossmann, Blow, Harding & Coller, 1964). This was used in the case of chymotrypsin (Blow *et al.*, 1964) and in insulin (Dodsen *et al.*, 1965).

The third and final stage is to determine the phases, given the results of the first two stages. Equations have been derived for this purpose in the case of two independent molecules within the same crystal (Rossmann & Blow, 1963). These equations were solved in a two-dimensional problem for the innermost 35 reflections, but success was probably partly duc to the somewhat linear shape of the molecule giving rise to a large low order reflection. The method is also exceedingly expensive in terms of computer time, but a simpler and more powerful method of solution was given by Rossmann & Blow (1964). Application of the latter to improving the phases of the two independent α-chymotrypsin molecules (Blow *et al.*, 1964) showed that in this case the method did not give a unique answer.

The present paper derives a set of equations for the third stage which are perfectly general. We show that a method based on that of Rossmann & Blow (1964), interlaced with refinement procedures, produces unique solutions, and that a general solution to the translation problem may be obtained simultaneously.

The equations

The structure factor $\mathbf{F}_p$ at the reciprocal lattice point $\mathbf{p}$ may be expressed as

$$\mathbf{F}_p = \sum_{n=1}^{N} \int_U \varrho_1(\mathbf{x}_n) \exp\{2\pi i \mathbf{p} \cdot \mathbf{x}_n\} d\mathbf{x}_n \tag{1}$$

where there are N identical molecules in the unit cell of the crystal, each molecule being enclosed within a volume U, and $\varrho_1(\mathbf{x}_n)$ is the electron density at the point $\mathbf{x}_n$ in the nth molecule. Let

$$\mathbf{x}_n = [\mathbf{C}_n]\mathbf{x}_1 + \mathbf{d}_n \tag{2}$$

where $[\mathbf{C}_n]$ is the rotation matrix and $\mathbf{d}_n$ the translation vector that relate the equivalent points $\mathbf{x}_1$ and $\mathbf{x}_n$ in the first and nth molecules repectively. Thus $[\mathbf{C}_1]=[\mathbf{I}]$, the identity matrix, and $\mathbf{d}_1=0$. If there is only one molecule per asymmetric unit then $[\mathbf{C}_n]$ and $\mathbf{d}_n$ are purely space group operators.

Since $\varrho_1(\mathbf{x}_n)=\varrho_1(\mathbf{x}_1)$ by definition, we have from (1) and (2)

$$\mathbf{F}_p = \sum_{n=1}^{N} \int_U \varrho_1(\mathbf{x}_1) \exp\{2\pi i \mathbf{p} \cdot ([\mathbf{C}_n]\mathbf{x}_1 + \mathbf{d}_n)\} d\mathbf{x}_1 \,. \tag{3}$$

Now let $\varrho(x)$ be the electron density at a point $\mathbf{x}$ in a second crystal which contains the same molecule so that $\varrho(\mathbf{x})=\varrho_1(\mathbf{x}_1)$ within the molecular volume U. If the 'second' crystal is the same as the first then ϱ and ϱ_1 are identical. Expressing $\varrho(\mathbf{x})$ in terms of a Fourier summation we get

$$\varrho(\mathbf{x}) = \frac{1}{V} \sum_{h=-\infty}^{+\infty} \mathbf{F}_h \exp\{-2\pi i \mathbf{h} \cdot \mathbf{x}\} \tag{4}$$

where $\mathbf{F}_h$ is the structure factor at the reciprocal lattice point $\mathbf{h}$ and V is the volume of the unit cell.

Let

$$\mathbf{x} = [\mathbf{C}] \cdot \mathbf{x}_1 + \mathbf{d} \tag{5}$$

where $[\mathbf{C}]$ is the rotation matrix and $\mathbf{d}$ the translation vector relating the equivalent points $\mathbf{x}_1$ and $\mathbf{x}$ in the 'p' and 'h' crystals respectively.

We can eliminate $\mathbf{x}$ from (4) by using (5), and this gives us $\varrho(\mathbf{x}_1)$ which, by definition, is identical with $\varrho_1(\mathbf{x}_1)$ within the volume U. Putting this into (3) we obtain

$$\mathbf{F}_p = \sum_{n=1}^{N} \int_U \frac{1}{V} \sum_{h=-\infty}^{+\infty} \mathbf{F}_h \exp\{-2\pi i \mathbf{h} \cdot ([\mathbf{C}] \cdot \mathbf{x}_1 + \mathbf{d})\} \exp\{2\pi i \mathbf{p} \cdot ([\mathbf{C}_n] \cdot \mathbf{x}_1 + \mathbf{d}_n)\} d\mathbf{x}_1$$

which, after rearrangement, becomes

$$\mathbf{F}_p = \frac{1}{V} \sum_{h=-\infty}^{+\infty} \sum_{n=1}^{N} \mathbf{F}_h \exp\{2\pi i (\mathbf{p} \cdot \mathbf{d}_n - \mathbf{h} \cdot \mathbf{d})\} \int_U \exp\{2\pi i (\mathbf{p} \cdot [\mathbf{C}_n] - \mathbf{h} \cdot [\mathbf{C}]) \cdot \mathbf{x}_1\} d\mathbf{x}_1 \,. \tag{6}$$

The integral part of the expression is the same as that described by Rossmann & Blow (1962) and is the Fourier transform of the volume U. It may be represented by a magnitude UG_{hpn} and a phase Ω_{hpn}. In the case of a sphere or a parallelepiped, the two most commonly used 'molecular envelopes', the phase is given by

$$\Omega_{hpn} = 2\pi (\mathbf{p} \cdot [\mathbf{C}_n] - \mathbf{h} \cdot [\mathbf{C}]) \cdot \mathbf{S}_1 \tag{7}$$

where $\mathbf{S}_1$ is the position of the geometric center of the first molecular envelope in the 'p' crystal.

$$\therefore\ \mathbf{F}_p = \frac{U}{V} \sum_{h=-\infty}^{+\infty} \sum_{n=1}^{N} \mathbf{F}_h \exp\{2\pi i (\mathbf{p} \cdot \mathbf{d}_n - \mathbf{h} \cdot \mathbf{d})\} G_{hpn} \exp\{2\pi i (\mathbf{p} \cdot [\mathbf{C}_n] - \mathbf{h} \cdot [\mathbf{C}]) \cdot \mathbf{S}_1\}$$

i.e.

$$\mathbf{F}_p = \frac{U}{V} \sum_{h=-\infty}^{+\infty} \sum_{n=1}^{N} \mathbf{F}_h G_{hpn} \exp\{2\pi i [\mathbf{p} \cdot (\mathbf{d}_n + [\mathbf{C}_n] \cdot \mathbf{S}_1) - \mathbf{h} \cdot (\mathbf{d} + [\mathbf{C}] \cdot \mathbf{S}_1)]\} \,. \tag{8}$$

Let $\mathbf{S}_n$ be the nth position of the centre of the volume U in the 'p' crystal and let $\mathbf{S}$ be a corresponding point in the 'h' crystal, then from (2) and (5) we get

$$\mathbf{S}_n = [\mathbf{C}_n] \cdot \mathbf{S}_1 + \mathbf{d}_n \quad \text{and} \quad \mathbf{S} = [\mathbf{C}] \cdot \mathbf{S}_1 + \mathbf{d} \,. \tag{9}$$

By writing the structure factors in terms of magnitude and phase and from (8) and (9) we arrive at the final equations

$$|\mathbf{F}_p| \exp\{i\alpha_p\} = \frac{U}{V} \sum_{h=-\infty}^{+\infty} |\mathbf{F}_h| \exp\{i\alpha_h\} \sum_{n=1}^{N} G_{hpn} \exp\{2\pi i (\mathbf{p} \cdot \mathbf{S}_n - \mathbf{h} \cdot \mathbf{S})\} \,. \tag{10}$$

As an example of an expression for G_{hpn} we can take the case of a sphere of radius R,

$$G_{hpn} = \frac{3(\sin 2\pi HR - 2\pi HR \cos 2\pi HR)}{(2\pi HR)^3} \,, \tag{11}$$

where H is the length of the vector $\mathbf{p} \cdot [\mathbf{C}_n] - \mathbf{h} \cdot [\mathbf{C}]$. The shape of this function is shown in Fig. 1 of Rossmann & Blow (1962). In general, as H increases G_{hpn} decreases, so only those values of **h** which make H small need be included in equation (10), the remaining **h** values giving rise to negligible values for G_{hpn}.

Once the rotation and translation parameters relating all molecules in every crystal have been determined, the only unknowns in (10) are the phases α_h and α_p.

It must be pointed out that (10) refers only to a single set of equations, whereas several such sets of equations may generally be obtained for a single problem. If we have two crystals A and B, then making A the 'h' crystal and B the 'p' crystal will produce a different set of equations than when A is the 'p' and B is the 'h' crystal. In addition, (10) refers to only one molecule in crystal 'h' – that located within the envelope centered on **S** – but generally there will be more than one molecule in the unit cell of this crystal. Different sets of equations result by taking **S** at each *independent* molecule in turn, but the same set of equations is obtained when the different positions of **S** are related by space-group symmetry. This is shown in the Appendix. It should also be noted that the 'h' and 'p' crystals can be identical, though if there is only one molecule per asymmetric unit, the equations reduce to $\mathbf{F}_p=\mathbf{F}_p$ and give no phase information. With more than one independent molecule, however, a legitimate set of equations is obtained.

Clearly, the more crystals and independent molecules there are, the more equations can be set up in relation to the number of unknown phases. The problem therefore becomes progressively more over-determined as the number of independent molecules increases.

Accuracy of the equations

In a practical case, it will be difficult to define an envelope of volume U within which a single molecule is completely contained without any part of any other

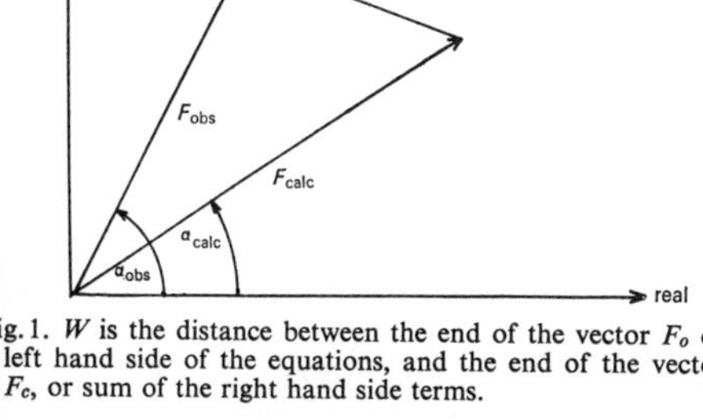

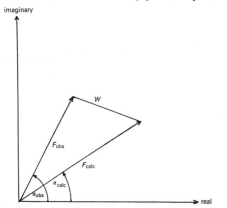

Fig. 1. W is the distance between the end of the vector F_o or left hand side of the equations, and the end of the vector F_c, or sum of the right hand side terms.

molecule. Our experiments have not allowed for this type of error. It is hoped that if only a small amount of electron density is present in the envelope in additon to the molecule, or if only a small part of the molecule is left outside the envelope, then the accuracy with which the equations are satified will not be greatly affected. Subsequent refinement of the structure should reveal the molecule more accurately. This, in turn, will lead to more accurate satisfaction of the equations.

The accuracy of the equations may be defined by the usual crystallographic R index. If $\mathbf{F}_o$ is the left hand side of an equation, $\mathbf{F}_c$ the resultant of the right hand side sum and W is the magnitude of the vector difference btweeen them, as in Fig. 1, we can define

$$R=\frac{\Sigma W}{\Sigma|\mathbf{F}_o|}.$$

The equations have been set up in a three-dimensional case (to be published) in which one crystal consisted of four identical molecules in the unit cell of space group $P2_1$ and another crystal of four molecules in the unit cell of space group $P2_12_12_1$. The magnitude of G_{hpn} was assumed to be negligible for arguments greater than 1·75 and only the fifty largest terms were considered in each equation. In this case the residual was 18%. In every one-dimensional case for which 'observed' structure factors were calculated and the known phases used for substitution in the equations, a residual of less than 3% was obtained. Even after introducing a 4% random error on the $|\mathbf{F}_o|$ values, R was less than 5%.

Solutions of the equations

We have solved these equations for the phases of unknown structures under certain limited conditions, using methods similar to those described by Rossmann & Blow (1963, 1964) in conjunction with iterative refinement procedures. In practice, however, only rough values of **S** and $\mathbf{S}_n$ in equation (10) will be known from packing considerations, so these were also refined during the solution of the equations. Fig. 2 shows a hypothetical one-dimensional structure in which there are three identical 'molecules' per asymmetric unit and which was used to test the equations. After imposing a 4% random error on the $|\mathbf{F}_o|$ values and starting with approximate relative positions of the molecules, all phases out to $h=44$ were determined with an average error of 31°. These are shown in Table 1 together with the structure amplitudes and the correct phases. Other structures, with three or four identical molecules in the asymmetric unit were also solved using the same techniques. However, when a one-dimensional structure with two molecules in the asymmetric unit was used, the phase determination was only satisfactory to $h=10$. The breakdown of phase determination in this case can be attributed to the fact that the two molecule structure contained less information than the three or four molecule structures.

Conclusions

The equations presented in this paper are completely general. They relate the structure factors of any number of crystal forms of the same molecule, or of only one crystal form if there is more than one molecule per asymmetric unit. The fact that the equations are satisfied has been demonstrated and their ability to solve one-dimensional structures indicates the possibility of using them for phase determination with real structures.

APPENDIX

We wish to show that equation (10) reproduces the correct Laue symmetry and phase relationships for the structure factors $\mathbf{F}_p$ regardless of the symmetry of crystal '*h*'.

Centric reflections

The N rotation matrices associated with the crystal '*p*' may be divided into pairs $[\mathbf{C}_n]$, $[\mathbf{C}_{N-n+1}]$ $(n=1, 2\ldots N/2)$ such that the operation $[\mathbf{C}_n][\mathbf{C}_{N-n+1}]^{-1}$ is a space-group rotation which gives rise to centric reflections in certain zones of the reciprocal lattice. It can be shown that, for a centric reflection

$$\mathbf{p}\,.\,[\mathbf{C}_n]=-\mathbf{p}\,.\,[\mathbf{C}_{N-n+1}] \quad (n=1,2\ldots N/2)\,. \qquad (1A)$$

Therefore

$$\mathbf{p}\,.\,[\mathbf{C}_n]-\mathbf{h}\,.\,[\mathbf{C}]=-\mathbf{p}\,.\,[\mathbf{C}_{N-n+1}]+\bar{\mathbf{h}}\,.\,[\mathbf{C}]\,. \qquad (2A)$$

As the magnitude of G_{hpn} is unaltered when the direction of the argument is reversed, we have from (2A)

$$G_{hpn}=G_{hp(N-n+1)}\,. \qquad (3A)$$

From equation (9) we have

$$\mathbf{S}_n=[\mathbf{C}_n]\mathbf{S}_1+\mathbf{d}_n\,. \qquad (4A)$$

Therefore, using (1A) it follows that

$$\mathbf{p}\,.\,\mathbf{S}_n=-\mathbf{p}\,.\,\mathbf{S}_{N-n+1}+\mathbf{p}\,.\,\mathbf{d}_n+\mathbf{p}\,.\,\mathbf{d}_{N-n+1}\,.$$

Therefore

$$\exp\{2\pi i\mathbf{p}\,.\,\mathbf{S}_n\}=\exp\{-2\pi i\mathbf{p}\,.\,\mathbf{S}_{N-n+1}\}\,, \qquad (5A)$$

since $\mathbf{d}_n+\mathbf{d}_{N-n+1}$ is a space group translation and for centric reflections $2\pi\mathbf{p}\,.\,(\mathbf{d}_n+\mathbf{d}_{N-n+1})$ will be equal to $2\pi m$, where m is an integer.

Now, rewriting (10) as

$$|\mathbf{F}_p|\exp\{i\alpha_p\}=\frac{U}{V}\sum_{h=-\infty}^{+\infty}\sum_{n=1}^{N/2}[|F_h|G_{hpn}\exp\{i(2\pi\mathbf{p}\,.\,\mathbf{S}_n-2\pi\mathbf{h}\,.\,\mathbf{S}+\alpha_h)\}+|\mathbf{F}_{\bar{h}}|G_{\bar{h}p(N-n+1)}\exp\{i(2\pi\mathbf{p}\,.\,\mathbf{S}_{N-n+1}-2\pi\bar{\mathbf{h}}\,.\,\mathbf{S}+\alpha_h)\}]$$

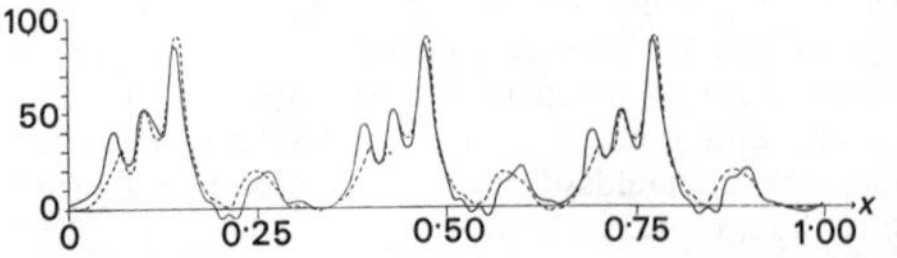

Fig. 2. Structure determination with three identical molecules per unit cell. The dashed line is the true structure, and the continuous line is the structure determined with an approximate knowledge of the position of the molecular centers and also $|\mathbf{F}_o|$ amplitudes which contained a 4 % experimenta error.

Table 1. *Phase determination of structure shown in Fig.* 2

h is the index of the correct structure amplitude $|F_o|$ and phase α^0_0. A random set of errors $\pm\varepsilon$ has been added to each $|F_o|$ Solution of the set of equations using coefficients based on the magnitudes $(|F_o|\pm\varepsilon)$ gave the phase angles α^0.

h	$\|\mathbf{F}_o\|$	$\|\mathbf{F}_o\|\pm\varepsilon$	α^0	α^0_0	h	$\|\mathbf{F}_o\|$	$\|\mathbf{F}_o\|\pm\varepsilon$	α^0	α^0_0
0	18·92	18·92	0	0	23	0·95	0·97	359	351
1	1·31	1·27	173	169	24	2·43	2·53	166	148
2	2·05	1·99	247	236	25	0·86	0·82	130	107
3	9·91	10·56	244	228	26	0·50	0·54	281	261
4	2·32	2·37	78	62	27	2·00	1·85	69	29
5	2·43	2·50	157	145	28	0·29	0·29	359	308
6	5·81	5·43	129	123	29	0·29	0·28	232	200
7	3·21	2·91	290	295	30	1·21	1·24	299	273
8	2·70	2·55	323	343	31	0·26	0·27	126	124
9	3·11	3·26	259	282	32	0·16	0·16	88	118
10	2·98	3·02	76	98	33	0·25	0·24	78	142
11	2·20	2·31	148	157	34	0·03	0·03	265	251
12	1·24	1·14	101	90	35	0·09	0·09	353	222
13	1·72	1·86	320	315	36	0·33	0·33	7	223
14	1·14	1·08	71	40	37	0·43	0·43	191	63
15	0·61	0·61	327	286	38	0·28	0·28	232	116
16	1·32	1·26	202	188	39	0·33	0·33	195	94
17	0·96	1·01	255	257	40	0·68	0·68	19	303
18	0·97	1·05	63	86	41	0·26	0·26	68	15
19	1·52	1·58	258	24	42	0·18	0·18	344	307
20	1·14	1·07	87	111	43	0·50	0·50	191	195
21	1·99	1·92	277	285	44	0·20	0·20	267	286
22	1·57	1·42	246	242					

Translation parameters

Initial values $S_1=0{\cdot}150;\ S_2=0{\cdot}520;\ S_3=0{\cdot}800$

Refined values $S_1=0{\cdot}169;\ S_2=0{\cdot}500;\ S_3=0{\cdot}800$

Correct values $S_1=0{\cdot}170;\ S_2=0{\cdot}500;\ S_3=0{\cdot}800$

we see from (3A) and (5A) that the above simplifies to

$$|F_p| \exp\{i\alpha_p\} = \frac{U}{V}\sum_{h=-\infty}^{+\infty}\sum_{n=1}^{N/2}|\mathbf{F}_h|G_{hpn}$$
$$\cos[2\pi(\mathbf{p}\,.\,\mathbf{S}_n-\mathbf{h}\,.\,\mathbf{S})+\alpha_h] \quad (6A)$$

and the right hand side is completely real. The result is independent of the nature of crystal 'h'.

A similar argument can be produced for any phases which are restricted to particular discrete values by space group symmetry, such as those produced by zonal reflections in space group $P2_12_12_1$. whose values must be $\pi/2$ or $3\pi/2$.

Systematic absences

If $\mathbf{S}_1$ and $\mathbf{S}_n$ in (4A) are related by a Bravais type translation (giving rise to systematic absences) then $[\mathbf{C}_n]=[\mathbf{I}]$. Also since systematic absences due to screw axes or glide planes lie on an axis or in a plane respectively, it is clear that, in this case,

$$\mathbf{p}\,.\,[\mathbf{C}_n]=\mathbf{p}$$

where $\mathbf{p}$ is the reciprocal lattice vector corresponding to a systematic absence. Hence, in all cases

$$\mathbf{p}\,.\,\mathbf{S}_n=\mathbf{p}\,.\,\mathbf{S}_1+\mathbf{p}\,.\,\mathbf{d}_n\,. \quad (7A)$$

Now, a factor in the summation over n in (10) is $\sum_{n=1}^{N}\exp(2\pi i\mathbf{p}\,.\,\mathbf{S}_n)$, which, from (7$A$), becomes

$$\sum_{n=1}^{N}\exp(2\pi i\mathbf{p}\,.\,\mathbf{S}_n)=\exp(2\pi i\mathbf{p}\,.\,\mathbf{S}_1)\sum_{n=1}^{N}\exp(2\pi i\mathbf{p}\,.\,\mathbf{d}_n)\,. \quad (8A)$$

But, if $\mathbf{p}$ is systematically absent we have

$$\sum_{n=1}^{N}\exp(2\pi i\mathbf{p}\,.\,\mathbf{d}_n)=0$$

since $\mathbf{d}_n$ represented the Bravais, glide or screw translation element. Hence, from (8A)

$$\sum_{n=1}^{N}\exp(2\pi i\mathbf{p}\,.\,\mathbf{S}_n)=0$$

and it is clear that the sum over n for each value of h in (10) will be zero, when $\mathbf{p}$ corresponds to a space-group systematic absence.

The effect of changing p to a Laue-symmetry related position

The structure factor $\mathbf{F}_p$ is defined as

$$|\mathbf{F}_p|=\int_v \varrho(\mathbf{x})\exp\{2\pi i\mathbf{p}\,.\,\mathbf{x}\}dV\,. \quad (9A)$$

Now, if $[\mathbf{C}_m]$ and $\mathbf{d}_m$ are space group operators, we have

$$\mathbf{x}=[\mathbf{C}_m]\mathbf{x}'+\mathbf{d}_m \quad (10A)$$

where $\mathbf{x}$ and $\mathbf{x}'$ are equivalent positions. Eliminating $\mathbf{x}$ between (9A) and (10A) we obtain

$$\mathbf{F}_p=\int_v \varrho(\mathbf{x}')\exp\{2\pi i\mathbf{p}\,.\,([C_m]\mathbf{x}'+\mathbf{d}_m)\}dV$$

Therefore

$$\mathbf{F}_p=\exp\{2\pi i\mathbf{p}\,.\,\mathbf{d}_m\}\int_v \varrho(\mathbf{x}')\exp\{2\pi i\mathbf{p}[\mathbf{C}_m]\mathbf{x}'\}dV\,.$$

If we now let

$$\mathbf{p}'=\mathbf{p}\,.\,[\mathbf{C}_m] \quad (11A)$$

then

$$\mathbf{F}_p=\exp\{2\pi i\mathbf{p}\,.\,\mathbf{d}_m\}\mathbf{F}_{p'}$$

or, after rearrangement,

$$\mathbf{F}_{p'}=\mathbf{F}_p\exp\{-2\pi i\mathbf{p}\,.\,\mathbf{d}_m\}\,. \quad (12A)$$

That is, the effect on the left hand side structure factor, when the point $\mathbf{p}$ is changed to the symmetry related position $\mathbf{p}'$, is to rotate the phase by $2\pi\mathbf{p}\,.\,\mathbf{d}_m$.

From (10), the right hand side of the equation for $\mathbf{F}_{p'}$ may be written

$$\frac{U}{V}\sum_{h=-\infty}^{+\infty}|\mathbf{F}_h|\exp\{i(\alpha_h-2\pi\mathbf{h}\,.\,\mathbf{S})\}\sum_{n=1}^{N}G_{hpn}$$
$$\exp\{2\pi i\mathbf{p}'\,.\,\mathbf{S}_n\} \quad (13A)$$

and it is clear that the only changes are in the summation over n. But the argument of $G_{hp'n}$ is $(\mathbf{p}'\,.\,[\mathbf{C}_n]-\mathbf{h}\,.\,[\mathbf{C}]$ or $(\mathbf{p}\,.\,[\mathbf{C}_m][\mathbf{C}_n]-\mathbf{h}\,.\,[\mathbf{C}])$ from (11A). Since $[\mathbf{C}_m]$ is a space group rotation, $[\mathbf{C}_m][\mathbf{C}_n]$ are also space group rotations and merely reproduce the set $[\mathbf{C}_n]$ in a different order. Let this new set be $[\mathbf{C}_l]$, then the argument of G becomes $(\mathbf{p}\,.\,[\mathbf{C}_l]-\mathbf{h}\,.\,[\mathbf{C}])$ and the set of $G_{hp'n}$ for all n is reproduced by the set G_{hpl} for all l in a different order.

Let us now apply the operators $[\mathbf{C}_m]$ and $[\mathbf{d}_m]$ to each $\mathbf{S}_n$ in turn. We then obtain $[\mathbf{C}_m]\,\mathbf{S}_n\pm\mathbf{d}_m$ which from (6) becomes

$$[\mathbf{C}_m][\mathbf{C}_n]\,\mathbf{S}_1+[\mathbf{C}_m]\,\mathbf{d}_n+\mathbf{d}_m\,.$$

If we now define $[\mathbf{C}_m]\mathbf{d}_n\pm\mathbf{d}_m$ to be $\mathbf{d}_l$ and $[\mathbf{C}_m][\mathbf{C}_n]$ as $[\mathbf{C}_l]$ as before, we then obtain $[\mathbf{C}_l]\mathbf{S}_1+\mathbf{d}_l$ which, by analogy with (4A), is clearly the set of equivalent positions $\mathbf{S}_l$. That is ,we can write

$$\mathbf{S}_l=[\mathbf{C}_m]\mathbf{S}_n+\mathbf{d}_m\,. \quad (14A)$$

We can now deal with the product $\mathbf{p}'\,.\,\mathbf{S}_n$ in the expression (13A) above.

From (11A),

$$\mathbf{p}'\,.\,\mathbf{S}_n=\mathbf{p}\,.\,[\mathbf{C}_m]\mathbf{S}_n\,.$$

Then from (14A)

$$\mathbf{p}'\,.\,\mathbf{S}_n=\mathbf{p}\,.\,(\mathbf{S}_l-\mathbf{d}_m)$$

and we can now rewrite (13A) as

$$\exp\{-2\pi i\mathbf{p}\,.\,\mathbf{d}_m\}\frac{U}{V}\sum_{h=-\infty}^{+\infty}|F_h|$$
$$\exp\{i(\alpha_h-2\pi\mathbf{h}\,.\,\mathbf{S})\}\sum_{l=1}^{N}G_{hpl}\exp\{2\pi i\mathbf{p}\,.\,\mathbf{S}_l\}\,,$$

which from (10) is clearly equal to $\exp\{-2\pi i\mathbf{p}\,.\,\mathbf{d}_m\}\mathbf{F}_p$. Thus the equations are unchanged by moving to Laue-symmetry related lattice points, apart from the application of the factor $\exp\{-2\pi i\mathbf{p}\,.\,\mathbf{d}_m\}$ which, from (12*A*), is necessary to preserve the symmetry in the phases.

The effect of changing **S** *to a space-group symmetry related position*

The argument of the exponential term in (10) involving **h** and **S** is

$$\varphi=\alpha_h-2\pi\mathbf{h}\,.\,\mathbf{S}\,.$$

Let us now use, instead of **S**, the space-group symmetry related position **S**′, where

$$\mathbf{S}=[\mathbf{C}']\mathbf{S}'+\mathbf{d}'$$

and [**C**′] and **d**′ are the space group operators. This space group operation has the effect in reciprocal space of producing symmetry related structure factors $\mathbf{F}_h$ and $\mathbf{F}_{h'}$ such that $\mathbf{h}'=\mathbf{h}[\mathbf{C}']$ and $\alpha_{h'}=\alpha_h-2\pi\mathbf{h}\,.\,\mathbf{d}'$ [see equations (11*A*) and (12*A*)]. If we sum the right hand side of (10) over **h**′ instead of **h**, φ' will be given by

$$\varphi'=\alpha_{h'}-2\pi\mathbf{h}'\,.\,\mathbf{S}'$$

i.e. $$\varphi'=\alpha_h-2\pi\mathbf{h}\,.\,\mathbf{d}'-2\pi\mathbf{h}\,.\,[\mathbf{C}'][\mathbf{C}']^{-1}(\mathbf{S}-\mathbf{d}')\,.$$

Therefore $\varphi'=\alpha_h-2\pi\mathbf{h}\,.\,\mathbf{S}=\varphi\,.$

Since φ is unchanged, it is clearly immaterial which of the equivalent positions of **S** is used in setting up the equations.

A corollary is that if **S** is changed to a molecular equivalent position, but one without any crystallographic equivalence, we form a different set of equations.

This work has been supported by NSF grant GB-02905 and NIH grant GM10704-03. We also thank the Purdue University Computer Science Centre for their assistance in the prompt running of programs. We thank Dr P. Tøllin and also Mrs J. Roberts and Mrs J. Parsons for their scientific and technical assistance in the preparation of this manuscript.

References

Blow, D. M., Rossmann, M. G. & Jeffery, B. A. (1964). *J. Mol. Biol.* **8**, 65.

Dodsen, E., Harding, M. M., Hodgkin, D. C. & Rossmann, M. G. (1966). *J. Mol. Biol.* **16**, 227.

Palmer, H. T., Palmer, R. A. & Dickerson, R. E. (1964). *Nature, Lond.* **202**, 1052.

Prothero, J. W. & Rossmann, M. G. (1964). *Acta Cryst.* **17**, 768.

Rossmann, M. G. & Blow, D. M. (1962). *Acta Cryst.* **15**, 24.

Rossmann, M. G. & Blow, D. M. (1963). *Acta Cryst.* **16**, 39.

Rossmann, M. G. & Blow, D. M. (1964). *Acta Cryst.* **17**, 1474.

Rossmann, M. G., Blow, D. M., Harding, M. M. & Coller, E. (1964). *Acta Cryst.* **17**, 338.

Sasada, Y. (1964). *Acta Cryst.* **17**, 611.

Reprinted from *Acta Crystallographica*, Vol. 23, Part 1, July 1967

Acta Cryst. (1967). **23**, 50

Phase Determination Using Non-crystallographic Symmetry

By Peter Main

Department of Biological Sciences, Purdue University, Lafayette, Indiana, U.S.A.

A three-dimensional hypothetical structure containing four crystallographically independent but chemically identical molecules in space group $P1$ has been solved. Each molecule contained ten carbon atoms separated by distances greater than 1·2 Å. The solution of the phases required only a knowledge of the structure amplitudes and the relative orientations and positions of the molecules.

1. Introduction

In a paper by Main & Rossmann (1966) (hereafter MR) there was described a method of phase determination which depended upon having chemically identical molecules in different crystallographic environments. Equating the electron densities of such molecules places restriction on the phases which are expressed by equation (10) of MR.

$$|\mathbf{F}_p| \exp\{i\alpha_p\} = \frac{U}{V} \sum_{h=-\infty}^{+\infty} |\mathbf{F}_h| \exp\{i\alpha_h\} \sum_{n=1}^{N} G_{hpn} \exp\{2\pi i(\mathbf{p}\,.\,\mathbf{S}_n - \mathbf{h}\,.\,\mathbf{S})\} \quad (1)$$

where $|\mathbf{F}_p|$, α_p, $|\mathbf{F}_h|$ and α_h are the structure amplitudes and their phases at the reciprocal lattice points $\mathbf{p}$ and $\mathbf{h}$ in either the same or different crystals. Each molecule is enclosed in an envelope of volume U, the centres of the N molecular envelopes in the 'p' crystal being at $\mathbf{S}_n(n=1,2\ldots N)$, while $\mathbf{S}$ is the centre of a molecular envelope in the 'h' crystal. The function G_{hpn} is the magnitude of the Fourier transform of the molecular envelope which is given both in magnitude and phase by

$$G_{hpn}\{\exp i\Omega_{hpn}\} = \int_U \exp\{2\pi i(\mathbf{p}\,.\,[\mathbf{C}_n] - \mathbf{h}\,.\,[\mathbf{C}])\mathbf{x}\}d\mathbf{x}\,, \quad (2)$$

where $[\mathbf{C}_n]$ is the rotation matrix describing the orientation of the nth molecule in crystal 'p' and $[\mathbf{C}]$ is the rotation matrix corresponding to the molecule centred on $\mathbf{S}$ in crystal 'h'.

MR showed that, using these equations in a one-dimensional case, the phases α_p and α_h could be determined with sufficient accuracy for the structure to be recognized in the resulting Fourier synthesis. This paper describes the method of phase determination used here and by MR, as well as the application of the technique to the solution of a hypothetical three-dimensional structure in the space group $P1$.

2. Method of phase determination

Because of the nature of the function G_{hpn}, the largest terms on the right hand side of equation (1) will tend to have $[\mathbf{h}]\approx[\mathbf{p}]$ or, more specifically, $\mathbf{h}$ and $\mathbf{p}$ will be such that the vector $(\mathbf{p}\,.\,[\mathbf{C}_n]-\mathbf{h}\,.\,[\mathbf{C}])$ is small. Initially, the only known phase will be $\alpha_o(=2\pi)$, so that the first phases to be determined will be those for which $|\mathbf{p}|$ is small as these will have the largest interactions with $\mathbf{F}_o$. Next, equations with $|\mathbf{p}|$ a little larger are used since these will have large interactions with those phases previously determined. The equations are therefore arranged in increasing order of their Bragg angle and knowledge of the phases is gradually extended outwards in reciprocal space. This is similar in outline to the method of Rossmann & Blow (1963).

The actual process of phase determination is to take one new phase, α_p, on the edge of the known part of reciprocal space and find its 'best' value by a search procedure. This is done by choosing an equation with α_p on the left hand side and summing the right hand side over all known values of α_h. Arbitrary values of α_p at say 5° intervals are substituted into the equation and the discrepancy between the two sides is calculated for each value of α_p. This is repeated for each equation which contains α_p explicitly on the left hand side and the sum of all the discrepancies for each angle is computed. That value of α_p which gives the lowest total discrepancy is considered to be the best present estimate of the phase, subject to the error introduced by the lack of knowledge or inaccuracy of the phases α_h. In the event that $\mathbf{h}$ and $\mathbf{p}$ refer to the same crystal, terms involving α_p may occur also on the right hand side, that is, those terms for which $\mathbf{h}=\pm\mathbf{p}$. This procedure is similar to that described by Rossmann & Blow (1964).

As estimates of more phases become known, phases determined earlier may now be redetermined with more accuracy. The determination of a batch of phases is therefore followed by a refinement of all known phases before further phase determination takes place. The refinement consists simply of substituting the present estimate of the phases in the right hand sides of the equations and performing the vector summation. The argument of each resultant is then taken as the new estimate of the phase angle appearing on the left hand side of the equation. Whenever the same phase appears explicitly on the left hand side of more than one equation, the argument of the vector sum of all the right hand sides is taken as the new estimate. The new set of phases is only accepted, however, if it reduces the residual of the equations as defined by MR.

That this process is one of refinement can be seen by examining its real space equivalent. By referring to the derivation of the equations by MR it can be seen that any one equation represents the structure factor $\mathbf{F}_p$ calculated from the assumption that all the molecules in crystal 'p' are identical with that centred on $\mathbf{S}$ in crystal 'h'. There will be approximately one such equation for each crystallographically independent molecule, so taking the vector average of the right hand side sums of these equations is the same as calculating structure factors from an electron density which is the average over all the independent molecules. It is this averaging process which produces the refinement, but since there is nothing in the procedure which forces the residual to decrease, it will rise again after several cycles and begin to oscillate.

3. Application to a trial structure

Because the equations (1) are non-linear, there immediately arose the problem of how to solve them and whether the solution would be unique. As a preliminary answer to these questions, the equations were applied to a variety of one-dimensional problems and were found to be successful (MR). Recently, a more satisfactory test of the method has been completed in which a hypothetical structure in the space group $P1$ was solved. The structure (Fig. 1) was made up of four identical molecules arranged in different orientations in the unit cell ($a=11{\cdot}8$, $b=11{\cdot}1$, $c=6{\cdot}8$ Å, $\alpha=\beta=\gamma=90{\cdot}0°$), each molecule consisting of ten equal carbon atoms separated by distances greater than 1·2 Å. The size of the molecule is immaterial as far as the method is concerned but, in order to attain atomic resolution with a minimum amount of work, the 10-atom molecule was chosen. The molecular envelope was chosen to be a sphere of radius 3·4 Å and, in order to avoid errors due to atoms spilling over into the wrong envelope, the molecules were given a larger than normal separation. This resulted in the calculated density of the crystal being 0·90 g.cm^{-3} and in this respect the crystal was rather ideal. After calculating structure factors to 1·0 Å resolution, the equations were set up using only the structure amplitudes and a knowledge of the relative positions and orientations of the molecules. In all, there were 1838 unique reflexions in the 1·0 Å limiting sphere but only the 1113 largest were used in the calculations. The magnitude of G_{hpn} was assumed to be negligible for arguments greater than $2\pi \times 1{\cdot}6$ and only the 60 largest terms were considered in each equation. (A previous attempt at solving the structure, using $2\pi \times 1{\cdot}1$ as the maximum argument of G_{hpn} and 40 terms in each equation, proved to be only partially successful.)

Putting the correct phases into the equations and calculating the residual produced the results shown in

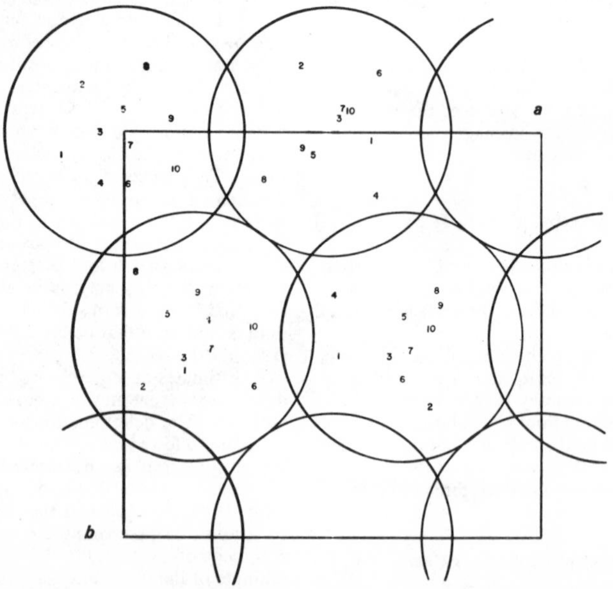

Fig. 1. Projections of the hypothetical structure onto the *ab* face of the unit cell. The unit cell contains four identical molecules in different orientations in the space group $P1$. Each molecule contains ten carbon atoms numbered 1–10.

Table 1. The overall residual was 22·7%, but doubtless this could be decreased by accepting larger arguments of G_{hpn} and including more terms in the equations. The average discrepancy in angle between the left and right hand sides of the equations was only about 10°, however.

Table 1. *Residuals obtained on substituting the correct phases into equations*

The residual R is defined as the sum of the magnitude of the lack of closure vectors of each equation divided by the sum of the magnitude of the left hand sides. The error $\Delta\alpha$ is the mean difference in angle between the two sides of the equation.

Resolution range	R	$\Delta\alpha$
∞ − 1·8 Å	18·8 %	9·4°
1·8 − 1·4	22·7	9·5
1·4 − 1·0	26·0	10·7

The method of phase determination outlined in § 2 was used, and when the calculations were terminated the average error in the 1113 phases determined was 13°. At this point the phases were still refining to more accurate values, but there seemed no need to pursue the calculations further as the structure was obviously solved and refinement was rather slow. A plot of error in phase angle against sin θ is shown in Fig. 2. The lower curve shows the errors at the termination of the calculations and the upper curve shows the errors at the stage where the phase determination had progressed to 1·35 Å resolution. Immediately after the 1·35 Å stage the accuracy of the determined phases increased dramatically. Presumably this was because a large number of atoms suddenly became resolved, changing the features of the electron density quite

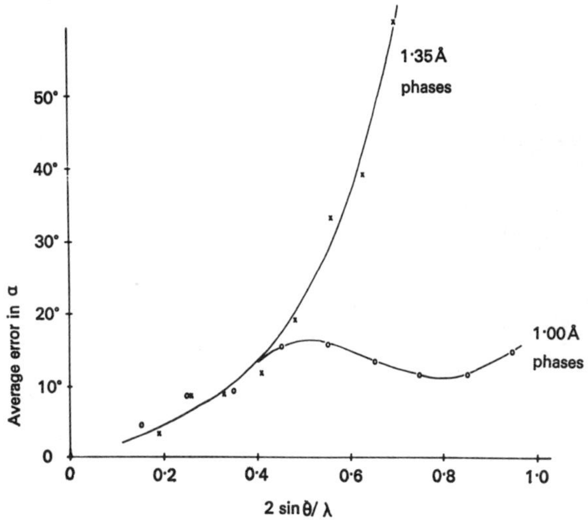

Fig. 2. Quality of phase determination as a function of resolution. The crosses show accuracy of phase determination using all equations up to a resolution 1·35 Å. An increase of resolution to 1·0 Å gave a dramatic improvement in phase determination as shown by the circles.

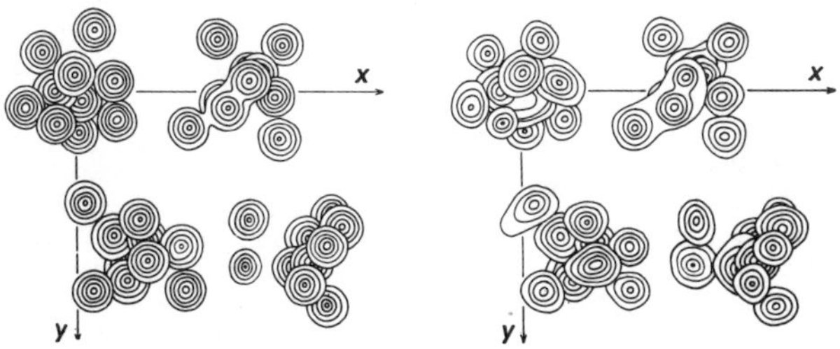

Fig. 3. Comparison of the three-dimensional electron density maps at 1·0 Å resolution viewed down the c axis. The map on the left has been computed with the correct phases, whereas the map on the right is based on the phases determined by the solution of the molecular replacement equations.

radically and allowing the residual of the equations to fall into a deep minimum.

The electron density calculated from the 1113 determined phases and the corresponding structure amplitudes, projected onto the *ab* face, is shown in Fig. 3. The true electron density calculated from all 1838 reflexions in the 1·0 Å sphere and the correct phases is also shown. All the features of the correct structure are clearly discernible in the determined structure – all the atoms are at least partially resolved, the vast majority being fully resolved, and no atom lies more than 0·15 Å away from its correct position, most of them being within 0·10 Å. The largest undesirable features in the determined structure are regions of negative electron density (some as low as $-1{\cdot}2$ e.Å^{-3}) between the molecules and outside of the molecular envelopes.

4. Discussion

An average error of only 13° in the phases of over 1000 reflexions may be attributed to the fact that the relative orientations and positions of all the molecules were known exactly, the molecular envelopes could be placed accurately and there was no experimental error in the structure amplitudes. In addition, there were four independent molecules, which is probably more than sufficient. The one-dimensional examples quoted by MR suggest that with only two independent molecules, the phase determination is likely to be less reliable and may even be quite random at high resolution.*

A number of questions remain unanswered by this trial of the molecular replacement method. It is not yet known what effect experimental error will have on the ability of the equations to determine accurate phases, although experiments with one-dimensional structures show that a small amount of error will have very little effect (MR). Errors in the placement† or shape‡ of the molecular envelopes will have an effect on the phase determination though, again, the extent of this effect has not been investigated. In the one-dimensional structures reported by MR the positions of the molecular envelopes were successfully refined by least-squares methods during phase determination, but in three dimensions this becomes an unwieldy computing problem and has not yet been programmed.

The application of the method described in this paper has been limited to the case of chemically identical but crystallographically independent molecules within the same crystal. Additional problems may exist, however, when the molecules are in different crystals. In the latter case, the structure factors $\mathbf{F}_p$ and $\mathbf{F}_h$ in equations (1) belong to different crystals, whereas in the problem treated in this paper they correspond to the same crystal.

The example given in this paper also assumes a knowledge of the absolute scale of the structure amplitudes. This is implied in the use of the $\mathbf{F}(000)$ term to determine some of the early phases. Furthermore, if this method is to be applied to a protein, we should consider the space outside the molecular envelopes to be filled uniformly by electron density representing the liquid of crystallization. As will be shown, these two factors are closely related.

Let us assume that all $\mathbf{F}_h$'s have been placed on a roughly absolute scale. Although it is possible to calculate $\mathbf{F}_h(000)$ from the total number of electrons in the cell, nevertheless, this value should be adjusted to be $k\,.\,\mathbf{F}_h(000)$ in order to bring it more accurately onto the same scale as the other structure amplitudes. Let ϱ_s be the average electron density of liquid between the molecular envelopes. We may now see that

$$\mathbf{F}_p = \sum_{n=1}^{N} \int_U \varrho(\mathbf{x}_n) \exp\{2\pi i\mathbf{p}\,.\,\mathbf{x}_n\}d\mathbf{x}_n + \int_{(V-NU)} \varrho_s \exp\{2\pi i\mathbf{p}\,.\,\mathbf{x}\}d\mathbf{x}$$

i.e.

$$\mathbf{F}_p = \sum_{n=1}^{N} \int_U \varrho(\mathbf{x}_n) \exp\{2\pi i\mathbf{p}\,.\,\mathbf{x}_n\}d\mathbf{x}_n + \int_V \varrho_s \exp\{2\pi i\mathbf{p}\,.\,\mathbf{x}\}d\mathbf{x} - \sum_{n=1}^{N} \int_U \varrho_s \exp\{2\pi i\mathbf{p}\,.\,\mathbf{x}_n\}d\mathbf{x}_n$$

$$\mathbf{F}_p = \sum_{n=1}^{N} \int_U [\varrho(\mathbf{x}_n) - \varrho_s] \exp\{2\pi i\mathbf{p}\,.\,\mathbf{x}_n\}d\mathbf{x}_n + \int_V \varrho_s \exp\{2\pi i\mathbf{p}\,.\,\mathbf{x}\}d\mathbf{x}\,.$$

The last term is zero unless $\mathbf{p}$ is zero, when this term is equal to $V\varrho_s$. Hence in all equations, apart from the $\mathbf{F}_p(000)$ equation, we simply replace $\varrho(\mathbf{x})$ by $[\varrho(\mathbf{x})-\varrho_s]$ which is equivalent to subtracting $V\varrho_s$ from $k\,.\,\mathbf{F}_h(000)$. The equations therefore remain in exactly the same form apart from the interactions with $\mathbf{F}_h(000)$.

We may rewrite the interactions with the $\mathbf{F}_h(000$ term as $[k(U/V)\mathbf{F}_h(000) - U\varrho_s]re^{i\varphi}$ when $|\mathbf{p}| \neq 0$, or b

---

* Since this paper was submitted, the author has shown that, using the techniques described here, phase determination with only two independent molecules does become random at high resolution, though not before useful structural information has been obtained.

† The order of magnitude of the error involved may be obtained as follows. Let us assume that the orientation error may be corrected by a rotation of $\delta\theta$ about an axis a distance r from the reference point S_n within the nth molecule. This corrects $\mathbf{S}_n$ to $\mathbf{S}_n + \delta\mathbf{S}_n$, where $\delta S_n = r\,.\,\delta\theta$ and the argument of the corresponding coefficient in the equation will be changed by $2\pi\mathbf{p}\,.\,\delta S_n$ radians. If we assume the magnitudes of all the coefficients with the same h are equal then the total error involved in the phase determined by that equation (i.e. α_p) is $2\pi\mathbf{p}\,.\,\sum_n \delta S_n$ radians. The value of $\delta\theta$ may be estimated from the rotation function and r will be approximately the distance between the non-crystallographic rotation axis and the centre of the molecule.

‡ A satisfactory envelope can be chosen for the monomer in R3 insulin from packing and other considerations. This envelope can be further refined from initial poor electron density maps. The degree of accuracy required in the first guess is, however, unknown and will undoubtedly vary from structure to structure.

$k(U/V)\mathbf{F}_h(000)$ when $|\mathbf{p}|=0$. Here $re^{i\varphi}$ represents the sum over n in equation (1). The constant quantity $[k(U/V)\mathbf{F}_h(000)-U\varrho_s]$ will appear in every equation except when $|\mathbf{p}|=0$, and may therefore be estimated by averaging the lack of closure of each equation. Also $k(1-U/V)\mathbf{F}_h(000)$ may be found from the $\mathbf{F}_p(000)$ equation. Hence k and ϱ_s can be determined, given reasonable initial estimates of these quantities. Since the size of the interaction $re^{i\varphi}$ decreases as $|\mathbf{p}|$ increases, the effect of salt concentration or an inaccurate knowledge of the absolute scale becomes rapidly less significant as we go out in reciprocal space.

The author is indebted to Dr M. G. Rossmann for his help and inspiration in this work, to Mr John Steele at Purdue University's Computer Sciences Center for giving valuable advice, and to Mrs Margaret Wonacott for aid in the preparation of the manuscript. This work was supported by N.I.H. grant GM 10704-03 and by N.S.F. grant GB 02905.

References

MAIN, P. & ROSSMANN, M. G. (1966). *Acta Cryst.* **21**, 67.
ROSSMANN, M. G. & BLOW, D. M. (1963). *Acta Cryst.* **16**, 39.
ROSSMANN, M. G. & BLOW, D. M. (1964). *Acta Cryst.* **17**, 1474.

Reprinted from *Acta Crystallographica*, Vol. 22, Part 6, June 1967

Acta Cryst. (1967). **22**, 758

A Linear Analysis of the Non-Crystallographic Symmetry Problem

BY R. A. CROWTHER

Medical Research Council Laboratory of Molecular Biology, Hills Road, Cambridge, England

Linear equations are derived which express constraints on the structure factors of a crystal having more than one identical molecule or subunit in the asymmetric unit. Solution of these equations leads to a series of functions having the required non-crystallographic symmetry. Any structure having the postulated symmetry can be expressed as a linear combination of these functions. This approach has the advantage that far fewer variables are needed to describe the system to a given resolution than in the conventional method using amplitudes and phases. The reduction in the number of variables is used as a measure of the information content of the equations.

Introduction

has been shown (Rossmann & Blow, 1963; Main & ɔssmann, 1966) that, when a crystal contains more an one identical molecule or subunit per asymmetric it, equations can be set up which imply constraints the phases of the structure factors. These equations ntain certain parameters relating to the relative ro- ional and translational positioning of the subunits thin the asymmetric unit. However, there exist meth- s for determining these parameters (Rossmann & ow, 1962; Rossmann, Blow, Harding & Coller, 1964) d it is assumed in all that follows that their values known.

Iterative methods for solution of the equations have been proposed which, for a number of simple trial structures, appear to converge to a unique answer, agreeing well with the known phases (Rossmann & Blow, 1964; Main & Rossmann, 1966). Both these papers attempt to derive values for the unknown phases and in doing so formally separate the amplitudes and phases of the structure factors as they appear in the equations. This means that the equations to be solved are non-linear from the beginning of the calculation.

The methods described in this paper formally keep the amplitude and phase together as an unknown complex structure factor. The equations are now linear in these complex structure factors and the powerful techniques of linear analysis can be applied to the system. It will be shown that to a given resolution there is only a finite number of independent density distributions which satisfy the non-crystallographic symmetry and that this number is considerably less than the number of phases needed in a conventional description of the system to this resolution. These density distributions are the Fourier transforms of a degenerate set of eigenvectors corresponding to a multiple eigenvalue of the matrix describing the geometry of the system. Such degenerate systems of eigenfunctions are familiar in quantum mechanics and other brances of applied mathematics. The important point about them is that any function which satisfies the conditions of the problem can be expressed as a linear combination of the allowed eigenfunctions. Thus, to solve a structure having known non-crystallographic symmetry, it is necessary to determine the coefficients in the expansion of the structure in terms of the allowed eigenfunctions. Since only the intensities of the diffraction pattern are available the equations for these coefficients are non-linear, but the number of unknowns is now much smaller than the number of phases that would have to be found in a conventional structure determination.

Setting up the equations

Let us now derive, in a suitably symmetrized form, the equations that the structure factors must obey when a crystal contains n identical subunits per asymmetric unit. For simplicity we consider space group $P1$, though the results can readily be extended to space groups of higher symmetry. In setting up the equations it is assumed that

(*a*) the geometry of the subunits is known;
(*b*) the subunits are identical;
(*c*) the density between the subunits is zero;
(*d*) the density is real.

One subunit U_1 is taken as the reference subunit and the positions of the other subunits U_j are specified relative to this. Suppose the position $\mathbf{x}_j$ of an element of density in the jth subunit is related to the position $\mathbf{x}_1$ of the corresponding element of density in the reference subunit by

$$\mathbf{x}_j = \mathbf{C}_j\mathbf{x}_1 + \mathbf{d}_j,\ (j=1,n)\,,$$

where $\mathbf{C}_1 = \mathbf{I},\ \mathbf{d}_1 = \mathbf{0}\,,$

so that $\varrho(\mathbf{C}_j\mathbf{x}_1 + \mathbf{d}_j) = \varrho(\mathbf{x}_1)$

when $\mathbf{x}_1$ lies within U_1. We may write the complex structure factor $F_{\mathbf{h}}$ as

$$F_{\mathbf{h}} = |F_{\mathbf{h}}| \exp(i\alpha_{\mathbf{h}}) = V \int_{\substack{\text{unit}\\ \text{cell}}} \varrho(\mathbf{x}) \exp(2\pi i \mathbf{h}\,.\,\mathbf{x}) d\mathbf{x}\,.$$

For reasons which will appear later it is more convenient to use assumption (*d*) and to work with the complex conjugate relation

$$F^*_{\mathbf{h}} = |F_{\mathbf{h}}| \exp(-i\alpha_{\mathbf{h}}) = V \int_{\substack{\text{unit}\\ \text{cell}}} \varrho(\mathbf{x}) \exp(-2\pi i \mathbf{h}\,.\,\mathbf{x}) d\mathbf{x}\,.$$

Using assumption (*c*) we may write this as a sum of integrals taken over the subunits

$$F^*_{\mathbf{h}} = V \sum_{j=1}^{n} \int_{U_j} \varrho(\mathbf{x}) \exp(-2\pi i \mathbf{h}\,.\,\mathbf{x}) d\mathbf{x}\,.$$

Transforming the variable of integration we have

$$F^*_{\mathbf{h}} = V \sum_{j=1}^{n} \int_{U_1} \varrho(\mathbf{x}_j) \exp(-2\pi i \mathbf{h}\,.\,\mathbf{x}_j) d\mathbf{x}_1\,.$$

We now have to express the identity of the subunits, assumption (*b*), in such a way that the algebraic symmetry is retained. This may be done by equating all the densities $\varrho(\mathbf{x}_j)$ in turn to $\varrho(\mathbf{x}_1)$, then to $\varrho(\mathbf{x}_2)$ and so on, thus generating the n relations

$$F^*_{\mathbf{h}} = V \sum_{j=1}^{n} \int_{U_1} \varrho(\mathbf{x}_k) \exp(-2\pi i \mathbf{h}\,.\,\mathbf{x}_j) d\mathbf{x}_1,\ (k=1,n)\,.$$

We may now add these n expressions giving

$$nF^*_{\mathbf{h}} = V \sum_{j=1}^{n} \sum_{k=1}^{n} \int_{U_1} \varrho(\mathbf{x}_k) \exp(-2\pi i \mathbf{h}\,.\,\mathbf{x}_j) d\mathbf{x}_1\,.$$

Replacing $\varrho(\mathbf{x}_k)$ by its Fourier series expansion

$$\varrho(\mathbf{x}_k) = \frac{1}{V} \sum_{\mathbf{p}} F_{\mathbf{p}} \exp(-2\pi i \mathbf{p}\,.\,\mathbf{x}_k)$$

gives

$$F^*_{\mathbf{h}} = \frac{1}{n} \sum_{j=1}^{n} \sum_{k=1}^{n} \int_{U_1} \sum_{\mathbf{p}} F_{\mathbf{p}} \exp(-2\pi i \mathbf{p}\,.\,\mathbf{x}_k) \exp(-2\pi i \mathbf{h}\,.\,\mathbf{x}_j)\, d\mathbf{x}_1$$

which, after rearrangement, becomes

$$F^*_{\mathbf{h}} = \sum_{\mathbf{p}} F_{\mathbf{p}} \left\{ \frac{1}{n} \sum_{j=1}^{n} \sum_{k=1}^{n} \int_{U_1} \exp[-2\pi i (\mathbf{h}\,.\,\mathbf{x}_j + \mathbf{p}\,.\,\mathbf{x}_k)] d\mathbf{x}_1 \right\}$$

This may be written more compactly as

$$F^*_{\mathbf{h}} = \sum_{\mathbf{p}} B_{\mathbf{hp}} F_{\mathbf{p}}\,, \qquad (1$$

where

$$B_{\mathbf{hp}} = \frac{1}{n} \sum_{j=1}^{n} \sum_{k=1}^{n} \int_{U_1} \exp[-2\pi i (\mathbf{h}\,.\,\mathbf{x}_j + \mathbf{p}\,.\,\mathbf{x}_k)] d\mathbf{x}_1\,.$$

It is shown in the Appendix that these equations r lating the structure factors are not only a necessa consequence of the identity of the subunits, but a also sufficient to ensure that identity.

Matrix formulation of the equations

The equations (1) express the value of an arbitra structure factor $F^*_{\mathbf{h}}$ as a weighted sum of structure f tors $F_{\mathbf{p}}$ taken over the whole of reciprocal space. T weighting factors $B_{\mathbf{hp}}$ are expressed in terms of t shape and the relative rotational and translational p ameters of the subunits within the asymmetric unit a are assumed calculable. For the purposes of compu tion it is necessary to truncate the summation o reciprocal space after a finite number of terms. Si the weighting factor falls off fairly rapidly with increasing distance between the points **p** and **h** in reciprocal space, it may be assumed that the truncation affects significantly only those reflexions lying close to the boundary of the region of reciprocal space being considered.

It is convenient at this stage to denote the reflexions $F_{\mathbf{h}}$ and $F_{\mathbf{p}}$ by scalar suffixes as F_r and F_s, the Friedel-related reflexions being denoted by F_{-r} and F_{-s}. The equations (1) now become

$$\sum_{S=-N}^{N} B_{rs}F_s = F_r^*, \; (r=-N,\dots N),$$

or, writing this in matrix notation,

$$\mathbf{BF}=\mathbf{F}^*, \tag{2}$$

where **B** is the $(2N+1)\times(2N+1)$ complex matrix of weighting factors and **F** is the complex column vector of structure factors

$$\mathbf{F}=\begin{pmatrix} F_{-N} \\ \vdots \\ F_0 \\ \vdots \\ F_N \end{pmatrix}.$$

We now combine equation (2) with the Friedel relationship which can conveniently be written in matrix form as

$$\mathbf{TF}=\mathbf{F}^*, \tag{3}$$

where

$$\mathbf{T}=\begin{pmatrix} 0 & & 1 \\ & \cdot^{\cdot^{\cdot}} & \\ 1 & & 0 \end{pmatrix}, \; \mathbf{T}^2=\mathbf{I}.$$

Premultiplication of the vector **F** by the matrix **T** has the effect of interchanging F_r and F_{-r}, $(r=1,N)$, so that **T** is in fact a re-ordering matrix. Combining (2) and (3) we have

$$\mathbf{BF}=\mathbf{TF}$$

or

$$\mathbf{HF}=\mathbf{F} \tag{4}$$

where $\mathbf{H}=\mathbf{TB}$.

Therefore

$$(\mathbf{H}-\mathbf{I})\mathbf{F}=0. \tag{5}$$

It can be seen from their definition that the elements of matrix **B** obey the symmetry relation

$$B_{-s-r}=B_{rs}^*$$

so that **B** is Hermitian about its second diagonal. Premultiplication by the matrix **T** has the effect of interchanging the diagonals, so that the matrix **H** is Hermitian about its leading diagonal (*i.e.* $H_{sr}=H_{rs}^*$). The rather complicated manipulations used in deriving the equations were necessary in order to produce a matrix of Hermitian type, thus simplifying further theory and computation.

Solution of the equations

The expression (5) represents a set of $(2N+1)$ homogeneous linear equations in the $(2N+1)$ complex variables F_r. Because of the way the equations were constructed, any solution of them will satisfy the Friedel relation and will have a Fourier transform which has identical density distributions inside the subunits and zero density outside the subunits. In general, however, there will be more than one independent solution and the general solution will be a linear combination of these.

To discover how many independent solutions there are to equations (5) we must consider (4) as a special case of the general eigenvalue problem

$$\mathbf{HF}=\lambda\mathbf{F}. \tag{6}$$

By comparing (4) and (6) we see that any eigenvector of **H** corresponding to an eigenvalue $\lambda=1$ will be a solution of equation (5). Conversely the number of linearly independent solutions of (5) is equal to the number of unit eigenvalues of the matrix **H**. Since **H** is Hermitian all its eigenvalues are real and it is possible to construct a set of $(2N+1)$ orthonormal eigenvectors.

Let us suppose that **H** has m unit eigenvalues and let us denote the corresponding orthonormal eigenvectors by $(\mathbf{u}_1,\dots\mathbf{u}_m)$. If we have a problem in which the density $\varrho(\mathbf{x})$ satisfies the postulated conditions of localization and local symmetry, it is possible by the above argument to express its transform **F** as a linear combination of the eigenvectors $(\mathbf{u}_1,\dots\mathbf{u}_m)$, namely

$$\mathbf{F}=\sum_{j=1}^{m}\mu_j\mathbf{u}_j.$$

By taking the Fourier transform of this equation we could equally well express the relation in real space (to the resolution to which we are working) and write

$$\varrho(\mathbf{x})=\sum_{j=1}^{m}\mu_j\varrho_j(\mathbf{x}),$$

where $\varrho_j(\mathbf{x})$ represents the Fourier transform of the eigenvector $\mathbf{u}_j$. The functions $\varrho_j(\mathbf{x})$ will be referred to as 'eigendensities'. It is important to note that the μ_j are real, since $\varrho(\mathbf{x})$ is real and since $\varrho_j(\mathbf{x})$ are real because $\mathbf{u}_j$ were constructed to satisfy the Friedel relation.

The eigendensities ϱ_j corresponding to an orthonormal set of eigenvectors $\mathbf{u}_j$ are also orthonormal, in the sense that

$$I_{jk}=\int_{\substack{\text{unit}\\\text{cell}}}\varrho_j(\mathbf{x})\varrho_k(\mathbf{x})d\mathbf{x}=\delta_{jk}.$$

This may be shown by replacing the densities by their Fourier series giving

$$I_{jk}=\int_{\substack{\text{unit}\\\text{cell}}}\sum_{\mathbf{h}}u_{j\mathbf{h}}\exp(-2\pi i\mathbf{h}\,.\,\mathbf{x})\sum_{\mathbf{p}}u_{k\mathbf{p}}\exp(-2\pi i\mathbf{p}\,.\,\mathbf{x})d\mathbf{x}$$

$$=\sum_{\mathbf{h}}\sum_{\mathbf{p}}u_{j\mathbf{h}}u_{k\mathbf{p}}\int_{\substack{\text{unit}\\\text{cell}}}\exp[-2\pi i(\mathbf{h}+\mathbf{p})\,.\,\mathbf{x}]d\mathbf{x}.$$

The integral vanishes unless $\mathbf{p}=-\mathbf{h}$ so that

$$I_{jk} = \sum_{\mathbf{h}} u_{j\mathbf{h}} u_{k,-\mathbf{h}}$$
$$= \sum_{\mathbf{h}} u_{j\mathbf{h}} u^{*}_{k\mathbf{h}}$$

since $\mathbf{u}_k$ satisfies the Friedel relation. Hence by the orthonormality of the eigenvectors we have

$$I_{jk} = \delta_{jk} .$$

We have so far considered only those eigenvectors and eigendensities corresponding to unit eigenvalues. What meaning can be attached to those eigenvalues

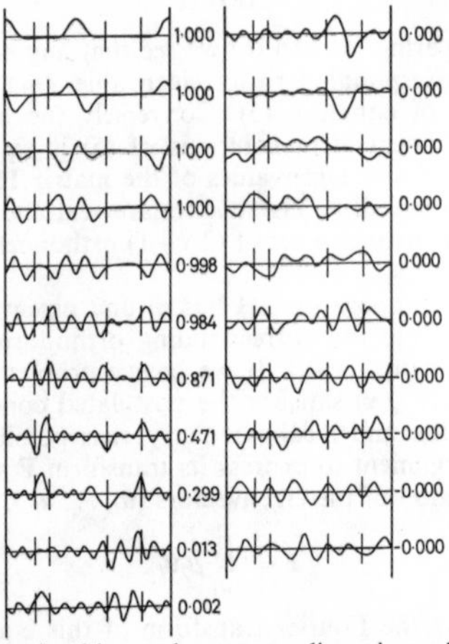

Fig. 1. Eigendensities and corresponding eigenvalues for a one-dimensional cell, line group 1, containing two identical subunits, each of fractional size 0·357 with centres at 0 and 0·431 respectively, reflexions from $h=-10$ to $h=+10$ being included.

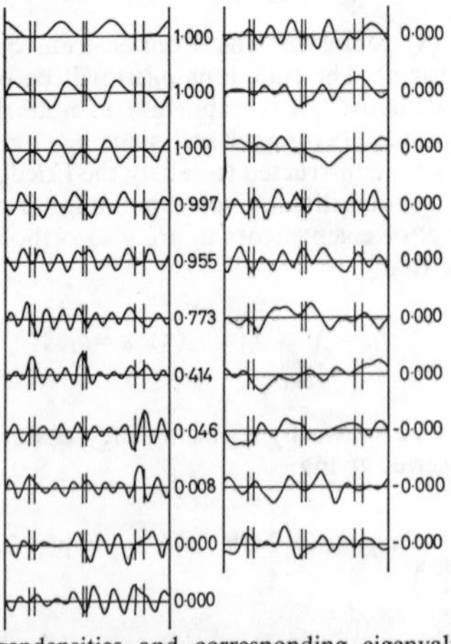

Fig. 2. Eigendensities and corresponding eigenvalues for a one-dimensional cell, line group 1, containing three identical subunits, each of fractional size 0·29 with centres at 0, 0·33 and 0·63 respectively (Main & Rossmann, 1966), reflexions from $h=-10$ to $h=+10$ being included.

which are not unity? It is shown in the Appendix that an eigenvalue λ_j can be expressed in terms of its corresponding eigendensity by

$$\lambda_j = \frac{\int_{\text{subunits}} [\varrho_j(\mathbf{x})]^2 d\mathbf{x} - \sigma_j^2}{\int_{\text{unit cell}} [\varrho_j(\mathbf{x})]^2 d\mathbf{x}} , \tag{7}$$

where σ_j^2 is a measure of the lack of equality of density within the various subunits. The first term in the numerator is a measure of the fraction of the total density which lies within the subunits and the denominator is a normalizing factor. The form of (7) implies that $0 \le \lambda_j \le 1$. If there is no density outside the subunits and the densities within the subunits are identical, so that $\sigma_j^2 = 0$, equation (7) gives $\lambda_j = 1$, as expected. If all the density lies outside the subunits, $\lambda_j = 0$. Some combinations of non-zero densities within the various subunits can also lead to a zero eigenvalue, though the exact form of these densities depends on the number of subunits.

Figs. 1 and 2 show the eigendensities and corresponding eigenvalues for two one-dimensional examples containing 2 and 3 subunits respectively. In each case reflexions from $h=-10$ to $h=+10$ are included. Because we are considering a truncated system and because of rounding errors during calculation there are no exactly unit eigenvalues. Also in any real problem the postulated conditions, in particular that of vanishing density outside the subunits, will not be exactly fulfilled, so that it is not clear how far an eigenvalue can depart from unity, while still considering the corresponding eigendensity as allowable. This will be discussed further in the next section. If we consider an allowed eigendensity to be one corresponding to an eigenvalue $\lambda \ge 0·95$, the two subunit case has six allowed eigendensities and the three subunit case has five.

Fig. 3 shows the eigendensities corresponding to the six largest eigenvalues for a two-dimensional case with two identical subunits.

As might be expected the behaviour within the subunits of the one-dimensional eigendensities is similar to that of the classical orthogonal polynomials. With increasing number of zeros in the interval the fitting that can be achieved, while working to a given resolution, becomes steadily worse and this is reflected in an increasing departure from unity of the corresponding eigenvalue. In the two-dimensional example of Fig. 3 it can be seen that the behaviour of the eigendensities within the subunits is analogous to the normal modes of vibration of a rectangular membrane, though there are departures from this because of the unsymmetric disposition of the subunits.

Information content of the equations

Let us now consider the above problem in a different way. Suppose we have a structure which is unknown but which has the postulated local symmetry, and that to a given resolution we have measured the intensities of N independent reflexions. In a conventional structure determination N phases have to be found. Using the above analysis, however, only m real parameters have to be determined, namely the coefficients in the expansion of the transform in terms of the m known allowed eigenvectors. We may write

$$\mathbf{F} = \sum_{j=1}^{m} \mu_j \mathbf{u}_j \,. \tag{8}$$

Since only the intensities of the reflexions are available the equations from which μ_j have to be found are non-linear, namely

$$|F_h|^2 = \sum_{j=1}^{m} \sum_{k=1}^{m} \mu_j \mu_k u_{jh}^* u_{kh},\ (h=0,1,\ldots N)\,.$$

The number of equations is now much greater than the number of unknowns and it should be possible to find best values of the parameters μ_j by a non-linear least-squares process, using a sliding filter of the type described by Diamond (1966). Using this technique it s possible to decide how many eigenvectors to include at each stage of the fitting procedure and in particular o decide how many eigenvectors are allowable. If the u_j are orthonormal the form of (8) implies an overall cale factor for the problem, since the μ_j must satisfy he relation

$$\sum_{j=1}^{m} \mu_j^2 = \sum_{h=-N}^{N} |F_h|^2 \,.$$

In Fig. 4 the number of allowed eigendensities is lotted against the number of independent reflexions ncluded, for a series of one-dimensional problems coniining 2, 3 and 4 subunits respectively. In this context igendensities corresponding to eigenvalues $\lambda \geq 0{\cdot}95$ ave been considered allowable. It can be seen that e plots are linear, though their exact form for a given umber of subunits will depend on the size and posioning of the subunits. The fact that the plots do not ass through the origin means that there is a certain inimum number of reflexions that has to be included efore it is possible to generate an eigendensity which tisfies the conditions of the problem. The gradient the plots, or the fractional decrease in the number parameters needed to describe the system, can be nsidered to represent the information gained by this ethod of analysis.

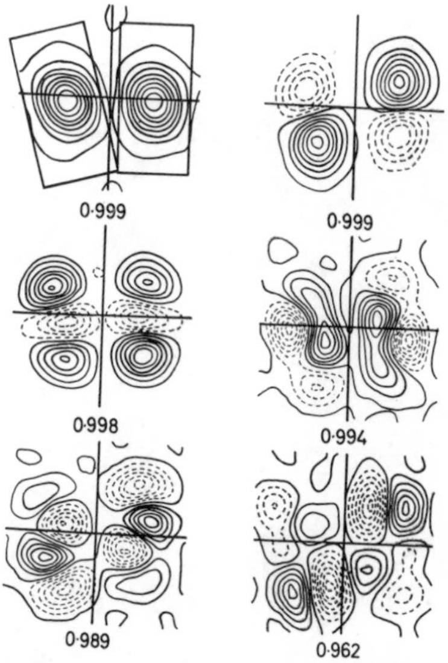

Fig. 3. Eigendensities corresponding to the six largest eigenvalues for a two-dimensional square cell, plane group $p1$, containing two identical subunits related by a rotation of 194° about the centre of the cell. The subunits are enclosed within rectangular boxes of fractional dimensions $0{\cdot}4 \times 0{\cdot}8$ and the centre of the reference subunit is at $x=0{\cdot}25$, $y=0$, as shown in the first diagram of the series. The innermost 49 reflexions are included.

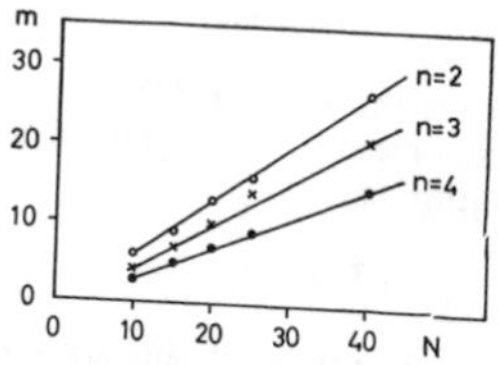

Fig. 4. Plots of m, the number of allowed eigenvectors, against N, the number of independent reflexions included, for one-dimensional examples containing 2, 3 and 4 identical subunits. Allowed eigenvectors are those corresponding to eigenvalues $\lambda \geq 0{\cdot}95$. For $n=2$, subunit size $=0{\cdot}357$, subunit centres at 0 and 0·431. For $n=3$, subunit size $=0{\cdot}29$, subunit centres at 0, 0·33 & 0·63. For $n=4$, subunit size $=0{\cdot}21$, subunit centres at 0, 0·22, 0·46 and 0·72.

Appendix

We wish to derive the relation (7) between an eigenvalue λ_j and its corresponding eigendensity $\varrho_j(x)$. The eigenvalue equation is

$$\mathbf{H}\mathbf{u}_j = \lambda_j \mathbf{u}_j .$$

Taking the scalar products of this with $\mathbf{u}_j^H$, the Hermitian transpose of $\mathbf{u}_j$, gives

$$\mathbf{u}_j^H \mathbf{H}\mathbf{u}_j = \lambda_j \mathbf{u}_j^H \cdot \mathbf{u}_j .$$

Therefore

$$\lambda_j = \frac{\mathbf{u}_j^H \mathbf{H}\mathbf{u}_j}{\mathbf{u}_j^H \cdot \mathbf{u}_j} . \quad (9)$$

Now

$$\mathbf{u}_j^H \cdot \mathbf{u}_j = \sum_{h=-N}^{N} |u_{jh}|^2 = \int_{\substack{\text{unit}\\ \text{cell}}} [\varrho_j(\mathbf{x})]^2 d\mathbf{x} . \quad (10)$$

Also

$$\mathbf{u}_j^H \mathbf{H}\mathbf{u}_j = \sum_h \sum_p u_{jh}^* H_{hp} u_{jp} .$$

Substitution for H_{hp} gives

$$\mathbf{u}_j^H \mathbf{H}\mathbf{u}_j = \sum_h \sum_p u_{jh}^* u_{jp} \left\{ \frac{1}{n} \sum_{k=1}^{n} \sum_{l=1}^{n} \int_{U_1} \exp[-2\pi i (\mathbf{h} \cdot \mathbf{x}_k + \mathbf{p} \cdot \mathbf{x}_l)] d\mathbf{x}_1 \right\} .$$

Therefore

$$\mathbf{u}_j^H \mathbf{H}\mathbf{u}_j = \frac{1}{n} \sum_{k=1}^{n} \sum_{l=1}^{n} \int_{U_1} \varrho_j(\mathbf{x}_k) \varrho_j(\mathbf{x}_l) d\mathbf{x}_1 \quad (11)$$

$$= \int_{\substack{\text{sub-}\\ \text{units}}} [\varrho_j(\mathbf{x})]^2 d\mathbf{x} - \frac{1}{n} \sum_{k=1}^{n} \sum_{l=1}^{k-1} \int_{U_1} [\varrho_j(\mathbf{x}_k) - \varrho_j(\mathbf{x}_l)]^2 d\mathbf{x}_1$$

$$= \int_{\substack{\text{sub-}\\ \text{units}}} [\varrho_j(\mathbf{x})]^2 d\mathbf{x} - \sigma_j^2 , \quad (12)$$

where σ_j^2 is a measure of the lack of equality of the subunits, comparing them in pairs in every possible way. Combining (9), (10) and (12) leads to the required relation between an eigenvalue λ_j and the corresponding eigendensity $\varrho_j(\mathbf{x})$, namely

$$\lambda_j = \frac{\int_{\substack{\text{sub-}\\ \text{units}}} [\varrho_j(\mathbf{x})]^2 d\mathbf{x} - \sigma_j^2}{\int_{\substack{\text{unit}\\ \text{cell}}} [\varrho_j(\mathbf{x})]^2 d\mathbf{x}} .$$

The form of this expression implies that $\lambda \leq 1$, equality occurring only if all the subunits are equal, and if there is zero density outside the subunits. We have therefore shown that any solution of the structure factor equations (1) derived above does satisfy the assumptions (*a*)–(*d*).

By writing (11) in the form

$$\mathbf{u}_j^H \mathbf{H}\mathbf{u}_j = \frac{1}{n} \int_{U_1} [\sum_k \varrho_j(\mathbf{x}_k)]^2 d\mathbf{x}_1$$

we obtain the alternative expression for λ_j,

$$\lambda_j = \frac{\frac{1}{n} \int_{U_1} [\sum_k \varrho_j(\mathbf{x}_k)]^2 d\mathbf{x}_1}{\int_{\substack{\text{unit}\\ \text{cell}}} [\varrho_j(\mathbf{x})]^2 d\mathbf{x}} ,$$

from which it follows that λ_j must be positive. We have therefore shown that the eigenvalues of the matrix $\mathbf{H}$ satisfy $0 \leq \lambda_j \leq 1$.

I am grateful to Dr D. M. Blow and Dr R. Diamond for many helpful discussions, both during the course of this work and in the preparation of the manuscript, to Imperial College, London, for making available facilities on their IBM 7090 computer, and to Mr T. H. Gossling, whose contour plotting program was used in preparing Fig. 3. I am indebted to the Medical Research Council for a Scholarship for Training in Research Methods.

References

DIAMOND, R. (1966). *Acta Cryst.* **21**, 253.

MAIN, P. & ROSSMANN, M. G. (1966). *Acta Cryst.* **21**, 67.

ROSSMANN, M. G. & BLOW, D. M. (1962). *Acta Cryst.* **15**, 24.

ROSSMANN, M. G. & BLOW, D. M. (1963). *Acta Cryst.* **16**, 39.

ROSSMANN, M. G. & BLOW, D. M. (1964). *Acta Cryst.* **17**, 1474.

ROSSMANN, M. G., BLOW, D. M., HARDING, M. M. & COLLER, E. (1964). *Acta Cryst.* **17**, 338.

Reprinted from *Acta Crystallographica*, Vol. 23, Part 1, July 1967

Acta Cryst. (1967). **23**, 173

Application of the molecular replacement equations to the heavy atom technique. By Michael G. Rossmann, *Department of Biological Sciences, Purdue University, Lafayette, Indiana, U.S.A.*

A set of non-linear phase equations is derived. The coefficients depend on the knowledge of structure amplitudes and the position of some 'heavy atoms'. An approximate set of phases based on structure factor calculations using the known heavy atoms can then be refined to satisfy the equations exactly. Thus non-heavy-atom structural information can be derived without interpretation of heavy-atom based Fourier maps which may require chemical information and intuition.

Main & Rossmann (1966) and Main (1967) have shown that the use of the molecular replacement equations may lead to a satisfactory solution of the phase problem whenever the asymmetric unit can be divided into different parts with related structures. Let us now divide the unit cell into a known (heavy-atom) and unknown part.

Let the structure factor of reflexion **p** of the known part of the cell be $\mathbf{f}_p$. Then by definition,

$$\mathbf{f}_p = \int_U \varrho(\mathbf{x}) \exp\{2\pi i \mathbf{p} \, . \, \mathbf{x}\} \, . \, d\mathbf{x} \, , \qquad (1)$$

where the integral is taken over the volume U of the known part of the cell, and $\varrho(\mathbf{x})$ is the total electron density distribution within the cell.

But

$$\varrho(\mathbf{x}) = \frac{1}{V} \sum_h \mathbf{F}_h \exp\{-2\pi i \mathbf{h} \, . \, \mathbf{x}\} \, . \, d\mathbf{x} \, . \qquad (2)$$

Hence by substituting (2) in (1) we have

$$\mathbf{f}_p = \frac{1}{V} \sum_h \mathbf{F}_h \int_U \exp\{2\pi i (\mathbf{p}-\mathbf{h}) \, . \, \mathbf{x}\} \, . \, d\mathbf{x} \, .$$

The integral can be easily evaluated if we consider each of the N known atoms to be enclosed in a sphere of radius R and centred at S_n, the total volume enclosed being U. Then

$$\int_U \exp\{2\pi i (\mathbf{p}-\mathbf{h}) \, . \, \mathbf{x}\} \, . \, d\mathbf{x} = \frac{4\pi R^3}{3} G_{hp} \sum_{n=1}^{N} \exp\{2\pi i (\mathbf{p}-\mathbf{h}) \, . \, S_n\} \, ,$$

where

$$G_{hp} = \frac{3\left[\sin(2\pi HR) - (2\pi HR)\cos(2\pi HR)\right]}{(2\pi HR)^3}$$

and

$$H = |(\mathbf{p}-\mathbf{h})| \, .$$

Hence

$$\mathbf{f}_p = \frac{4\pi R^3}{3V} \sum_h \mathbf{F}_h G_{hp} \left[\sum_{n=1}^{N} \exp\{2\pi i (\mathbf{p}-\mathbf{h}) \, . \, \mathbf{S}_n\} \right] . \qquad (3)$$

The equations (3) are of the same form as the molecular replacement equations, although there will be many more significant terms per equation owing to the slower decrease of G as H increases. They express the relationship between the structure factors $\mathbf{F}_h$ when part of the cell is of known structure.

Now $\mathbf{f}_p$ can be calculated and an initial solution of the phases of $\mathbf{F}_h$ can be found from the usual heavy-atom techniques. Improvement of these phases can then be made by the methods described in the paper by Main (1967) in order to achieve better satisfaction of equations (3). Hence the heavy-atom phases may be improved without any chemical knowledge. An application of these equations may therefore be of help when a heavy atom is sufficiently weak not to permit easy recognition of chemical information, when resolution is too poor for recognition of chemical groups, or when approximate phases have been determined by means of poorly isomorphous derivatives.

This work was supported by N.S.F. grant GB-02905 and by N.I.H. grant GM-10704-03.

References

Main, P. & Rossmann, M. G., (1966). *Acta Cryst.* **21**, 67.
Main, P. (1967). *Acta Cryst.* **23**, 50.

D. APPLICATIONS

Reprinted from *Acta Crystallographica*, Vol. 17, Part 6, June 1964

Acta Cryst. (1964). **17**, 768

The relative orientation of molecules of crystallized human and horse oxyhaemoglobin. By John W. Prothero and Michael G. Rossmann, *M.R.C. Laboratory of Molecular Biology, Hills Road, Cambridge, England*

The horse oxyhaemoglobin molecule consists of four sub-units, namely two α and two β chains, packed in a tetrahedral array (Cullis, Muirhead, Perutz, Rossmann & North, 1962). Human reduced (deoxy) haemoglobin has a similar structure, except that the β chains are translated 7 Å apart (Muirhead & Perutz, 1963). This increased separation of the β chains is probably associated with deoxygenation, but the possibility exists that it merely reflects a difference between human and horse oxyhaemoglobin. The failure of human oxyhaemoglobin crystals to form isomorphous derivatives has hindered X-ray analysis by the isomorphous replacement method. However a method (based on the 'rotation function') of determining the relative orientation of two similar proteins in different crystal lattices was recently described (Rossmann & Blow, 1962). This note reports, as a preliminary step in the structural analysis of human oxyhaemoglobin, the application of the rotation function to a comparison of human and horse oxyhaemoglobin.

Horse oxyhaemoglobin crystals are monoclinic with space group $C2$ and cell dimensions $a=108{\cdot}9$, $b=63{\cdot}5$, ; $=54{\cdot}9$ Å, $\beta=110{\cdot}9°$. The molecular twofold axis lies along the crystallographic twofold axis (*i.e.* parallel to). In addition, the molecule possesses an approximate 222 point group symmetry with one of the pseudo twofold axes making an angle of about 5° with the a axis. On the other hand human oxyhaemoglobin crystals are tetragonal with space group $P4_12_12$ and with cell dimensions of $a=54{\cdot}3$, $c=196{\cdot}4$ Å. In this case the molecular diad must lie along the [110] and symmetry related directions (Perutz, 1953).

The rotation function program calculates the degree of concurrence arising when the Patterson vectors of one protein are superimposed, in a sphere around the origin, on those of another protein. In order to superimpose the self-Pattersons of human and horse oxyhaemoglobin correctly it is necessary to align the [010] direction of the horse oxyhaemoglobin molecule with the [110] direction of the human oxyhaemoglobin molecule. This result could be obtained by re-indexing the tetragonal unit cell. Maximum agreement between the Pattersons would then be obtained by rotating the tetragonal cell through an unknown angle (say θ) about the common axis. An alternative and more general procedure is to produce alignment of the [010] and [110] directions and rotation through an angle θ in one operation. That is, the tetragonal cell may be rotated through an angle $\varkappa$ about a rotation axis whose position in the monoclinic cell is defined in terms of the polar coordinates ψ and φ (Rossmann & Blow, 1962, Fig. 4).

Assume that initially the b and c axes of the first crystal are placed on top of the b and c axes of the second crystal, respectively. If the molecular twofold axes are coincident for a given rotation $\varkappa$, then it can be shown that the position of the rotation axis is given by:

$$y^2=\frac{1-\sqrt{2}\cos\varkappa}{\sqrt{2}(1-\cos\varkappa)}$$

where $\cos\psi=y$

and $$\cos\varphi=(\sqrt{2}-1)y/(1-y^2)^{\frac{1}{2}}$$

It is convenient to define the angle θ, which measures the amount of rotation of one crystal with respect to the other around the twofold axis, as the angle between the monoclinic a axis and the tetragonal c axis. Both these arbitrary directions are perpendicular to the molecular twofold axes (Fig. 1). The sign of θ is taken so that it is positive when the tetragonal c axis lies between the monoclinic a and c axes. The angle θ is related to $\varkappa$ by

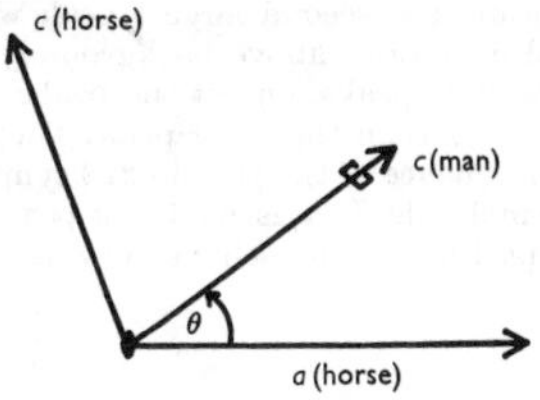

Fig. 1. Relationship between the horse and human oxyhaemoglobin groups viewed down the superimposed molecular twofold axes. θ defines the amount of rotation.

$$\theta=110{\cdot}9°-\cos^{-1}\left[\frac{\sqrt{2}-1+2\sqrt{2}\cos\varkappa}{\sqrt{2}+1}\right].$$

Values of θ from 0° to 180° were explored using 6 Å intensity data and a radius of integration of 35 Å. The 'shaded G' function was used. The latter applies a weighting varying exponentially between 1 and 0·1 between the inside and outside of the sphere of integration. Smaller weights near the outside of the sphere emphasize that more cross-vectors between molecules might be found here. A simple sharpening was brought about by omitting all terms whose spacing was greater than 10 Å. The results are shown in Fig. 2. The two curves correspond to unsharpened data (the dashed line) and sharpened data (the continuous line).

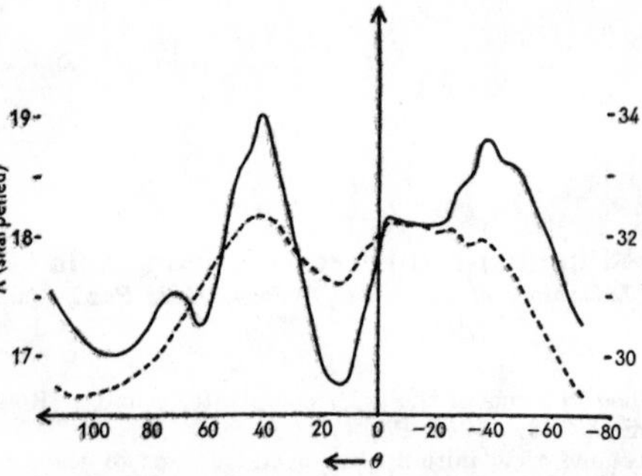

Fig. 2. Rotation function when the [010] direction of horse oxyhaemoglobin is rotated by the angle θ about the [110] human oxyhaemoglobin Patterson. The shaded line is the unsharpened 6 Å rotation function, while the full line represents the data sharpened by omitting all terms with spacing greater than 10 Å.

A check on the level of the background of the rotation function was made by calculating 28 points for values of $\varkappa$ between 0° and 360° in 10° to 15° increments, when $\psi=35{\cdot}5°$, $\varphi=54{\cdot}5°$. This section contains the peak at $\theta=40°$. By averaging the rotation function values, omitting the points which lay within 7·5° of the large peak, the mean value (corresponding to the persistent origin overlap) of R was found to be 17·6 units, and the r.m.s. deviation from the mean was 0·4 units. Thus the peak at $\theta=40°$, with $R=18{\cdot}97$, is 3·6 standard deviations above the mean. The second largest peak was less than two standard deviations above background.

Fig. 2 shows two peaks, one of the peaks being rather broader and lower than the other peak. These two peaks arise as a consequence of the pseudo 222 symmetry of the haemoglobin molecule. That is, while one peak corresponds to the superposition of the self-Pattersons of an α onto an α chain and of a β onto a β chain, the other peak corresponds to the superposition of the self-Pattersons of the α onto β and β onto α chains. If the haemoglobin molecules were to contain exact 222 symmetry then the two peaks would be of the same height. Furthermore, in the Patterson the directions of the two different pseudo twofold axes of the molecule must make equal and opposite angles with the tetragonal fourfold axis. Thus if the monoclinic Patterson is positioned on top of the tetragonal Patterson, so as to superimpose the corresponding pseudo twofold directions, there will be good agreement, whereas at an equal and opposite angle with the tetragonal c axis the agreement will not be as good. As the arbitrary reference line from which θ is measured in the monoclinic system coincides to within 5° of the molecular pseudo twofold axis, the two peaks should occur at $\pm\theta$, approximately. Fig. 2 shows the two peaks to be at $\theta=40°$ (sharp) and $-37°$ (broad).

The agreement of the position of the peak at θ with that at $-\theta$ to within 3°, and the agreement with the results of Perutz (1953) who showed from optical birefringence experiments that θ must be either 35° or —15° establishes the relative orientation of the two molecules as lying between $\theta=35°$ and 40°. The large size of the peak at $\theta=-37°$ might suggest that the superposition of the 222 symmetrical parts of the molecular Pattersons agree better than the non-symmetrical parts.

We are grateful for discussions with Dr. M. F. Perutz, and to Dr. Hilary Muirhead for allowing us to use her human oxyhaemoglobin data. All calculations were made on the IBM 7090 computer, assisted by the IBM Endowed Time scheme.

References

Cullis, A. F., Muirhead, H., Perutz, M. F., Rossmann, M. G. & North, A. C. T. (1962). *Proc. Roy. Soc.* A. **265**, 161.

Muirhead, H. & Perutz, M. F. (1963). *Nature, Lond.* **199**, 633.

Perutz, M. F. (1953). *Acta Cryst.* **6**, 859.

Rossmann, M. G. & Blow, D. M. (1962). *Acta Cryst.* **15**, 24.

J. Mol. Biol. (1964) 8, 65–78

The Arrangement of α-Chymotrypsin Molecules in the Monoclinic Crystal Form

D. M. Blow, Michael G. Rossmann and B. A. Jeffery
Medical Research Council Laboratory of Molecular Biology, Hills Road Cambridge, England

Crystals isomorphous with α-chymotrypsin, but containing platinum at four specific sites, were obtained by soaking crystals of α-chymotrypsin in solutions containing chloroplatinite and iodoplatinite. This isomorphous substitution was insufficient by itself to reveal the molecular structure. It has been used in combination with the rotation and translation functions to define the molecular arrangement. The molecules lie in bands parallel to the c axis, adjacent molecules being related by 180° rotation about a^*, without translation. The platinum ions all lie close to the local twofold axes relating adjacent molecules.

1. Introduction

We have obtained so far only one satisfactory type of isomorphous substitution for monoclinic α-chymotrypsin. Although we have calculated an electron density map based on this single derivative, the error in such a calculation was too great to allow us to make any interpretation of the tertiary structure within the molecule; nor was it possible to decide on the boundary between the two independent 23,000 mol. wt. molecules within the crystallographic asymmetric unit. We therefore calculated the rotation function (Rossmann & Blow, 1962) and translation function (Rossmann, Blow, Harding & Coller, 1964) from which it was possible to find the exact arrangement of molecules in the unit cell. The results were shown to be consistent with the isomorphous replacement results.

In this paper we wish to describe the derivation of the molecular arrangement. We are now using the non-crystallographic symmetry between the molecules in order to improve the phases by means of the technique described by Rossmann & Blow (1963). We hope that the subsequent electron density map will be sufficiently clear for more detailed interpretation.

2. The Crystals

α-Chymotrypsin was crystallized in monoclinic plates from ammonium sulphate solutions of pH near 4·2. This form of chymotrypsin was first studied by Bernal, Fankuchen & Perutz (1938). The crystals belonged to space group $P2_1$, and had unit cell parameters $a = 49{\cdot}6$ Å, $b = 67{\cdot}8$ Å, $c = 66{\cdot}5$ Å, $\beta = 102°\ 10'$. There are two molecules of molecular weight 23,000 in the crystallographic asymmetric unit.

In choosing this form for further study, we have been troubled continually by its particular drawback, which is persistent twinning about the c^* (or the a) axis, as first noted by Bernal *et al.* (1938) (Plate I). Untwinned crystals, unless they are exceptionally well formed, cannot be identified by optical means, and a strongly exposed 3° $h0l$ precession photograph is needed to discover whether a crystal is acceptable.

3. Isomorphous Replacement Results

A large range of heavy atom compounds has been screened for their ability to bind to definite sites on the enzyme. Only one type of useful interaction has been found, that with the planar complex haloplatinites:

chloroplatinite $(PtCl_4)^{2-}$
bromoplatinite $(PtBr_4)^{2-}$
iodoplatinite $(PtI_4)^{2-}$

Substituted crystals were obtained by addition of the potassium haloplatinite to the mother liquor in which the chymotrypsin crystals were grown. In every case the heavy metal binds at the same points in the structure. Figure 1 shows the 5·8 Å resolution, *h0l* difference Patterson projections for the $(PtCl_4)^{2-}$ and $(PtI_4)^{2-}$ derivatives.

Three-dimensional data to 5·8 Å resolution were collected from a series of twenty-one sets of precession photographs of α-chymotrypsin. Similar data were collected from $(PtCl_4)^{2-}$ and $(PtI_4)^{2-}$-substituted α-chymotrypsins: thirty-two sets of precession photographs were needed for observation of the significant anomalous scattering with Cu Kα radiation. Data for each compound were internally scaled by a least-squares method (Rollett & Sparks, 1960), using EDSAC 2. Standard error estimates were made on the basis of reflexions measured in more than one set of precession photographs. The over-all standard error (including very weak reflexions) gave

$$\frac{\sigma(F)}{|\bar{F}|} = 0{\cdot}065 \text{ (unsubstituted)};\ 0{\cdot}066\ (+K_2PtCl_4);\ 0{\cdot}056\ (+K_2PtI_4).$$

No attempt was made to correct for absorption: the crystals chosen were generally rather small (plates ~0·05 mm thick), because small crystals were less frequently twinned.

Three-dimensional difference Patterson functions, with coefficients $(|F_H|-|F|)^2$, were calculated for both heavy atom substituents. Typical sections of the difference Patterson function for K_2PtCl_4 are shown in Fig. 2. An arrangement of four heavy atom groups in the asymmetric unit explains all the major peaks satisfactorily, including the elongation of the partially resolved peaks. The platinum atoms are in two pairs, members of each pair being separated by 7 to 8 Å. The axis of one pair is approximately parallel to the crystallographic *b* axis; the axis of the other pair is practically along a^*. The difference Patterson function for K_2PtI_4 was extremely similar, as regards all major peaks and also the highest uninterpreted peak.

The heavy atom parameters derived from these Patterson functions and the over-all scale factors were refined on EDSAC 2 by the procedure described by Rossmann (1960). The refined parameters used for phase determination are given in Table 1. The "weights" of the four atoms A, B, C, D relate to the arbitrary scales adopted for the size of the structure amplitudes. We do not believe that the anisotropic shape parameters (defined by Cullis, Muirhead, Perutz, Rossmann & North, 1961) are particularly meaningful, but nevertheless the choice of these six parameters affects the apparent value of *Z* and *vice versa*.

Despite the clarity of the difference Patterson function, the "*R* factor"

$$\frac{\sum_{h0l} \|F_H|-|F\|-\Delta f_c}{\sum_{h0l} \|F_H|-|F\|}$$

in the (*h0l*) zone was very poor. For the K_2PtCl_4 compound it was 0·50; for the K_2PtI_4 compound, 0·59.

Using the refined parameters for determining phase angles a Fourier synthesis of the unsubstituted protein was calculated. Because of the very similar nature of the $PtCl_4{}^{2-}$ and the $PtI_4{}^{2-}$ substituents, this corresponded virtually to a "single isomorphous replacement" (Blow & Rossmann, 1961) and was not expected to provide a very accurate picture

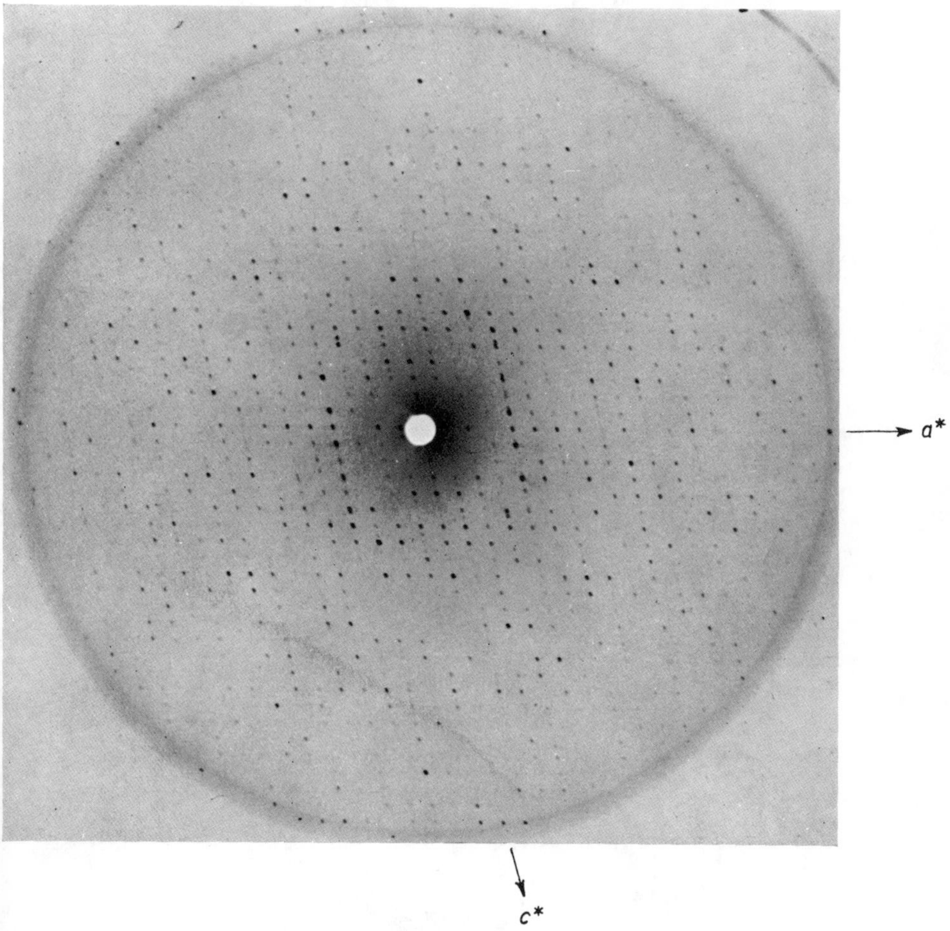

PLATE I. $h0l$ photograph of chymotrypsin, showing a small amount of twinning.

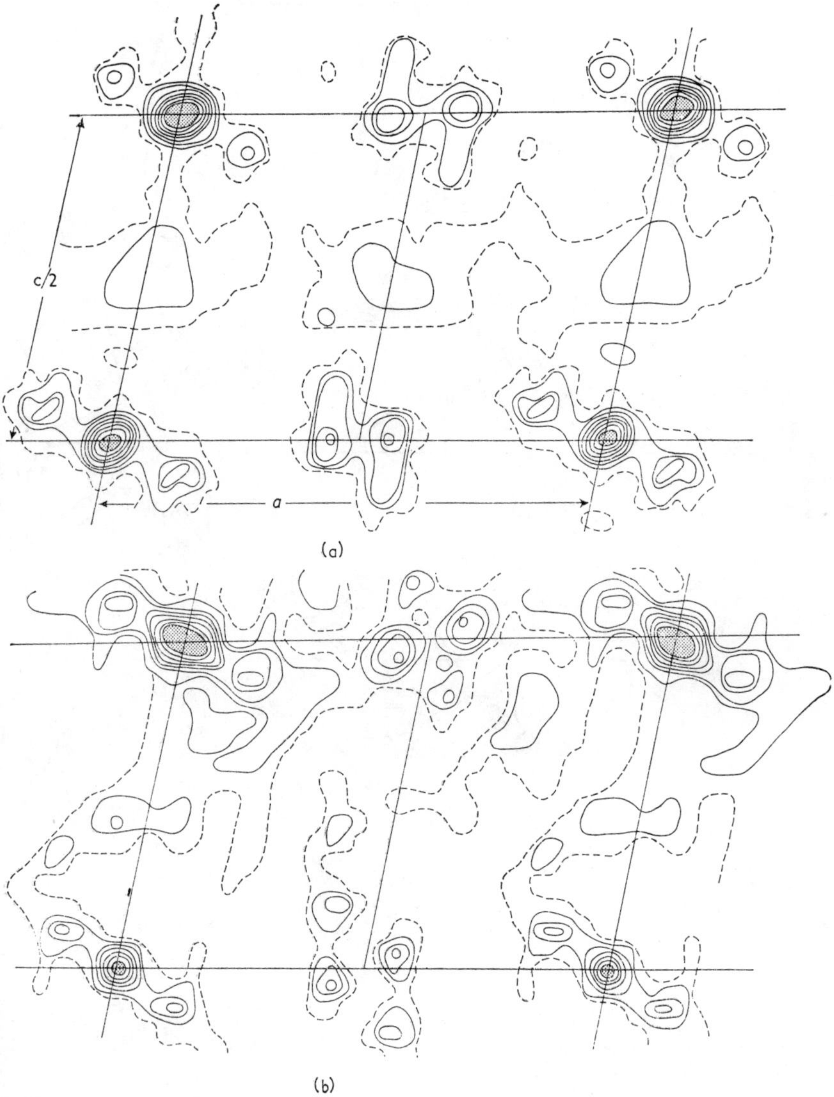

FIG. 1. $h0l$ difference Patterson projections at 5·8 Å resolution, (a) for chymotrypsin + K_2PtCl_4; (b) for chymotrypsin + K_2PtI_4.

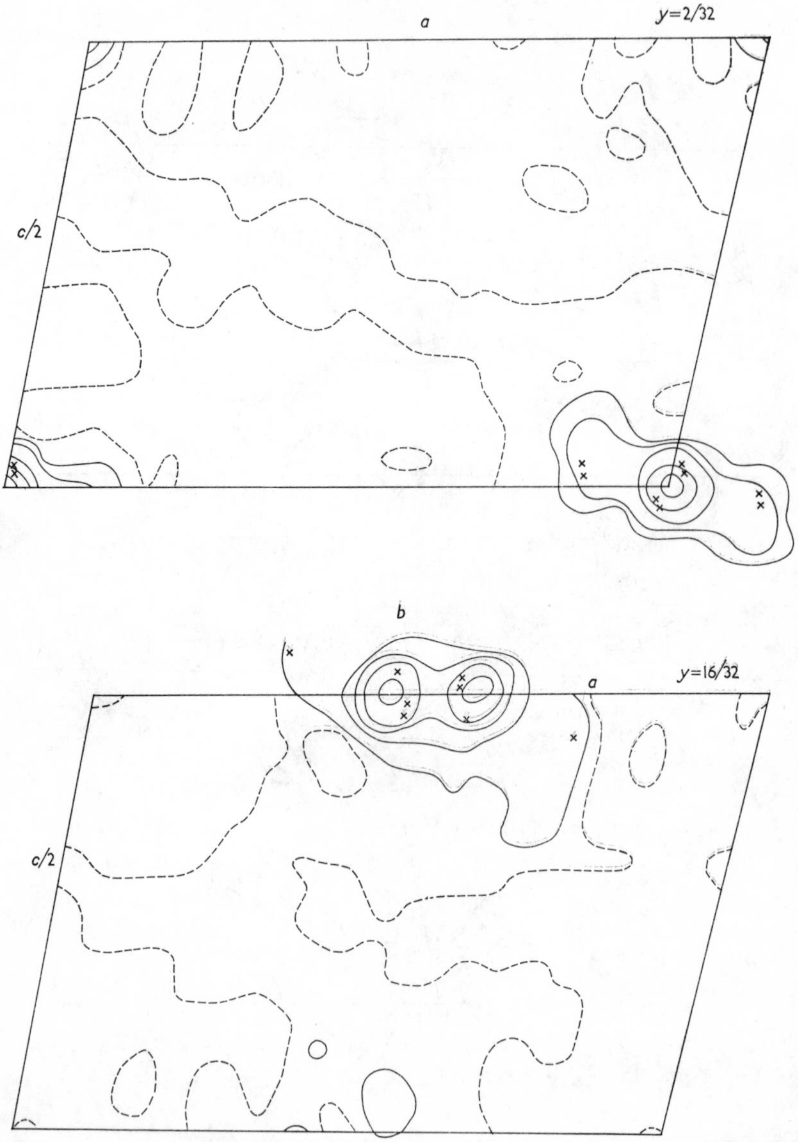

FIG. 2. Sections from the 5·8 Å resolution difference Patterson function for chymotrypsin $+K_2PtCl_4$. Crosses mark the positions of heavy-atom vectors.

(a), $y = 2/32$, showing elongation of peak due to overlapping vectors. The density near the origin is due to a peak at $y = 4/32$, not fully resolved from the origin peak. (b), $y = 16/32$, the Harker section. The highest unexplained density lies on this section.

of the molecule. Furthermore, the arrangement of heavy atoms was such as to produce a partial centre of symmetry which will result in strong images of the protein enantiomorph appearing in the Fourier synthesis.

It had been hoped to improve the phase determination by means of the measured anomalous dispersion. It is, however, necessary to decide on the absolute configuration of the heavy atoms before the correct sign of the anomalous dispersion is known (Blow & Rossmann, 1962). Two Fourier syntheses were calculated. To these the anomalous dispersion phase correction was applied in opposite senses. It had been hoped that we would be able to "see" the molecules more clearly in one of these two results. Unfortunately this was not the case.

TABLE 1

Heavy atom parameters

	Weight	Fractional coordinates			Shape parameters					
	Z	x	y	z	β_{11}	β_{22}	β_{33}	β_{12}	β_{23}	β_{13}
					$(PtCl_4)^{2-}$					
A	130·4	0·2299	0·0621	0·0098	0·0011	0·0022	0·0003	0·0080	−0·0004	−0·0016
B	106·9	0·2306	0·9422	0·0049	0·0020	0·0057	−0·0021	−0·0033	0·0034	−0·0014
C	105·2	0·2224	0·0294	0·4860	0·0041	−0·0033	−0·0003	0·0024	−0·0005	0·0097
D	114·6	0·3632	0·0242	0·5224	0·0022	−0·0041	0·0179	0·0121	−0·0010	−0·0018
					$(PtI_4)^{2-}$					
A	156·1	0·2293	0·0634	0·0153	0·0003	0·0045	0·0001	0·0051	0·0007	−0·0037
B	145·1	0·2399	0·9400	0·9913	0·0002	0·0030	−0·0007	0·0075	−0·0060	−0·0024
C	127·2	0·2294	0·0275	0·4759	0·0015	0·0016	0·0048	0·0021	0·0064	−0·0013
D	131·6	0·3535	0·0282	0·5148	−0·0009	0·0013	0·0122	0·0019	−0·0049	0·0049

The most obvious features of this Fourier synthesis were deep "holes" at each heavy atom site. By repeating the whole calculation for each derivative separately, it was found that the "holes" were largely due to the PtI_4^{2-} derivative, and that they could be removed by applying an over-all scale factor of 1·20 to the $|F|$ values of the PtI_4^{2-} derivative (on the basis of a scale factor of 1·00 given by the least squares refinement). Two further methods were used to study the scale factor: refinement of the $(h0l)$ data and "Wilson statistics" (Green, Ingram & Perutz, 1954), giving values of 0·95 and 1·07 respectively, relative to the result of the three-dimensional refinement program. Ultimately a mean value of 1·06 was used, which greatly reduced the "holes" at the heavy atom sites.

The final isomorphous replacement Fourier synthesis was interpretable in some respects. A region containing strong features ran through the cell in a band parallel to c. The band at height $y = 0$ was clearly separated from that at $y = \frac{1}{2}$ by a region of rather uniform density at $y = \frac{1}{4}$; similarly the bands were fairly clearly separated in the x direction. Each band had to represent two molecules, but the confusing jumble of chains and lumps of high density within the band could not readily be separated out into molecules, nor could two similar configurations of density be picked out within the band. This remained true even though we knew the rotation operation relating the two molecules.

4. Results from Non-crystallographic Symmetry

The volume of the unit cell and crystal density indicate that there are two chymotrypsin molecules in the asymmetric unit. The rotation function (Rossmann & Blow, 1962) was used to determine their relative orientations. The rotation function evaluates the "overlap" (or agreement) between the original Patterson function and a Patterson function rotated in a way specified by three variables (κ, ψ, ϕ). If this rotation corresponds to the rotation relating two molecules it will bring all vectors relating electrons within one molecule (the "self-Patterson function") into coincidence with all such vectors within the other molecule, giving a large value for the rotation function. Since the self-Patterson function tends to be in the region nearer to the origin, the "overlap" is evaluated in a sphere centred on the origin; the radius chosen for chymotrypsin was generally 30 Å or 35 Å.

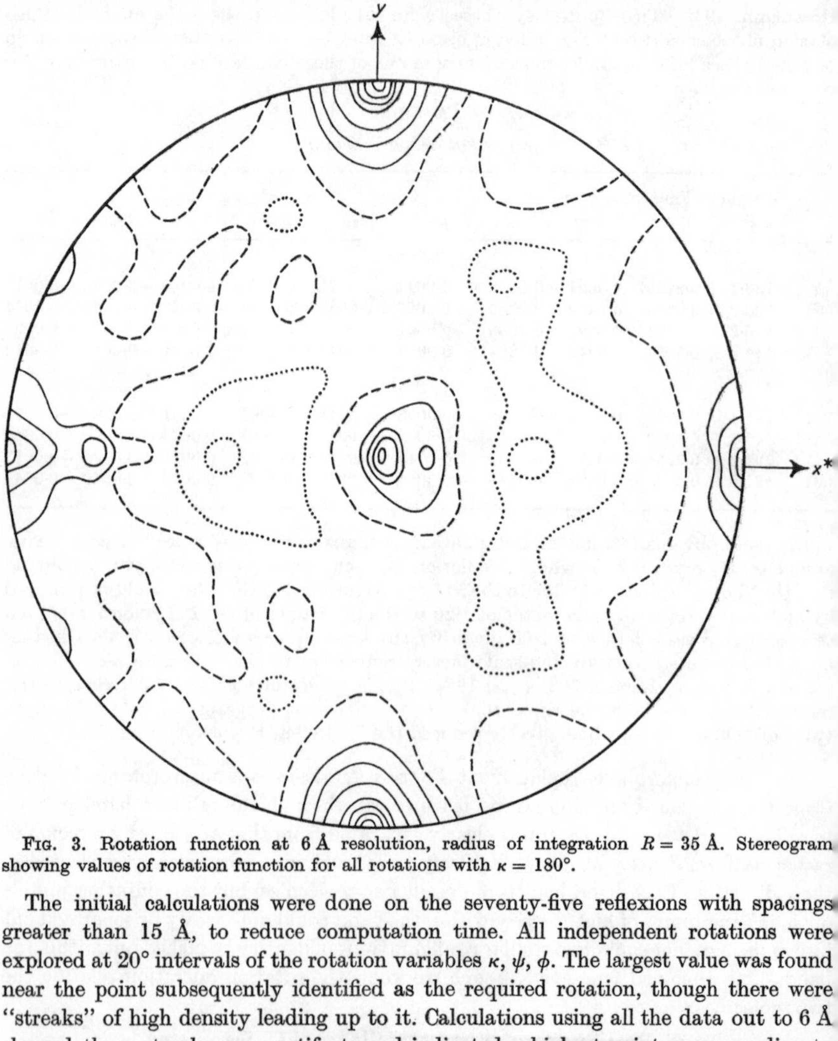

FIG. 3. Rotation function at 6 Å resolution, radius of integration $R = 35$ Å. Stereogram showing values of rotation function for all rotations with $\kappa = 180°$.

The initial calculations were done on the seventy-five reflexions with spacings greater than 15 Å, to reduce computation time. All independent rotations were explored at 20° intervals of the rotation variables κ, ψ, ϕ. The largest value was found near the point subsequently identified as the required rotation, though there were "streaks" of high density leading up to it. Calculations using all the data out to 6 Å showed these streaks were artifacts and indicated a highest point corresponding to a rotation κ of 180° about an axis almost exactly parallel to the crystallographic c axis. (If two molecules are related by such a rotation the crystallographic twofold axis implies that there are also pairs of molecules related by 180° rotation about an axis parallel to a^*.) As a final demonstration that this peak is highly significant, all possible rotations of 180° were examined at 10° intervals of the variables ψ, ϕ. These results are presented in Fig. 3.

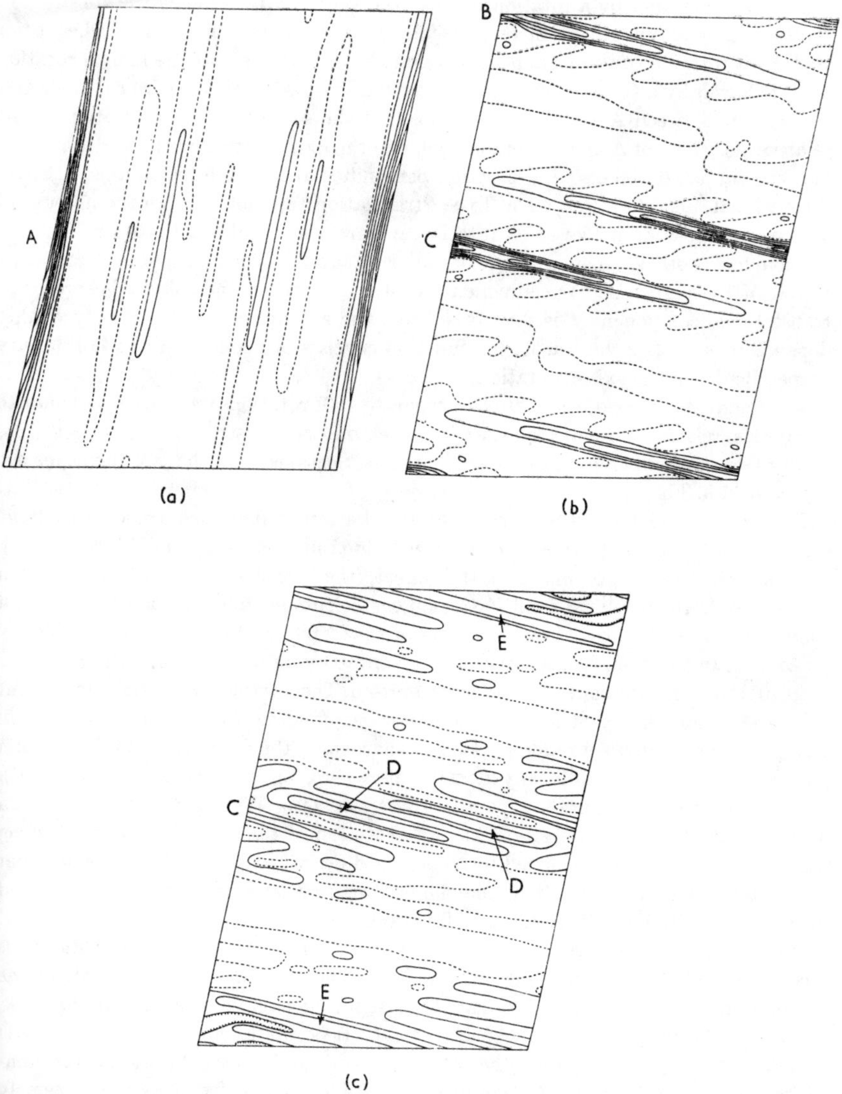

FIG. 4. Patterson space translation functions, using all terms between 10 Å and 6 Å resolution. Radius of integration $R = 30$ Å. The Patterson function was set equal to zero within a radius of $R_0 = 30$ Å around the origin.

(a), rotation about a^*, section $y = 0$; (b), rotation about c, section $y = 0$; (c), rotation about c, section $y = \frac{1}{2}$. The streak C on this section is a continuation of the streak in the section $y = 0$.

The next problem was to determine the relative positions of the molecules in the unit cell. In a recent paper (Rossmann *et al.*, 1964) it is shown that when two molecules A and B are related by a rotation of 180°, the vector $\mathbf{A}_i\mathbf{B}_j$ between the ith atom of molecule A and the jth atom of molecule B may be superimposed on the vector $\mathbf{B}_i\mathbf{A}_j$ by a rotation of the Patterson function through 180° about the known rotation axis, followed by a translation $2\boldsymbol{t}$ parallel to the axis of rotation, where $\boldsymbol{t}$ is the screw translation between A and B in real space. At the same time, an indication of the relative positions of A and B perpendicular to the axis is given by the localization of the superimposed vectors in a direction perpendicular to the rotation axis. A three-dimensional function which we call the "translation function" shows the amount of vector superposition achieved on rotation and translation of one Patterson function relative to the other, within a sphere of radius R, as a function of the screw translation $\boldsymbol{t}$, and of the perpendicular component, $\boldsymbol{s}$, of the centre of the sphere. Whereas the translational component, $\boldsymbol{t}$, is sharply defined, the amount of overlap is only weakly dependent on $\boldsymbol{s}$, and the translation function consists of planar "streaks" of density perpendicular to the axis of rotation.

As already mentioned, there are two separate 180° rotations, both perpendicular to the y axis, relating pairs of molecules in the chymotrypsin structure. These will give rise to two quite different translation functions. Sections from the two functions are reproduced in Fig. 4.

Superposition of the self-vectors in the two Patterson functions would cause large unwanted origin peaks to appear in the translation functions, which might well swamp the required peaks. To minimize this effect, the translation functions shown in Fig. 4 have been calculated from Patterson coefficients modified in such a way that a sphere of radius R_0, centred on the origin of the Patterson functions, has its density set to zero. In addition, it was found that the lowest-order terms, with spacings greater than 10 Å, reduced the contrast, and were omitted. These terms are strongly dependent on the electron density of the mother liquor surrounding the protein molecules; in addition this represents a crude method of sharpening the data. The appearance of a peak A, more than double any density elsewhere, on the line $x = 0$ (Fig. 4(a)), indicated that the translation $\boldsymbol{t}$, parallel to a^*, was zero. While it was possible that a peak appearing in such a position was an extension of the peak due to overlapping self-vectors, not entirely removed by the method described above, there was no other dominating peak in the function, and the next highest peak could not be interpreted consistently with the other translation function.

Four distinct streaks arise in the translation function when the axis of rotation is chosen parallel to the c axis (Fig. 4(b) and (c)). One streak, B, passing through the origin, is caused by imperfect removal of the self-Patterson vectors. A similar streak, C, passing through $z = c/2$, is a special streak. It occurs because two neighbouring Patterson origins are so placed that they can be superimposed by one of the non-crystallographic rotations. The volume occupied by the self-vectors is sufficiently large to produce a significant local twofold axis half-way between them (Fig. 5). These streaks B and C have maximum density in the section $y = 0$ (Fig. 4(b)). Similarly, the presence of a local twofold axis through the cross-Patterson vectors (i.e. vectors of the type $\mathbf{A}_i\mathbf{B}_j$) in neighbouring unit cells generates additional twofold axes half-way between them (Fig. 5). Thus there are two streaks, D and E, rather than one, having maximum density in the section $y = b/2$, which are caused by overlap of cross-vectors. They are separated by $c/2$, and correspond to translations along c of $-0{\cdot}11c$ and

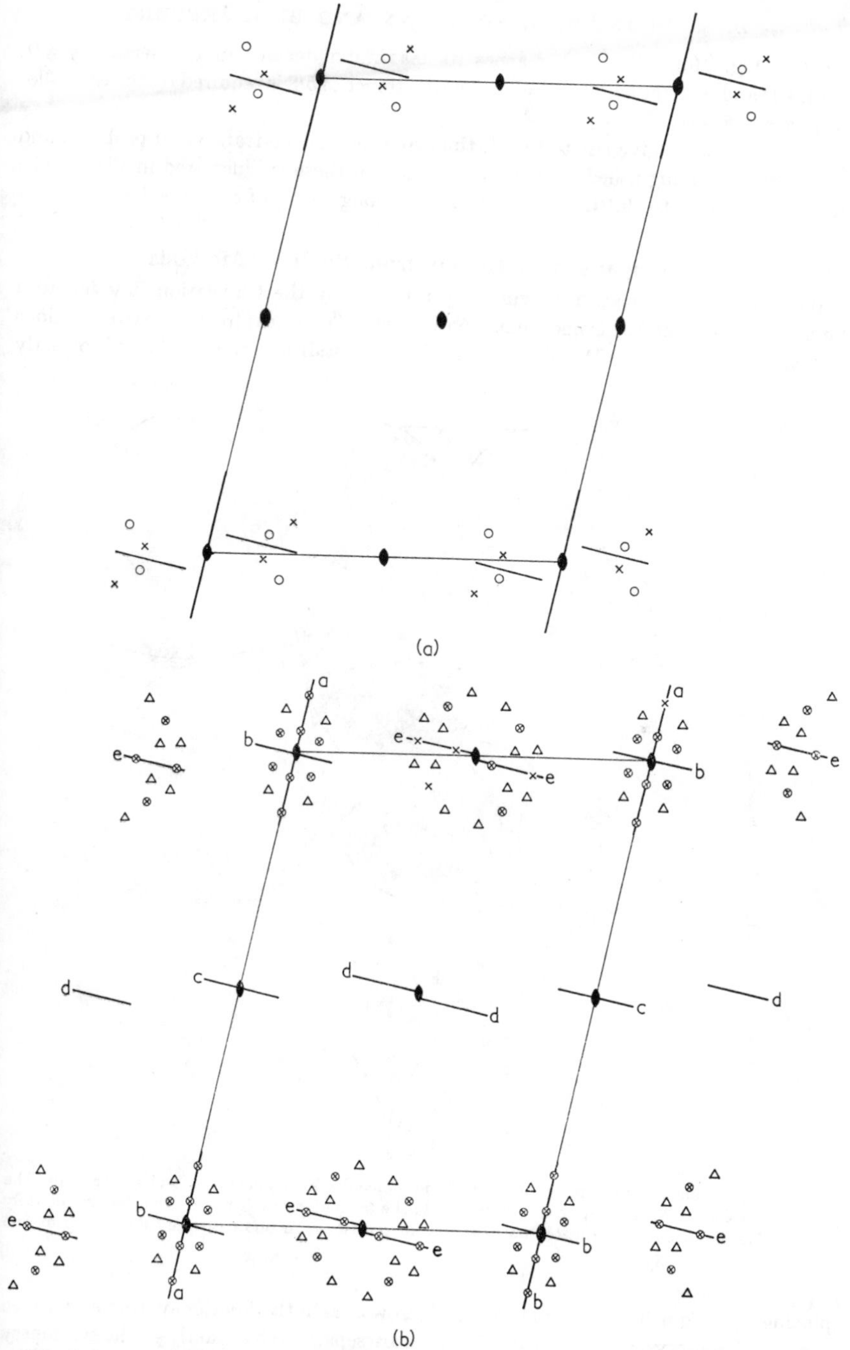

FIG. 5. (a) A point atom arrangement with the non-crystallographic symmetry found in α-chymotrypsin, although space group $P2$ has been chosen for clarity. One molecule is represented by two atoms, one above, the other below the plane of the paper.

(b) The corresponding point Patterson function. It shows local symmetry elements a, b and e which give rise to the streaks A, B and E on the translation function, as well as the additional special symmetry elements c and d which cause the streaks C and D on the translation maps.

+0·39c (Fig. 4(c)). Streak A reaches its maximum density in the section $y = 0$; streaks D and E in the section $y = b/2$. The difference of $b/2$ is required by the crystallographic screw axis.

Streaks D and E give rise to two distinct solutions of the translation problem, and these are not distinguished by the method. One of these is illustrated in Fig. 6. The other corresponds to shifting the twofold axes along c by $\frac{1}{4}$ of a unit cell.

5. Comparison of Results from the Two Methods

We now have to relate the symmetry revealed by the translation function to a Fourier map obtained by isomorphous replacement. There are already the two solutions corresponding to streaks D and E; we now have, in addition, the problem of correctly

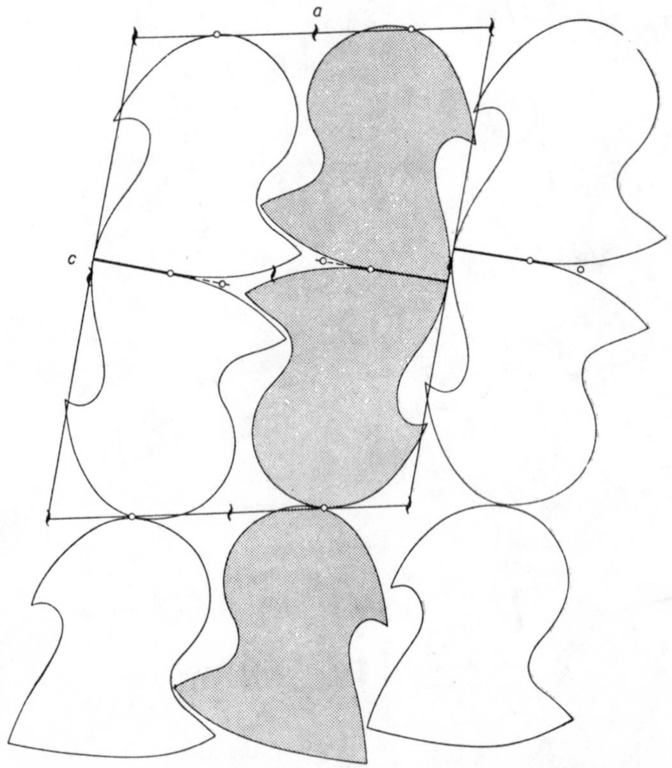

FIG. 6. Diagram to show the symmetry of the molecular arrangement in α-chymotrypsin. The shaded "molecules" are at approximately $y = \frac{1}{2}$; the unshaded "molecules" are at approximately $y = 0$. The small circles indicate the heavy-atom positions; in one case they lie on top of one another.

placing the origin. There are four distinct screw axes in the Fourier synthesis. Because the sets of non-crystallographic twofold axes are separated by exactly $\frac{1}{2}c$, the symmetry near to the axis at (0,0) and (0,$\frac{1}{2}c$) is the same (Fig. 6). The symmetry near to ($\frac{1}{2}a$,0) is different. There are thus only two possible ways of placing the origin of any Fourier map on the predicted arrangement of non-crystallographic symmetry elements in Fig. 6. In addition there is the usual "y-coordinate" problem for the monoclinic system, similar to that which has become familiar in myoglobin and haemoglobin (see, for instance, Cullis *et al.*, 1961). (A further problem which could arise, but causes no trouble in this case, is the enantiomorphy of the molecular arrangement compared to that of the Fourier synthesis. The molecular arrangement in this case is not enantiomorphous.)

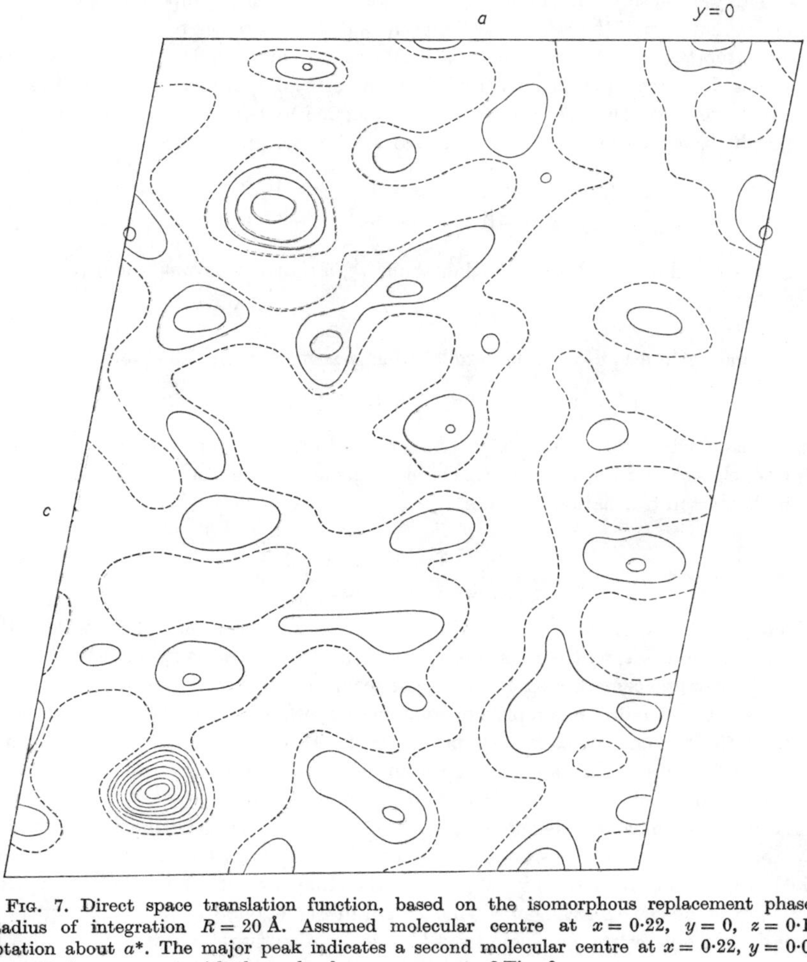

FIG. 7. Direct space translation function, based on the isomorphous replacement phases. Radius of integration $R = 20$ Å. Assumed molecular centre at $x = 0{\cdot}22$, $y = 0$, $z = 0{\cdot}12$, rotation about a^*. The major peak indicates a second molecular centre at $x = 0{\cdot}22$, $y = 0{\cdot}02$, $z = 0{\cdot}89$, in agreement with the molecular arrangement of Fig. 6.

There were thus four distinct ways in which the translation function results could be related to the isomorphous replacement results, and in each of these the origins could be displaced by any y value. The method adopted for testing these was a calculation based on the isomorphous replacement Fourier synthesis in much the same way as the translation function was calculated from the Patterson function.

A point in the unit cell was selected as representing an approximate molecular centre. The amount of superposition between all points within a radius R of this point and a rotated and translated version of the same Fourier synthesis was evaluated, as a function of the translation, for all possible translations. As in the Patterson translation function there are two possible versions of such a calculation, depending on which of the two rotation operations is selected, but crystallographic symmetry demands that the two maps give exactly the same information. Figure 7 shows a section of such a map. This section shows the major peak and also the next most important peak, which is approximately half the height. By assigning a molecular centre to a position midway between the two possible twofold axis positions, the four possible types of arrangement could be tested with only two different sets of coordinates for the possible molecular centres. The y coordinates were assigned as the most probable from the isomorphous replacement results. The two sets of coordinates were

$$(1)\quad x = 0{\cdot}22, \qquad y = 0, \qquad z = 0{\cdot}12,$$
$$(2)\quad x = -0{\cdot}22, \quad y = 0, \qquad z = -0{\cdot}12.$$

Using the coordinates (1), and rotation about a^*, a major peak was found (Fig. 7) at

$$x = 0{\cdot}22, \qquad y = 0{\cdot}02, \qquad z = 0{\cdot}89,$$

corresponding to a twofold axis parallel to a^* passing through the point

$$x = 0{\cdot}22, \qquad y = 0{\cdot}01, \qquad z = 0{\cdot}005$$

exactly as illustrated in Fig. 6. No prominent peaks were found when the coordinates (2) were chosen as molecular centre. These results are fully consistent with the results of the Patterson translation function.

6. Discussion

The consistency of the results of the rotation and translation functions with the isomorphous replacement results confirms that both are essentially correct. That the isomorphous replacement results are very inaccurate is demonstrated by superposing sections of the isomorphous replacement Fourier synthesis in such a way that related parts of the two molecules superimpose (Fig. 8). However, we believe they form a starting point from which a correct structure may be obtained by application of the non-crystallographic symmetry (Rossmann & Blow, 1963).

A feature which had worried us, as soon as the rotation function results were obtained, was that the heavy atom positions appeared to be completely inconsistent with them. The results of the translation function show that they are consistent in a very special way. In the molecular arrangement illustrated in Fig. 6, one pair of heavy atoms lies exactly on a non-crystallographic twofold axis; another twofold axis passes half-way between the pair of heavy atom sites separated parallel to b. Thus in each case the heavy atoms lie very close to a local twofold axis relating two molecules. The largest shift of heavy atom position required to give exact agreement with the non-crystallographic symmetry is 1·0 Å.

Chymotrypsin is known to form dimers in concentrated solutions (Schwert, 1949) and it is pertinent that adjacent molecules along c form what we may call "proper" dimers (that is, they are related by 180° rotation without translation so that like regions of the molecule are in contact). It appears that the $PtCl_4$ groups can participate in this like-with-like interaction. In fact both of the non-crystallographic axes perpendicular to c (those at $z = \sim 0$ and those at $z = \sim \frac{1}{2}$) are the axes of "proper" dimers, though presumably only one of these types persists in solution.

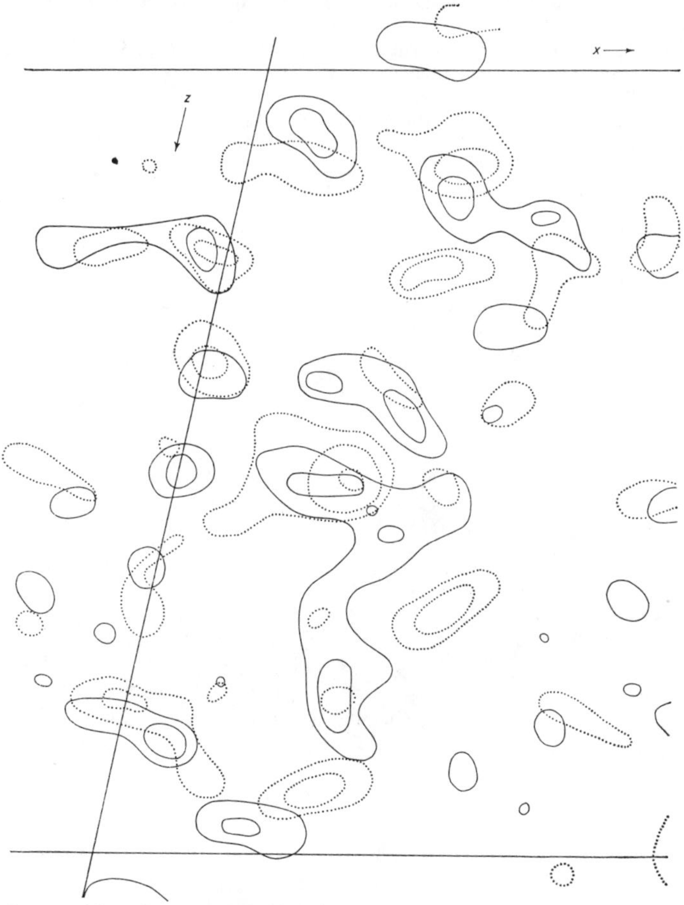

FIG. 8. Superposition of two sections of the isomorphous replacement Fourier synthesis in the way indicated by the molecular arrangement. Only the region of the structure corresponding roughly to the molecules which should superimpose is illustrated.

We would like to thank Ann Tench for her part in the early preparative work, Dr. R. J. Pollitt for his preparation of heavy-atom substituents for the active centre of the enzyme, and Geoffrey Fox and Joyce Wheeler for their help with some of the programming. We have had loyal assistance in the data handling and computing from Denise Thomas, Daphne Strachan, Tony Sainty, Diana Singleton, Jill Collard and Angela Campbell.

The isomorphous replacement calculations were done on EDSAC 2, and we thank the Director and staff of the University Mathematical Laboratory for their helpful cooperation. The rotation and translation functions were calculated on the IBM 7090 at the London Data Centre, and part of the work was assisted under the IBM Endowed Time scheme. Fourier syntheses on the IBM 7040 were calculated by the program ERFR 2 by W. G. Sly, D. P. Shoemaker and J. H. Van den Hende.

REFERENCES

Bernal, J. D., Fankuchen, I. & Perutz, M. F. (1938). *Nature*, **141**, **523**.
Blow, D. M. & Rossmann, M. G. (1961). *Acta Cryst.* **14**, 1195.
Blow, D. M. & Rossmann, M. G. (1962). *Acta Cryst.* **15**, 1060.
Cullis, A. F., Muirhead, H., Perutz, M. F., Rossmann, M. G. & North, A. C. T. (1961). *Proc. Roy. Soc.* A, **265**, 15.
Green, D. W., Ingram, V. M. & Perutz, M. F. (1954). *Proc. Roy. Soc.* A, **225**, 287.
Rollett, J. & Sparks, R. (1960). *Acta Cryst.* **13**, 273.
Rossmann, M. G. (1960). *Acta Cryst.* **13**, 221.
Rossmann, M. G. & Blow, D. M. (1962). *Acta Cryst.* **15**, 24.
Rossmann, M. G. & Blow, D. M. (1963). *Acta Cryst.* **16**, 39.
Rossmann, M. G., Blow, D. M., Harding, M. & Coller, E. (1964). *Acta Cryst.*, in the press.
Schwert, G. W. (1949). *J. Biol. Chem.* **179**, 665.

J. Mol. Biol. (1966) **16**, 227–241

The Crystal Structure of Insulin

III. Evidence for a 2-fold Axis in Rhombohedral Zinc Insulin

ELEANOR DODSON, MARJORIE M. HARDING†, DOROTHY CROWFOOT HODGKIN
Chemical Crystallography Laboratory, South Parks Road, Oxford, England
AND MICHAEL G. ROSSMANN‡
M.R.C. Laboratory of Molecular Biology, Cambridge, England

The existence of non-space-group symmetry elements in rhombohedral 2 Zn insulin and 4 Zn insulin crystals has been investigated. A rotation function shows the existence of a 2-fold axis perpendicular to the crystallographic *c*-axis (3-fold) and making an angle of 44° with the *a*-axis. A translation function, and independent arguments from the Patterson series, show that this is a 2-fold axis, without translation parallel to its length. In 2 Zn insulin the 2-fold axes pass through or within 0·5 Å of a 3-fold or, less probably, a 3-fold screw axis; in 4 Zn insulin they are about 1 Å from it.

1. Introduction

Both 2 Zn and 4 Zn insulin rhombohedral crystals and also the orthorhombic series of insulin salts have asymmetric units which contain two protein monomers of molecular weight about 6000. Insulin dimers also occur in many insulin solutions and may well be identical with the asymmetric unit of these crystals. In 1960, Low & Einstein published evidence for the presence, in the crystals of orthorhombic insulin sulphate, of non-space-group 2-fold axes of symmetry which relate pairs of monomers within each insulin dimer; these require the two molecules in any one dimer to be identical in configuration. They also suggested, and their suggestion has been discussed in some detail by Marcker & Graae (1962), that in the rhombohedral zinc-containing crystals similar 2-fold axes might exist within each insulin dimer, oriented perpendicular to the 3-fold axis in the crystal structure and intersecting it.

The rotation and translation functions recently developed (Rossmann & Blow, 1962; Rossmann, Blow, Harding & Coller, 1964) make it possible to investigate in a precise way the relation between subunits within any crystal. We have therefore applied these functions to the data for 2 Zn and 4 Zn insulin and have re-examined the Patterson distribution described in the preceding paper (Harding, Hodgkin, Kennedy, O'Connor & Weitzmann, 1966) in the light of our results. Our evidence shows the existence and orientation of 2-fold axes in the crystals and imposes limits on their position.

† Present address: Chemistry Department, University of Edinburgh, West Mains Road, Edinburgh 9, Scotland.
‡ Present address: Purdue University, Lafayette, Ind., U.S.A.

As described earlier, 2 Zn and 4 Zn pig insulin crystals both have the space group $R3$; the dimensions of the equivalent hexagonal cells are $a = 82{\cdot}5$, $c = 34{\cdot}0$ Å; and $a = 80{\cdot}7$, $c = 37{\cdot}6$ Å, respectively.

2. The Rotation Function

If there are two identical molecules in the asymmetric unit of a crystal, it is possible to make every atom of molecule I coincide with the corresponding atom of molecule II by a rotation of molecule I about some axis and a translation in some direction. The self-Patterson of molecule I, i.e. the array of vectors between atoms in this molecule, can be made to coincide with the self-Patterson of molecule II by the same rotation about an axis which is in the same direction but passes through the origin of Patterson space. The Patterson distribution will consist of these two self-Pattersons together with all the vectors between atoms in different molecules; the cross vectors are not, in the general case, related by the rotation axis through the origin. The orientation relationship between the two molecules can be found by rotating the Patterson function until the rotated and original functions are brought into maximum coincidence. Rossmann & Blow (1962) have shown that this is most conveniently done in practice by calculating a rotation function $R(\kappa,\psi,\phi)$ in reciprocal space, using $(F)^2$ values. The operation is equivalent to taking a sphere of radius R around the origin of the Patterson distribution, rotating this through $\kappa°$ about an axis defined by the polar co-ordinates ψ and ϕ (see Fig. 1), superimposing this rotated Patterson on the unrotated one, forming the product of the two vector densities at all points and then integrating over the whole sphere.

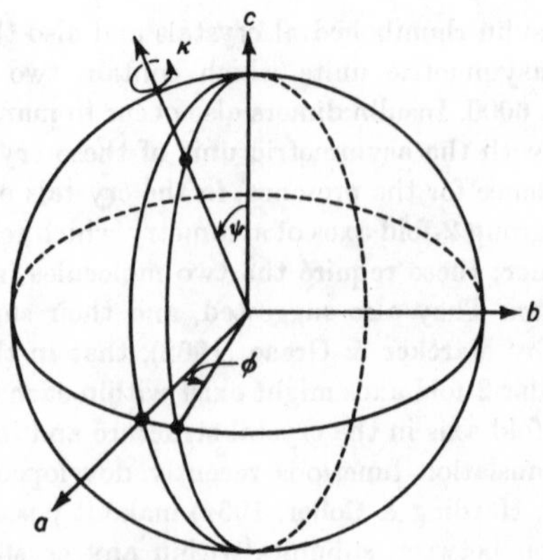

FIG. 1. The relation between the hexagonal crystallographic axes and the angles ψ, ϕ, used in the rotation function.

In the space group $R3$, an asymmetric unit of the rotation function lies within the range $\kappa = 0$ to 180°, $\psi = 0$ to 180° and $\phi = 0$ to 60°; other rotations and axes are related by the space group symmetry.

The method of calculation described by Rossmann & Blow (1962) was followed. nitially, intensity data for 2 Zn insulin for planes with spacings > 10 Å were used to alculate $R(\kappa,\psi,\phi)$ over a coarse grid with intervals of 20° in each angle (Fig. 2).

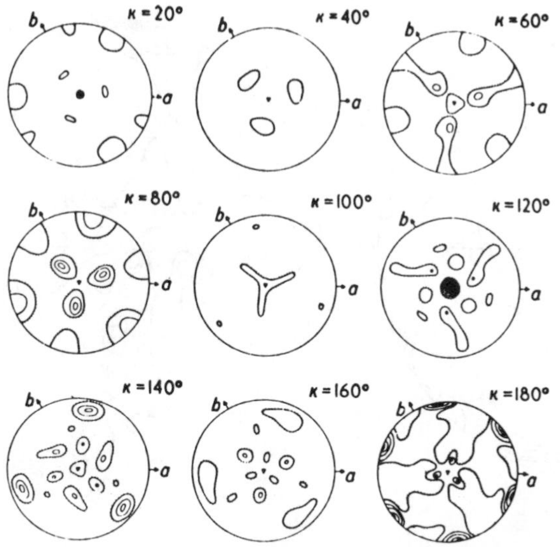

FIG. 2. Stereograms representing the results of the rotation function calculated for 2 Zn insulin t 10 Å resolution, self-Patterson radius taken as 30 Å. The "origin" peak at $\kappa = 120°$, $\psi = 0°$ presents the crystallographic 3-fold rotation axis. The dotted contour line represents the rotation nction at a level of 25% of the origin peak. The full lines are contours at intervals corresponding 10% of the origin peak.

ntensity data to 6 Å resolution (a little over 200 independent reflections) were then sed to calculate R (180°, ψ, ϕ) for both 2 Zn and 4 Zn insulin, which showed large axima in the same position for both crystal forms (Fig. 3(a) and (b)). The peak axima in both compounds were found to be at $\kappa = 180°$, $\psi = 90°$, $\phi = 44°$. Each f the angles is probably correct to about 2°. Finally, 4·5 Å data for 2 Zn insulin were sed to calculate R (180°, 90°, ϕ) which shows an even larger maximum (Fig. 3(d)). igure 3(c) demonstrated that the maximum lies accurately at $\kappa = 180°$ by mapping (κ, 90°, 44°). This means that a rotation of 180°, i.e. a 2-fold axis, perpendicular to and at 44° to a, is required to make the self-Pattersons coincide.

Since 2-fold axes in the same crystallographic direction had been found in both Zn and 4 Zn insulin, a further calculation was made to examine the relations between he two structures. A rotation function R (κ, 90°, 44°) illustrated in Fig. 4, was com- uted to compare a sphere of 2 Zn insulin Patterson with 4 Zn insulin Patterson. The axima are at $\kappa = 0°$ and 180°, which suggests that there is very little, if any, elative rotation of the molecules in the two structures.

The peak heights of the rotation functions at $\kappa = 0°$ and 180° are given in Table 1. hese show that the 2-fold axes in the crystal are quite powerful, relative to the 3-fold xes; 88% of the vectors, as observed at 6 Å resolution, in the 2 Zn crystal and 76% n the 4 Zn crystal conform with 2-fold symmetry.

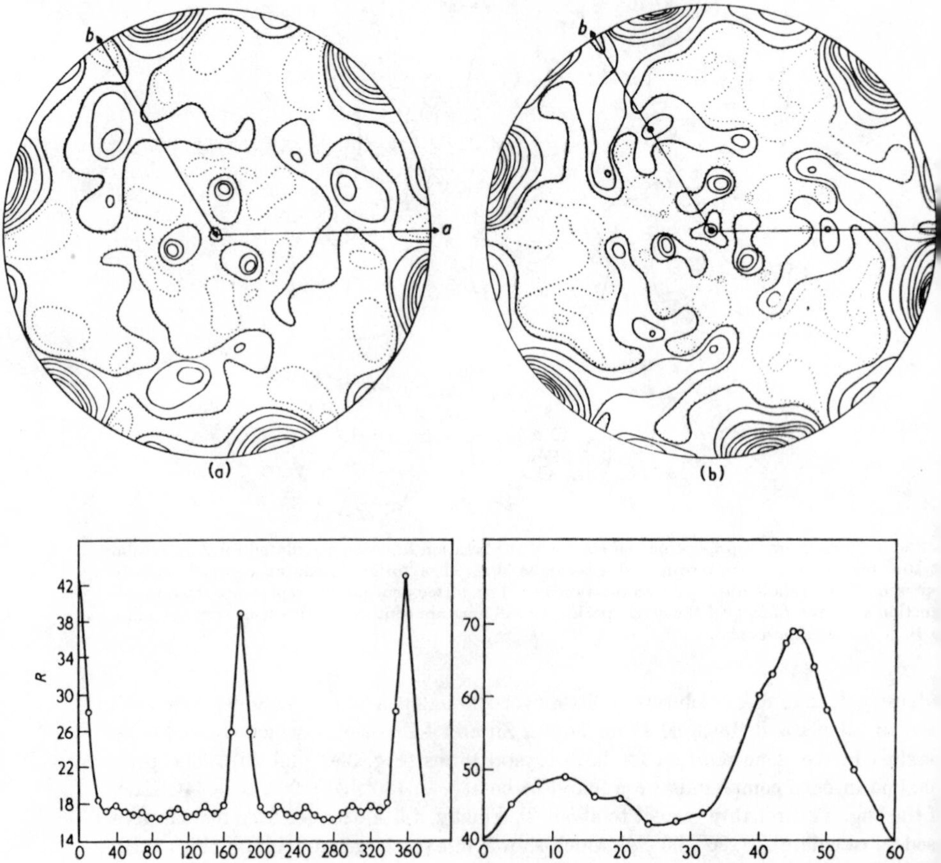

Fig. 3. Stereograms represent R (180°, ψ, ϕ) for (a) 2 Zn insulin and (b) 4 Zn insulin at 6 Å resolution and radius of integration = 30 Å; (c) shows $R(\kappa, 90°, 44°)$ for 2 Zn insulin at 6 Å resolution using a 35 Å radius self-Patterson sphere; (d) shows $R(180°, 90°, \phi)$ for 2 Zn insulin at 4·5 Å resolution using a 30 Å radius self-Patterson sphere.

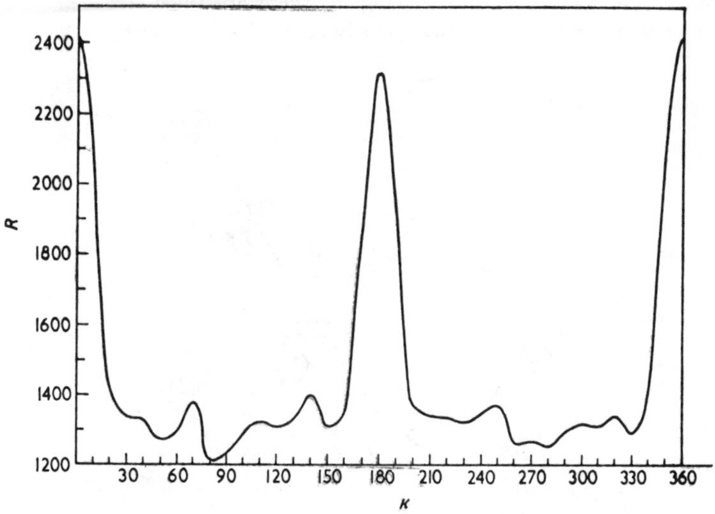

FIG. 4. Rotation function $R(\kappa, 90°, 44°)$ at 6 Å resolution showing relationship between 2 Zn and 4 Zn insulin.

TABLE 1

Relative heights of 3-fold and 2-fold rotation function peaks

	$R(0, 0, 0)$	$R(180°, 90°, 44°)$
2 Zn insulin	100	88
4 Zn insulin	100	76
2 Zn–4 Zn comparison	100	96

3. The Translation Function

The observation that there are 2-fold axes in the 2 Zn and 4 Zn insulin crystals perpendicular to the 3-fold axes formally leaves open the question of their position relative to the symmetry elements of the crystal, 3-fold and 3-fold screw axes. It also formally leaves undetermined whether the 2-fold axes are 2-fold rotation or screw axes. Figure 5 illustrates the four conceivable types of arrangement of 2-fold axes and 2-fold screw axes relative to 3-fold axes.

The translation function described by Rossmann *et al.* (1964) is designed to find the vector distances, Δ, between two molecules related by a 2-fold screw axis. Δ has a precise component, t, parallel to the 2-fold screw axis; its other components perpendicular to this which relate the molecular centres cannot be precisely defined when the molecule is complicated and irregular in shape. A rotation of the Patterson function about the direction of the axis, combined with a translation, $2t$, parallel to the axis, brings the cross vector patterns of the two identical molecules into coincidence. In practice, the operation of rotation and translation can be carried out by the calculation of an appropriate Fourier series starting with (F^2) terms.

Within a rhombohedral unit cell (Fig. 5) there are three screw axis relations between pairs of identical molecules, namely A_1 and B_1, A_2 and B_3, and A_3 and B_2.

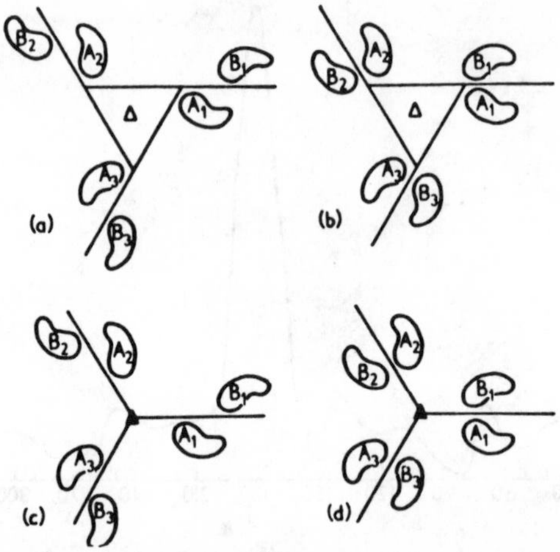

FIG. 5. (a) An arrangement of six molecules obeying a non-crystallographic rotation relation and a crystallographic 3-fold axis. (b), (c) and (d) Show three special cases which might arise.

These screw translations are related: if p is the perpendicular distance of the 2-fold axis relating A_1 to B_1 from the origin 3-fold axis, as in Fig. 6, and t the screw translation from A_1 to B_1, then the other screw translations are:

$$A_2 \ldots B_3\ t_{A_2B_3} = \sqrt{3}p - t/2$$

$$A_3 \ldots B_2\ t_{A_3B_2} = -\sqrt{3}p - t/2$$

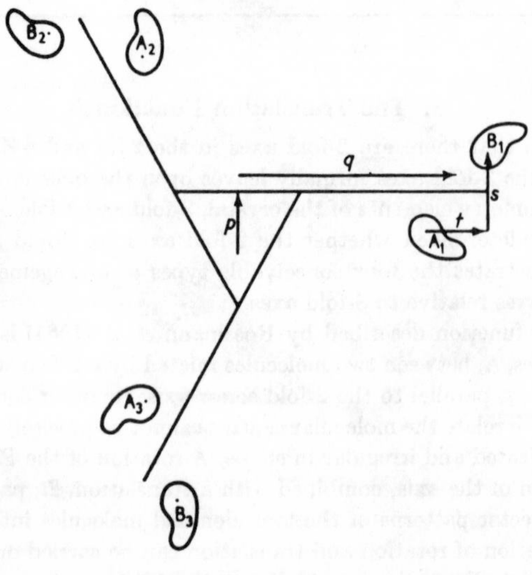

FIG. 6. General arrangement of six molecules obeying non-crystallographic screw axis relations

Sections of T (Δ) have been calculated for 2 Zn and 4 Zn insulin with different values of r, the radius inside which all cross vectors can be expected and with and without the origin peak and its surroundings removed to allow for the extra effect of the self vectors in this region (Rossmann *et al.*, 1964). Sections at $z = 0$, perpendicular to the c axis are shown in Fig. 7. The rotation axis used for all these functions was $\psi = 90°$, $\phi = 44°$, $\kappa = 180°$. T (Δ) is plotted in terms of the crystallographic hexagonal axes and the direction of t, parallel to the rotation axis, has been drawn in afterwards. As might be expected, the peaks are sharp in the direction of t but extended in the plane perpendicular to it. As shown they provide evidence on the relative arrangement of the molecules as seen in projection only in Fig. 5.

The main maxima consist of long ridges passing through the origin and at the rhombohedral lattice repeats. On the 2 Zn insulin map at high resolution, (Fig. 7(a)), they are almost the only feature and strongly suggest that here $t_{A_1B_1}$, $t_{A_2B_3}$ and $t_{A_3B_2}$ are all equal and very close to 0, i.e. that the insulin molecules are related by 2-fold axes that pass through a 3-fold axis as in Fig. 5(d). The small slope of the main maximum to the $t = 0$ line might be due to the 2-fold rotation axis having an orientation angle slightly greater, about 45°, to a, than the angle used in the calculation, or a position very slightly displaced, probably less than 0·3 Å from the 3-fold axis. At lower resolution there is a marked tendency for peaks to occur roughly midway between the main maxima, which could indicate an alternative position for the 2-fold axis, displaced by half a unit cell from the 3-fold axis. It seems most likely that these peaks are in the nature of a series termination effect; at low resolution the largely unresolved Patterson peak density superimposes on itself through rotation and translation in this region. The effect is enhanced, as might be expected, by the removal of the inner part of the Patterson function in the calculation (compare Fig. 7(b) and (c)).

The 4 Zn patterns at low resolution are very similar to those of 2 Zn insulin, indicating that the molecular positions are not greatly different. In the high resolution pattern (Fig. 7(d)), the long ridges running through the origin and equivalent positions are each clearly broken into two maxima. One set of these corresponds closely with the maxima in the 2 Zn pattern and here too suggests that the 2-fold axis is at 45° to a. The second set of peaks marks the differentiation of the cross Patterson vectors and strongly suggests that the 2-fold axis passes close to, but not through, the 3-fold axis. From the distance apart of the two peaks at the same s level, the distance of the 2-fold axis from the 3-fold axis can be estimated as about $1{\cdot}6/\sqrt{3}$, i.e. about 0·9 Å.

4. Discussion

The conclusions drawn from the rotation and translation functions for 2 Zn and 4 Zn insulin are supported by a direct examination of the Patterson functions. These show very clearly the features to be expected for Patterson maps derived from structures in which there are 2-fold axes running (1) through, and (2) at a small distance from, a 3-fold axis as in Figs 8 and 9.

The type of arrangement found for 2 Zn insulin (Fig. 8(a)) is one of high symmetry. All the vectors between atoms within one group of six molecules should have the symmetry $32m$, as a result of adding the Patterson centre of symmetry to the molecular symmetry 32. The mirror planes and 2-fold axes in the Patterson distribution, since they are not space group symmetry elements, are limited in their extent by the

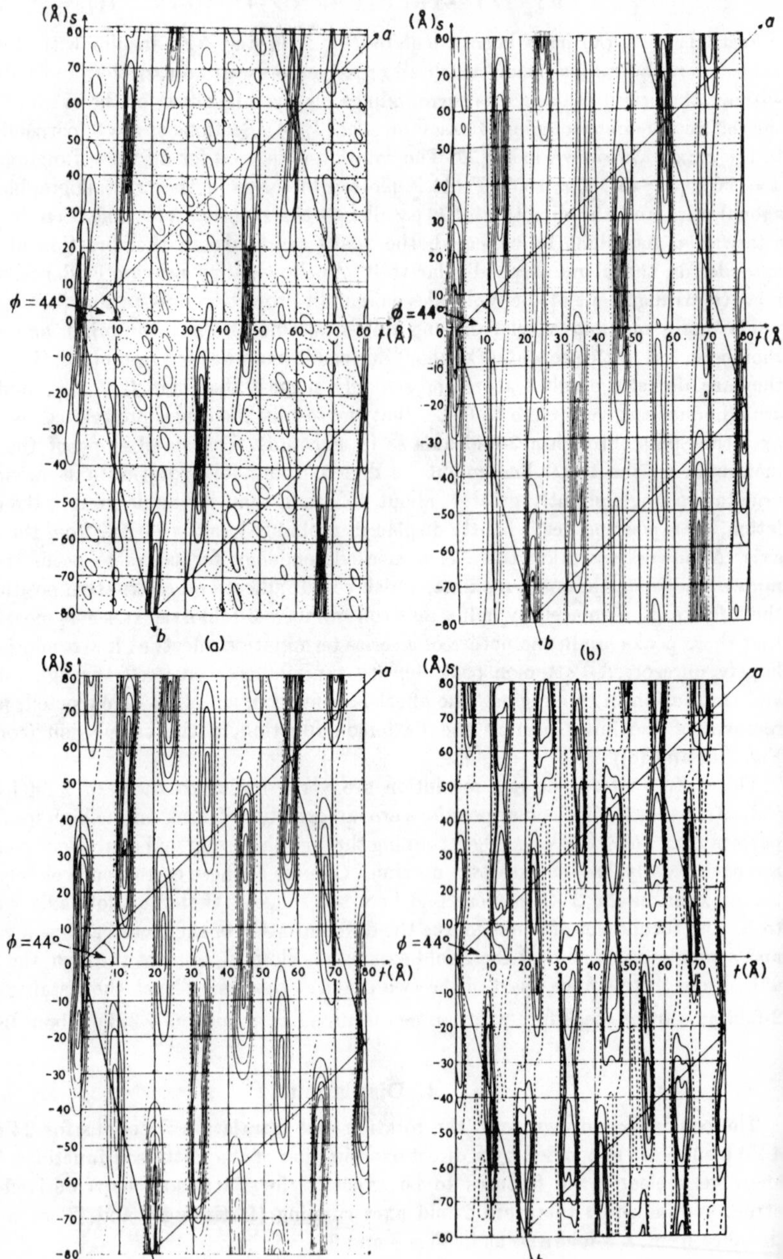

FIG. 7

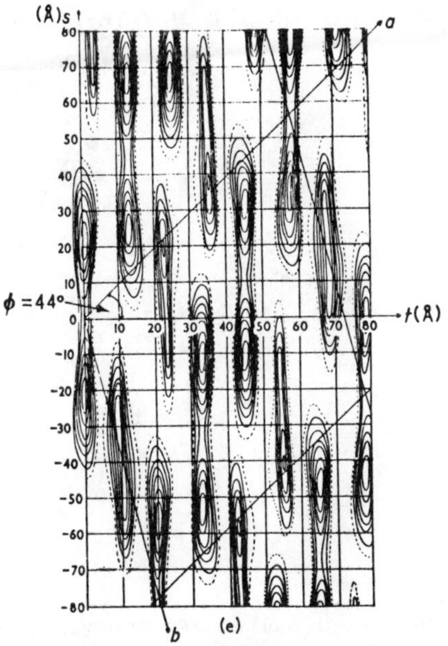

FIG. 7. Various translation functions in the hexagonal plane $z = 0$.

(a) 2 Zn insulin with self-Patterson removed within a sphere of 20 Å. Radius of integration 20 Å. Resolution 4·5 Å. Data sharpened by omitting all reflections with spacing greater than 10 Å.

(b) 2 Zn insulin without removal of self-Patterson. Radius of integration 20 Å. Resolution 6 Å.

(c) 2 Zn insulin with self-Patterson removed within a sphere of 22 Å. Radius of integration 16 Å. Resolution 6 Å.

(d) 4 Zn insulin with self-Patterson removed within a sphere of 22 Å. Radius of integration 20 Å. Resolution 3·5 Å.

(e) 4 Zn insulin with self-Patterson removed within a sphere of 22 Å. Radius of integration 16 Å. Resolution 6 Å.

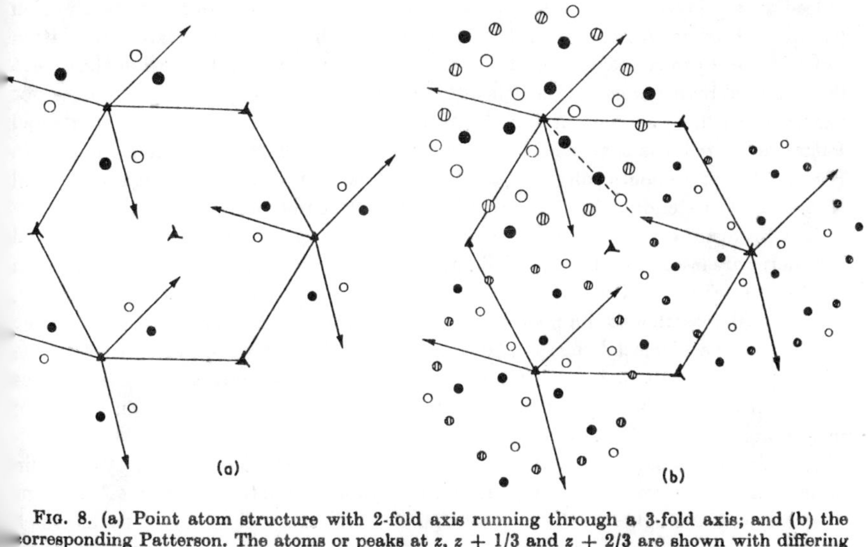

FIG. 8. (a) Point atom structure with 2-fold axis running through a 3-fold axis; and (b) the corresponding Patterson. The atoms or peaks at z, $z + 1/3$ and $z + 2/3$ are shown with differing radii; atoms within one asymmetric unit at different z heights are shaded differently.

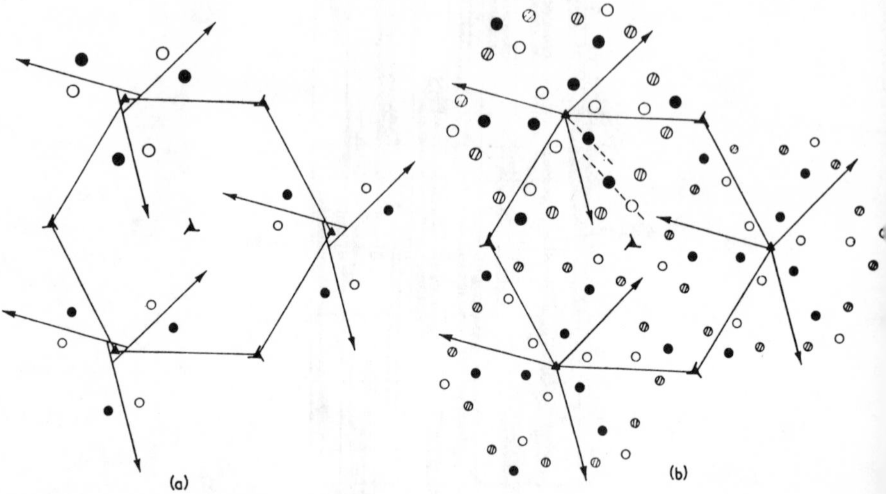

FIG. 9. (a) Point atom structure with 2-fold axis at a distance p from a 3-fold axis; and (b) the corresponding Patterson. Conventions as in Fig. 8.

interpenetration of the vector patterns around neighbouring lattice points. In the 6 Å resolution Patterson maps (Harding *et al.*, 1966) all the strong peaks actually lie on the mirror planes or midway between them. The very simplicity of the maps calls for some caution in their interpretation; the pattern could be produced by the existence of one prominent chain direction in the insulin asymmetric unit and was indeed interpreted in this way in early attempts to understand the distribution (compare Lindley & Rollett, 1955). However, both the rotation and translation functions and direct inspection of the Patterson maps at high resolution show that the observed high symmetry persists as far as the data extend. The mirror planes, for example, can be traced as in Fig. 10 in individual sections of the 2·2 Å sharpened Patterson distributions to a distance of about 30 Å (compare the streak length in Fig. 7(a)); approximate mirror planes can also be seen directly in single reciprocal lattice layers extending to the limit of the reflections observed.

In 4 Zn insulin, particularly in the high-resolution maps, the effects of additional symmetry are less marked than in 2 Zn insulin, and conform quite well to the situation indicated in Fig. 9(b). One can trace, as in Fig. 11, with perhaps some over optimism, lines of peaks parallel to the mirror planes through the origin of the Patterson, in the position of the displaced mirror planes to be expected for a structure in which the 2-fold axis lies at about 1 Å from the 3-fold axis. The preferred position is perhaps best identified by the comparison of the Patterson projections for 2 Zn and 4 Zn insulin illustrated in Fig. 12.

Probably the best general evidence for the position of the 2-fold axes in the insulin crystals is that derived not so much from the translation relations as from calculations of relative peak heights in the rotation function. The number of vector peaks which should be related by a 2-fold axis through the origin are very different in the four

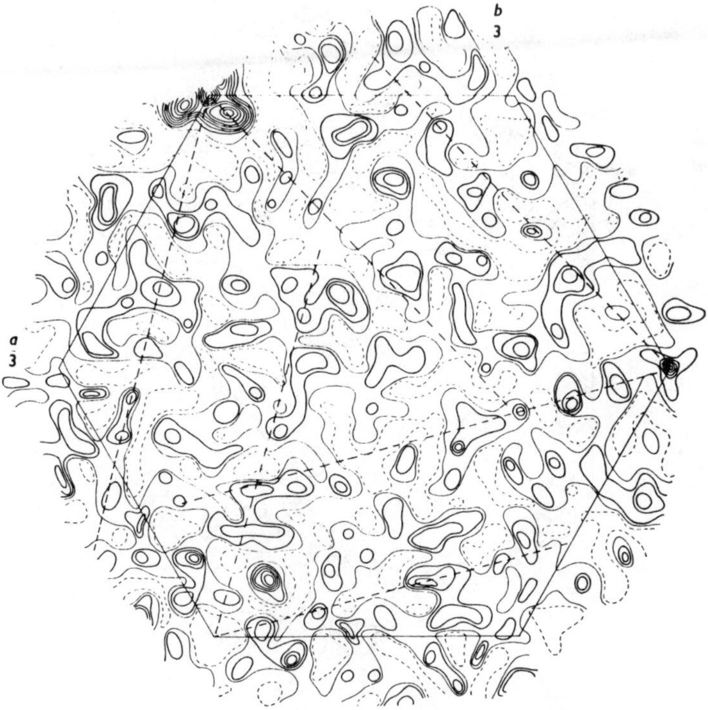

FIG. 10. Section at $z = 6/48$ of 2 Zn Patterson at 2·2 Å resolution.

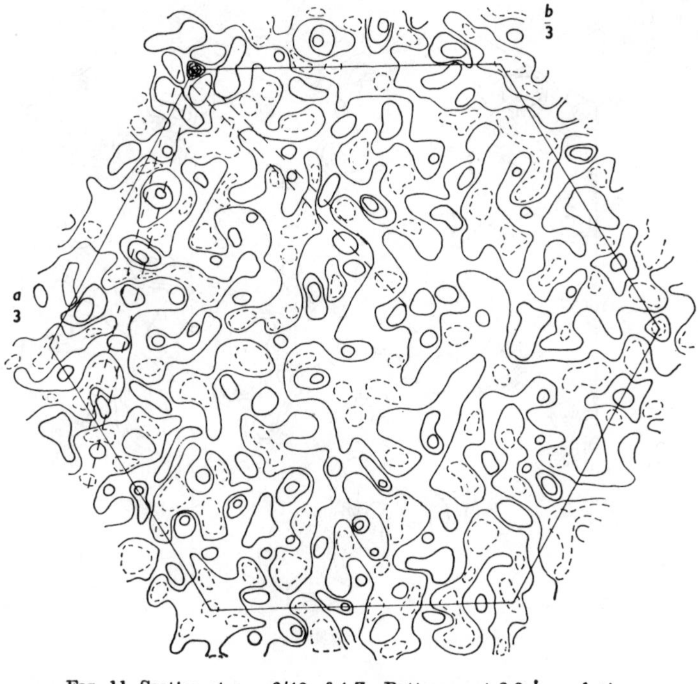

FIG. 11. Section at $z = 6/48$ of 4 Zn Patterson at 2·2 Å resolution.

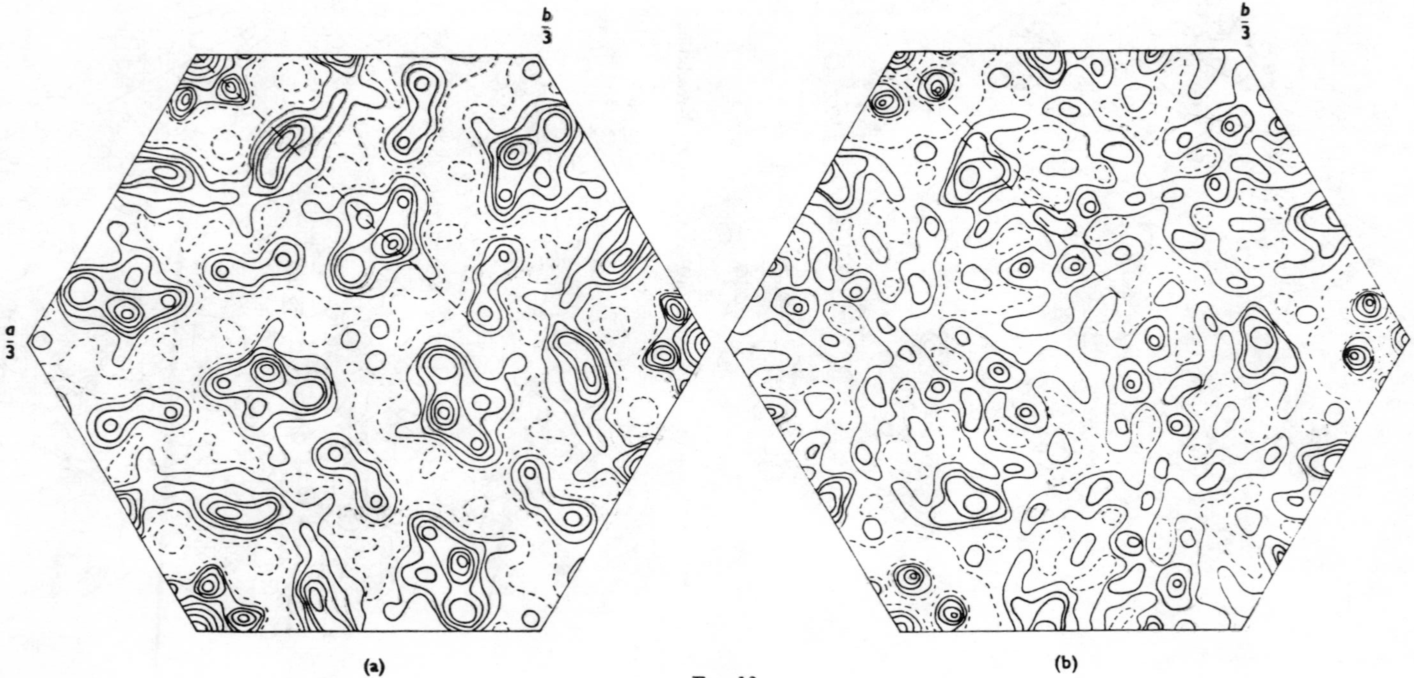

FIG. 12

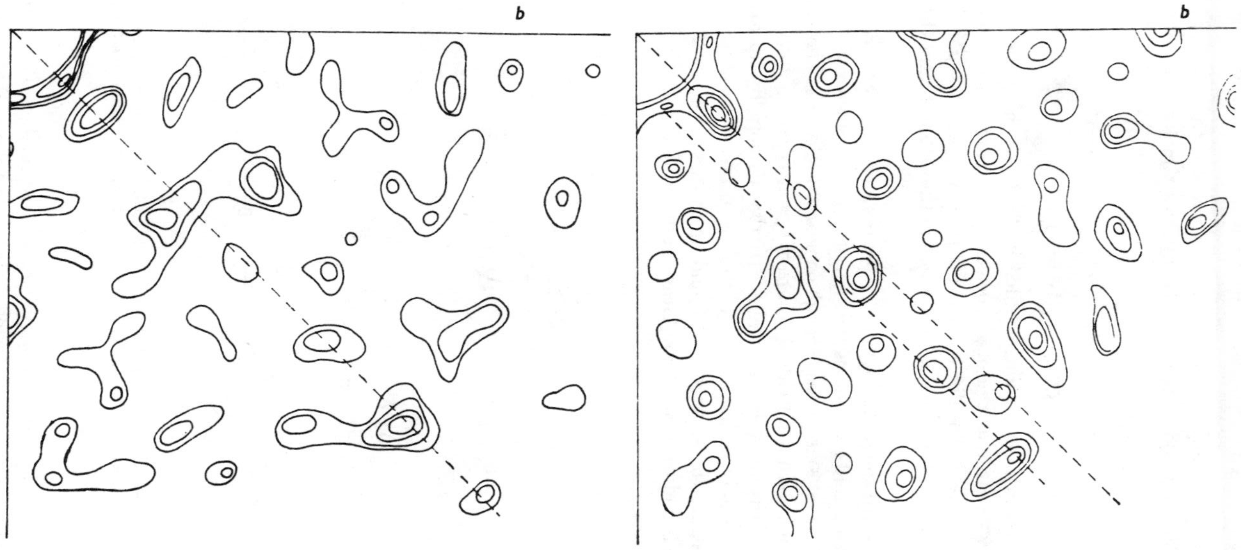

(c) (d)

Fig. 12. Comparison of the Patterson projections of 2 Zn and 4 Zn insulin.

(a) and (b) Pattern unit corresponding with Figs 8(b) and 9(b) (unsharpened).

(c) and (d) Enlarged portions of asymmetric unit of the sharpened Patterson projections. The mirror plane passing through the origin is shown in both maps; the displaced dotted line in the 4 Zn map corresponds with a value of p of 0·9 Å.

examples pictured in Fig. 5. They are given below, where n is the number of ator in each molecule and therefore $36\,n^2$ vectors arise in the six molecules.

(a)	(b)	(c)	(d)
$6n^2$	$8n^2$	$6n^2$	$36n^2$

(where n is large and $n\,(n-1) \simeq n^2$)

The observed situation in 2 Zn insulin recorded in Table 1, where the 2-fold ax rotation peak is nearly as large as the origin peak, clearly corresponds to case (d the corresponding peak in 4 Zn insulin is only a little lower, again suggesting th the six monomers conform to the 2-fold axis less well in the latter crystal than in t former.

One problem remains. All the formal symmetry relations so far described are show by structures in which a 2-fold axis passes through or near a 3-fold screw axis, as we as by those in which a 2-fold axis passes through or near a 3-fold axis. The ambigui is due to the difficulty of isolating individual groups of symmetry related vectors in t complicated vector patterns observed for insulin. Strictly therefore, by the argumen so far discussed, we can only define the translation relations as seen in projectio along c. We may illustrate the arrangement found up to this point, for 2 Zn insul by Fig. 13, where the 3-fold axis may lie at either position, I, II, or III.

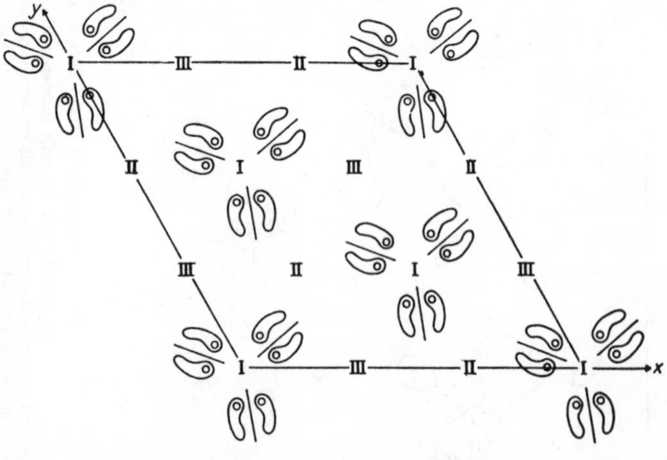

FIG. 13. Type of real space arrangement of molecules in 2 Zn insulin according to the resu of the rotation and translation functions. These do not distinguish whether there is a 3-fold axis I, II, or III.

It is possible, tentatively to carry the argument a stage further. The comparis of the wet and air-dried 2 Zn insulin Patterson distributions shows that there is ve close similarity of the vector patterns around each origin, provided one pattern turned 6° around the 3-fold axis relative to the other. The relations suggest that he one can distinguish the effect on the vector pattern of moving apart and rotati hexamer units which are essentially coherent around the 3-fold axis. The symmet of the coherent vector pattern is $32m$, and correspondingly it seems likely that t hexamers have the symmetry 32, i.e. that the 3-fold axis is at I in Fig. 13. The argument is a little weakened by the diffuse character of the low-resolution maps. However, in the 4 Zn insulin maps one can certainly begin to distinguish vectors between dimers and within one dimer unit. Here the hexamer around the 3-fold axis appears to have the symmetry 3, approximating to 32. The relations between the two crystals can be easily understood if there are, in both crystals, identical dimers co-ordinated around zinc ions. In 2 Zn insulin an arrangement is suggested in which ligands from three insulin molecules are attached to each zinc ion; in 4 Zn insulin, three of the zinc ions may surround the 3-fold axis and each be attached to only one insulin molecule.

The type of arrangement found in 2 Zn insulin is that proposed by Low & Einstein and by Marcker & Graae. It is perhaps worth adding, since Marcker & Graae expressed some concern over this problem, that it is not inconsistent with the asymmetric growth of insulin crystals observed by Schlichtkrull (1957). If the effective unit is a hexamer of 32 symmetry, the crystals may well grow by contact around one or other of the 3-fold screw axes. These are both asymmetric in character and are differently related to the two insulin molecules in a dimer.

Further evidence on the existence of insulin hexamers is described in a forthcoming paper on monoclinic insulin crystals (G. Ferguson and M. G. Rossmann, manuscript in preparation).

We are most grateful to Dr M. F. Perutz for suggesting the application of the rotation and translation functions to the X-ray data on insulin and to Dr David Blow for frequent, very helpful and stimulating discussions. We wish to thank the Cambridge University Mathematical Laboratory, IBM United Kingdom Ltd., and the Oxford University Computing Laboratory, for all the computing we have been allowed to do. We also thank Miss Jill Collard, Miss Angela Campbell (at Cambridge) and Mrs Sabina Cole, Miss Gwen Humphries and Miss Ann Cropper (at Oxford) for assistance in various stages of the work. We gratefully acknowledge the financial assistance of the Rockefeller Foundation.

REFERENCES

Harding, M. M., Hodgkin, D. C., Kennedy, A. F., O'Connor, A. & Weitzmann, P. D. J. (1966). *J. Mol. Biol.* **16**, 212.

Lindley, H. & Rollett, J. S. (1955). *Biochim. biophys. Acta*, **18**, 183.

Low, B. W. & Einstein, J. R. (1960). *Nature*, **186**, 470.

Marcker, K. & Graae, J. (1962). *Acta. Chem. Scand.* **16**, 41.

Rossmann, M. G. & Blow, D. M. (1962). *Acta Cryst.* **15**, 24.

Rossmann, M. G., Blow, D. M., Harding, M. M. & Coller, E. (1964). *Acta Cryst.* **17**, 338.

Schlichtkrull, J. (1957). *Acta Chem. Scand.*, **11**, 484.

[Reprinted from the Journal of the American Chemical Society, **85**, 353 (1963).]

INTERPRETATION OF THE PATTERSON FUNCTION OF CRYSTALS CONTAINING A KNOWN MOLECULAR FRAGMENT. THE STRUCTURE OF AN *ALSTONIA* ALKALOID[1]

Sir:

The interpretation of the Patterson function can be greatly facilitated if the molecules composing the crystal contain a rigid group of atoms with a known nternal geometry. We wish to outline a computer procedure by which the known presence of such a group can be exploited to yield a refinable approximation to the crystal structure.

The unit cell coördinates (x_0,y_0,z_0), $(x_1,y_1,z_1),\cdots$, $x_{n-1},y_{n-1},z_{n-1})$ of the n atoms in the rigid group are xpressible in terms of six parameters: the coördinates $x_0,y_0,z_0)$ of a point in the group, and the Euler angles $,\theta,\psi$, defining the orientation of the group with respect o a Cartesian coördinate system, fixed in relation to he crystal axes. A practical computer procedure for etermining the probable values of these parameters is two-stage search of the Patterson function. The rst stage computes a modified minimum function[2]

$$M_p(\phi,\theta,\psi) = \mathrm{Min}\{P_1,P_2,\cdots,P_p\}$$

ith $p = n(n-1)/2$, where the P's are the values of e Patterson function at the vertices of the p vectors etween the n atoms of the group. The "most robable" values of ϕ, θ and ψ are the coördinates of e highest peak in this three-dimensional function. he second stage executes a similar search of the atterson function with all vectors between the group orientation (ϕ,θ,ψ) and its symmetry-related groups the unit cell. The number, q, of such vectors depends on the number of symmetry-related groups, ., on the multiplicity of the positions of the space oup. The function $M_q(x_0,y_0,z_0)$ is less than three-dimensional whenever the space-group symmetry allows e origin to be arbitrarily specified in one or more nensions. The coördinates of the maximum in $_q(x_0,y_0,z_0)$ are the tentative values of the translanal parameters x_0,y_0,z_0. If the peak value of $_q(x_0,y_0,z_0)$ is less than that of $M_p(\phi\theta\psi)$, an improved by the minimum criterion, may be accomplished trial and error adjustment of ϕ, θ, and ψ so as to ximize $M_{p+q}(\phi,\theta,\psi,x_0,y_0,z_0) = \mathrm{Min}\{M_p(\phi\theta\psi), M_q(x_0,$- $z_0)\}$.

Having thus deduced a set of approximate coördinates the rigid-group atoms the rest of the structure can explored by means of multiple Patterson supersition techniques.

We have used this approach to determine the structe of Alkaloid C (m.p. 168–169°. $[\alpha]^{25}\mathrm{D}$ +200° c = 1.0 in ethanol) from *Alstonia Muelleriana*, t isolated by Gilman,[3] and characterized by him having the approximate composition $C_{19-20}H_{20}O_3N_2$, giving an ultraviolet spectrum indicating the sence of an oxindole group. Crystals of this comnd are monoclinic, space group $P2_1$, containing molecules per unit cell of dimensions a = 9.09 Å., 13.11 Å., c = 7.14 Å. and β = 95°8′. The crystal cture was determined using 1437 photographically rded and integrated reflections.

rotational and translational search of Patterson ce was carried out using the vectors, respectively, in and between the ten atom (n = 10) oxindole groups of known internal geometry.[4] The rotational minimum function $M_{45}(\phi\theta\psi)$ showed two dominant peaks, whose relative positions corresponded, very nearly, to a 180 degree rotation about an axis along the carbon–oxygen bond, reflecting the near twofold symmetry of the oxindole group about this axis. The higher one of the two peaks was subsequently found to represent the correct orientation. The two-dimensional function $M_{55}(x_0,z_0)$ for the $q = n(n+1)/2 = 55$ independent vectors from the oxindole group in orientation $(\phi\theta\psi)$ to its screw-axis related group unambiguously gave the location of the two groups relative to the 2_1 screw axis. Finally a 20-fold Patterson superposition $M_{20}(xyz)$ was computed using the atom coördinates of the two oxindole groups. This yielded the positions of all remaining carbon, nitrogen and oxygen atoms; their respective chemical identity was brought out by the subsequent least-squares refinement. Difference Fourier syntheses calculated following several cycles of refinement revealed all hydrogen atoms. Using anisotropic thermal parameters for the nonhydrogen atoms the refinement continued to R = 0.062. The empirical formula is $C_{20}H_{22}O_3N_2$. Figure 1 shows the electron density distribution and the relative configuration of the molecule. The absolute configuration chosen for the figure is the one whose C(15) configuration is the same as that deduced for ajmalicine.[5] A fuller account of the results will be presented elsewhere.

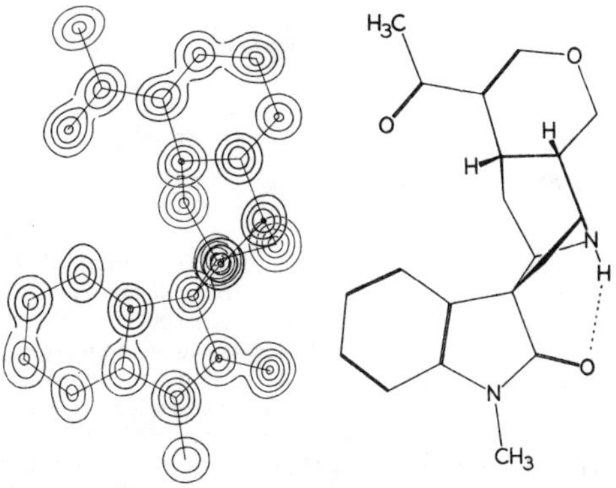

Fig. 1.—Electron density distribution and structure of the molecule.

The calculations were performed on an IBM 7090 computer. The Patterson function with origin peak removed, sharpened by $\exp(4.5 \sin^2\theta/\lambda^2)$, and computed on a 15 × 15 × 60 grid, was stored in the magnetic core storage using a packed word format. A total of about 150 minutes of computer time was used for the three searches of Patterson space, that is, for deducing the complete, refinable trial structure from the Patterson function. In retrospect it is clear that the computing time could have been reduced by at least a factor of two without risk of overlooking any significant peaks in the minimum functions.

Support of this investigation by Grant G-21408 from the National ce Foundation, and by Grant H-4179 from the National Heart Ine, U. S. Public Health Service, is gratefully acknowledged.

M. J. Buerger, "Vector Space," John Wiley and Sons, Inc., New York, , 1959 p. 242.
R. E. Gilman, Ph.D. Thesis, University of Michigan, 1959.
(4) H. Pandraud, *Acta Cryst.*, **14**, 901 (1961).
(5) E. Wenkert and N. V. Bringi, *J. Am. Chem. Soc.*, **81**, 1474 (1959); E. Wenkert, B. Wickberg and C. L. Leicht, *ibid.*, **83**, 5037 (1961); M. Shamma and J. B Moss, *ibid.*, **83**, 5038 (1961).

Department of Chemistry
University of Michigan
Ann Arbor, Michigan

C. E. Nordman
Kazumi Nakatsu

[Reprinted from the Journal of the American Chemical Society, 87, 2059 (1965).]

The Structure of Villalstonine[1]

Sir:

Alkaloid B (m.p. 235–270 dec. (*in vacuo*), $[\alpha]^{25}D$ +79° (*c* 1.0, pyridine)) isolated from *Alstonia muelleriana* Domin by Elderfield and co-workers[2] was characterized by them as an indole alkaloid of approximate composition $C_{40}H_{50}O_4N_4$. A tentative identification[3] of Alkaloid B with villalstonine[4] has been confirmed by a comparison of single crystal X-ray diffraction patterns.[5] We wish to report the result of a crystallographic study which establishes the molecular structure of villalstonine and confirms the recently revised[6] empirical formula as $C_{41}H_{48}O_4N_4$.

Crystals of villalstonine from methanol solution are monoclinic and belong to space group $P2_1$. The unit cell of dimensions a = 13.756 Å., b = 13.645 Å., c = 10.045 Å., and β = 101° 41′ contains two molecules of the alkaloid and two molecules of methanol. The Patterson function was calculated using 3337 observed, independent X-ray intensities, densitometrically evaluated from integrated oscillation photographs. The solution of the structure made use of the known presence in the molecule of a rigid group of 11 atoms in known configuration, namely an indole group and two adjacent carbon atoms. Rotational and translational searches[7] of the Patterson function yielded several plausible positions for the two symmetry-related (2_1) rigid groups in the unit cell. A vector-space refinement procedure was employed in making a choice among these possibilities. This procedure, programmed for the IBM 7090, refines the atomic coordinates of a partially known crystal structure by optimizing the fit of the interatomic vectors to the stored, three-dimensional Patterson function. The best-fitting set of refined atom coordinates was then used as the basis for a 22-fold Patterson superposition, which yielded the positions of most of the remaining atoms. Difference Fourier syntheses and least-squares refinement ultimately established the complete structure, with R = 0.059 for the observed reflections.

(1) This investigation was supported by Public Health Service Research Grants HE 04179 and HE 08612 from the National Heart Institute.

(2) R. C. Elderfield, R. E. Gilman, and A. Okano, to be published; R. E. Gilman, Ph.D. Thesis, University of Michigan, 1959.

(3) R. C. Elderfield, private communication.

(4) T. M. Sharp, *J. Chem. Soc.*, 1277 (1934); T. A. Henry, "The Plant Alkaloids," 4th Ed., The Blakiston Co., Philadelphia, Pa., 1949, p. 718.

(5) We are grateful to Dr. A. Chatterjee for sending us a sample of authentic villalstonine.

(6) A. Chatterjee and G. Ganguli, *J. Sci. Ind. Res.* (India), **23**, 178 (1964).

(7) C. E. Nordman and K. Nakatsu, *J. Am. Chem. Soc.*, **85**, 353 (1963).

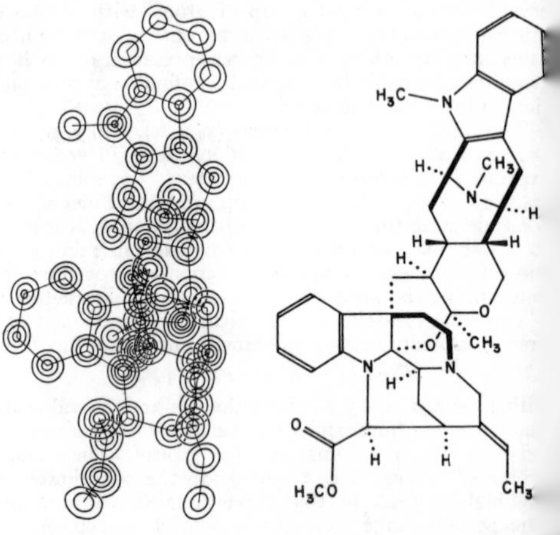

Figure 1. Electron density in the villalstonine molecule, contou at 2, 4, 6, . . . e. Å.$^{-3}$, and a schematic structural formula.

The structure and relative configuration of villalst nine are shown in Figure 1. The lower part of t figure matches the structure of pleiocarpamine,[8] cc firming the observation[9] that the latter alkaloid is product of the acid-catalyzed fission of villalstoni The other half of the villalstonine molecule does r appear to correspond to any alkaloid whose structure known at the present time. However, the skeleton this half is closely related to that of Alkaloid C,[2,7] oxindole alkaloid from the same source, *A. muelleria*

The absolute configuration of villalstonine is proba that of Figure 1, which is based on the probable absol configuration of pleiocarpamine,[8] which in turn based on the rule of uniform absolute stereochemis at C-15 of yohimbinoid alkaloids.[10] In this connect it should be noted that the previously publis configuration[7] for Alkaloid C, which was supposed have conformed to the C-15 rule,[10] was in actual f the mirror image of what had been intended.

(8) M. Hesse, W. von Philipsborn, D. Schumann, G. Spite M. Spiteller-Friedmann, W. I. Taylor, H. Schmid, and P. Ka *Helv. Chim. Acta*, **47**, 878 (1964).

(9) B. S. Joshi and W. I. Taylor, unpublished; M. F. Bartlet Sklar, A. F. Smith, and W. I. Taylor, *J. Org. Chem.*, **28**, 2197 (196

(10) E. Wenkert and N. V. Bringi, *J. Am. Chem. Soc.*, **81**, (1959); E. Wenkert, B. Wickberg, and C. L. Leicht, *ibid.*, **83**, (1961).

C. E. Nordman, S. K. K
Department of Chemistry, University of Mic
Ann Arbor, Mic

Programmed »Faltmolekül« Method

R. HUBER

Abteilung für Röntgenstrukturforschung am Max-Planck-Institut für Eiweiss- und Lederforschung, München und Physikalisch-Chemisches Institut der Technischen Hochschule München. Abteilung für Strukturforschung, München, West Germany.

A number of solutions have been proposed for determining the orientation and translation parameters of a known molecule or molecular fragment in the unit cell. These methods can be divided into two types: one operating in reciprocal space (Rossmann & Blow, 1962; Tollin & Cochran, 1964; Crowther & Blow, 1967), the other in real space (Hoppe, 1957; Nordman & Nakatsu, 1963; Huber, 1965; Braun, Hornstra & Leenhouts, 1969). The formalism of the two types of methods is in principle interconvertible. The differences and relative merits seem to reside mainly in the different criteria of fit, calculation procedures, and approximations which have to be used.

The purpose of this article is to describe the programmed Faltmolekül (convolution molecule) method, a Patterson search method operating in real space (Hoppe, 1957; Huber, 1965; Hoppe & Paulus, 1967).

The convolution molecule

The Faltmolekül or convolution molecule will be referred to as *CM*. The electron density in the unit cell ϱ can be described as the sum of the electron densities of the individual molecules

$$\varrho = \sum_{k}^{K} \varrho_M(\mathbf{E}_k \cdot \mathbf{r}_k) \qquad (1)$$

ϱ_M is the electron density of an individual molecule described from an arbitrary origin and in an arbitrary orientation. ϱ_M is transformed by the matrix $\mathbf{E}_k$ and translated by the vector $\mathbf{r}_k$ to coincide with the actual position of the kth molecule in the unit cell. The summation is to be made over the K molecules in the general equivalent positions of the space group. $\mathbf{E}_1$ and $\mathbf{r}_1$ are the unknown parameters, the other matrices and vectors being related to these by the symmetry operations of the space group.

A relation equivalent to (1) exists connecting the inverted electron density functions ϱ^* and ϱ_M^*

$$\varrho^* = \sum_{k}^{K} \varrho_M^*(\mathbf{E}_k \cdot \bar{\mathbf{r}}_k) \qquad (2)$$

The Patterson function P is the convolution product $\varrho\varrho^*$

$$P = \varrho\varrho^* = \sum_{k}^{K} \varrho_M\varrho_M^*[\mathbf{E}_k \cdot 0] \qquad (3a)$$

$$+\sum_{k}^{K}\sum_{\substack{k' \\ k\neq k'}}^{K} \varrho_M(\mathbf{E}_k)\varrho_M^*(\mathbf{E}_{k'})\,[\mathbf{r}_k - \mathbf{r}_{k'}] \qquad (3b)$$

The Patterson function, therefore, consists of two kinds of *CM*. The *K CM* of type *A* in Eq. (3) represent the self-vector sets of the *K* molecules in the unit cell. They are centred in the origin (translation independent) and have the orientations of the molecules derived from them. (We will refer to these *CM* as self-*CM*.) The *CM* of type *B* represent the cross-vector sets. Their *structure* is orientation dependent, as molecules of different orientations are folded (mixed *CM*). They are centred at the vertices of the difference vectors of the particular molecular positions, as shown in Fig. 1. Replacing the electron density function ϱ_M in Eq. (3) by point atoms, it might easily be seen that the translational part in (3) is the vector set of the general equivalent positions.

As an example I will derive the *CM* structure of a crystal structure in space group $P2_1$ containing 2 molecules/unit cell. The two self-*CM* are the self-vector sets of the two symmetrically related molecules. $\mathbf{E}_1$ is an orientation matrix, depending on the three Eulerian angles ψ, θ, φ (defined later). As space group $P2_1$ involves only rotations, $\mathbf{E}_2$ is also an Eulerian matrix of the angles $-\psi, -\theta, 180° + \varphi$ into which the angles ψ, θ, φ are transformed by the operation of the two-fold axis about y. As the general equivalent positions in $P2_1$ are x, y, z ($\mathbf{r}_1$) and $-x, \frac{1}{2}+y, -z$ ($\mathbf{r}_2$), the two mixed *CM* are centred at positions $2x$, $\frac{1}{2}$, $2z$ and $-2x$, $\frac{1}{2}$, $-2z$ respectively. (A derivation of the *CM* positions for all triclinic to orthorhombic space groups is given by Will, 1964.)

The most important principles can be summarized as follows:

1. If there are K symmetrically related molecules in the unit cell, the Patterson structure contains K^2 *CM*. Only K of these, however, are independent, $K.(K-1)$ being related by the symmetry of Patterson space.

2. One of these K-independent *CM* is translation independent and centred in the

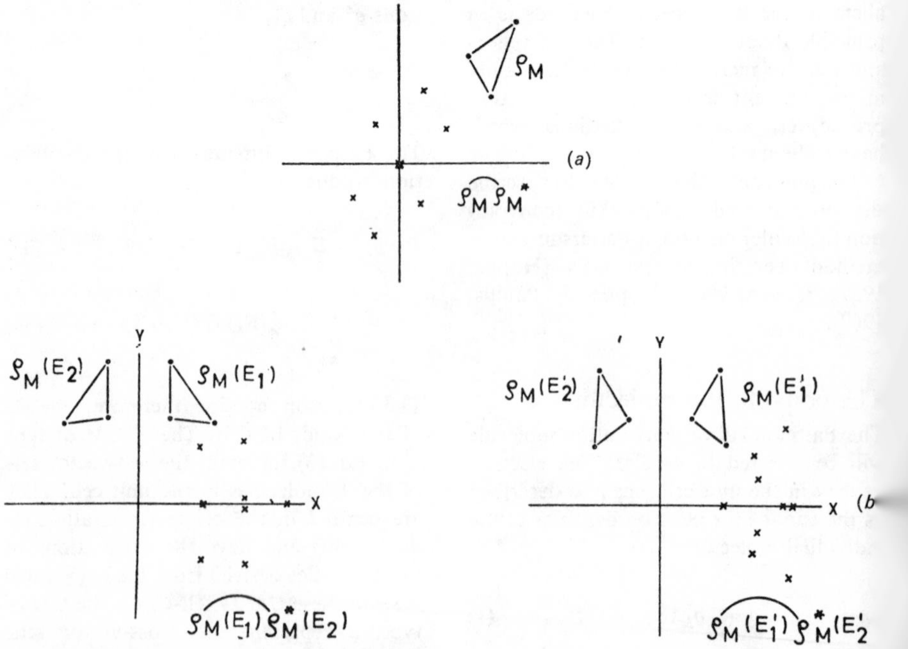

Fig. 1. Two-dimensional point structure ϱ_M and self-CM (Fig. 1a). The self-CM is centred in the orig and has the orientation of the structure derived from it. Its structure is orientation independent. $\varrho_M(\mathbf{E}_1)$ and $\varrho_M(\mathbf{E}_2)$ are related by a mirror line y (Fig. 1b). The mixed CM $\varrho_M(\mathbf{E}_1)\varrho^*_M(\mathbf{E}_2)$ is centr at the vertex of the difference vector of $\varrho_M(\mathbf{E}_1)$ and $\varrho_M(\mathbf{E}_2)$. It shows the symmetry of the Patters structure at its position, that is, a mirror line x. Its structure depends on the orientation of ϱ_M as t comparison of the two mixed CM shows.

origin of the Patterson function. $K-1$ are translation dependent.

3. Most *CM* exhibit certain symmetry properties, reflecting the symmetry of the Patterson function at their particular positions (all self-*CM* have a centre of symmetry; the mixed *CM* have a mirror plane perpendicular to their y axis in $P2_1$).

4. If there is more than one molecule in the asymmetric unit, *CM* exist which represent all possible combinations of vector sets between these independent molecules.

5. In centrosymmetric space groups, the *CM* centred in the origin and on Harker sections (Lipson & Cochran, 1957) have multiple weight.

Principle of the calculation

Eq. (3) shows that the *CM* structure depends in principle on six variables $\psi, \theta, \varphi, x, y, z$ (in space group $P2_1$ the variable y is arbitrary).

It is possible, however, to separate the orientation and translation determinations into a two-step operation, the first step being the orientation determination using translation independent self-*CM* centred in the origin. If the orientation is known, the mixed *CM* can be calculated and the translation determined.

Criterion of fit

There are several ways of defining a criterion for the best fit between a *CM* and the Patterson function (Rossmann & Blow, 1962; Nordman & Nakatsu, 1963). As the Patterson function is a superposition of all the *CM* which are positive everywhere, it should be expected that all values of a particular (correctly scaled) *CM* are lower than the corresponding values of the Patterson function if it is in the correct orientation (or translation). Therefore, the following function can be defined

$$R(\psi,\theta,\varphi) = \Sigma(P - \varrho_M \varrho_M^*[\psi,\theta,\varphi])^2 \qquad (4)$$

the summation being made over all points of the *CM* which fall on points of the Patterson function lower than the *CM*. This function should be zero at the correct angles ψ, θ, φ, deviations being caused by errors in scaling of the *CM* and Patterson function and in the geometry of the model. An analogous function is defined for the translation determination.

Calculation procedure

1. The *CM* are calculated in two steps.

A. Structure factors are calculated for the two molecules to be folded.

B. The *CM* is then the Fourier synthesis calculated with the product of these structure factors as coefficients. The advantage of this procedure is that the *CM* are directly comparable to the Patterson function if they are calculated using the same scale, overall temperature factor, and resolution.

2. Next the orientation is determined by rotating a self-*CM* about the three Eulerian angles and calculating the value of R for every set of angles. It would be best to use all grid points of the Fourier synthesis of $\varrho_M \varrho_M^*$, but this is too time consuming. Therefore, we only use the peaks of the *CM*, which are generally built up by overlapping vectors. The inclusion of single weight vectors proves to be unnecessary, as their height is in most cases below the level of the Patterson function. As these points generally do not coincide with grid points of the Patterson function, we make a linear interpolation using the four neighbouring points.

3. Having determined the orientation, we transform the model coordinates according to this orientation and calculate the mixed *CM*.

4. These *CM* are translated in the Patterson function and the function R is calculated for every step. No interpolation is necessary as the grids of the Patterson function and of the *CM* have the same orientation.

The calculation of the *CM* by a structure factor calculation and a Fourier synthesis provides an easy means of subtracting *CM* which have been determined in their orientation or translation from the Patterson function and so increasing the contrast of the *R* function for following *CM* searches.

The coefficients of such a modified Patterson function are $|F_{\mathrm{H}}|^2-|F_{CM,\mathrm{H}}|^2$, where $F_{CM,\mathrm{H}}$ are the structure factors of a particular correctly oriented and translated *CM*.

Eulerian angles

In our definition the Eulerian angles ψ,θ,φ produce rotations about Cartesian axes, resulting in a transformation matrix (Eulerian matrix) $\boldsymbol{E}$.

$$\boldsymbol{E}=\begin{vmatrix}\cos\psi & -\sin\psi & 0\\ \sin\psi & \cos\psi & 0\\ 0 & 0 & 1\end{vmatrix}\cdot\begin{vmatrix}1 & 0 & 0\\ 0 & \cos\theta & -\sin\theta\\ 0 & \sin\theta & \cos\theta\end{vmatrix}\cdot\begin{vmatrix}\cos\varphi & 0 & \sin\varphi\\ 0 & 1 & 0\\ -\sin\varphi & 0 & \cos\varphi\end{vmatrix} \quad (5)$$

so that $\mathbf{r}(\psi,\theta,\varphi)=\boldsymbol{E}\,.\,\mathbf{r}_0$. $\mathbf{r}_0$ is a vector in the reference system of the model, $\mathbf{r}(\psi,\theta,\varphi)$ is the rotated vector. This corresponds to the following definition of the Eulerian angles:

ψ rotates about z to give $x'y'z'$,
θ rotates about x' to give $x''y''z''$,
and φ rotates about y'' to give $x'''y'''z'''$.

The range of rotations necessary to cover all possible orientations is

ψ	0–360°
θ	0–180°
φ	0–360°

This range is reduced further by symmetries of the *CM* and the Patterson function. Only the rotational symmetries, however, may be taken into account, as inversion operations cannot be produced by rotations about Eulerian angles. As an example, if the *CM* has a twofold axis about its *y*-axis, the relation holds $\mathbf{R}(\psi,\theta,\varphi)=\mathbf{R}(\psi,\theta,\varphi+180°)$. If the Patterson function has a twofold axis about *b* (Patterson symmetry in space group $P2_1$ of our example), then $\mathbf{R}(\psi,\theta,\varphi)=\mathbf{R}(-\psi,-\theta,\varphi+180°)$. These relations may be derived from the matrix $\boldsymbol{E}$ [Eq. (5)] (Tollin, Main & Rossmann, 1966).

In crystal systems with oblique axes, a transformation into a Cartesian system is necessary, so that

$$\mathbf{r}(\psi,\theta,\varphi)=\boldsymbol{A}\,.\,\boldsymbol{E}\,.\,\boldsymbol{B}\,.\,\mathbf{r}_0$$

where $\boldsymbol{B}$ transforms $\mathbf{r}_0$ from the model reference system into a Cartesian system, and $\boldsymbol{A}$ transforms from the Cartesian system into the crystal system.

Programs

With the exception of two short subroutines, all programs are written in Fortran for a 32 *K* machine. As the Patterson function has to be kept in the core storage, we found it necessary to pack two values in a 36-bit word of storage.

The calculation time (IBM 7090) for an orientation search can be given approximately by the formula $t=nc/350$ (sec) where n is the number of peaks of a particular *CM* and c is the number of sets of Eulerian angles. A characteristic example with $n=50$ and $c=5800$ (ψ,θ,φ, 0–180°, 10° interval) takes $t\sim 14$ min. The translation search is approximately twice as fast. To these numbers, the time for calculating the *CM* has to be added, *i.e.* about 10 min/*CM*.

Experience

A number of structures has been solved by this method. Ecdyson (Huber & Hoppe, 1965), γ-Rhodomycinon (Röhrl, 1969), Bicyclo-2,2,1 Heptadien 2,5-Dicarbonsäure 2,3 (Steigemann, 1968), 1,6-Oxido-cyclo-decapentaen (Brodherr, 1969), Bullvalen (Amit, Huber & Hoppe, 1968), Tetramethylcyclohept-azulen (Qasba, Brandl, Hoppe & Huber, 1969), 2,2 Dimethyl-Thioindoxyl-1,1-Dioxyd (Preuss, 1969), 21-Hydroxy-Ecdyson (Dammeier, 1969), Neo-Phorbol (Hoppe, Brandl, Strell, Röhrl, Gassmann, Hecker, Bartsch, Kreibich, Szczepanski, 1967).

Two structure determinations will be discussed, one (γ-Rhodomycinon, Röhrl, 1969) because it contains two molecules, *i.e.* 52 light atoms/asymmetric unit, and the other (Neo-Phorbol) because it shows an interesting combination of *CM* and heavy atom methods.

Fig. 2 shows the known part of the γ-Rhodomycinon molecule which was used for the calculations. It contains 20 atoms out of 27 per molecule. The space group is $P2_1$. The rotational symmetries of the Patterson function and the self-*CM* (two-fold axis along **b** of the Patterson function and 222 symmetry of *CM*) restrict the range of Eulerian angles to

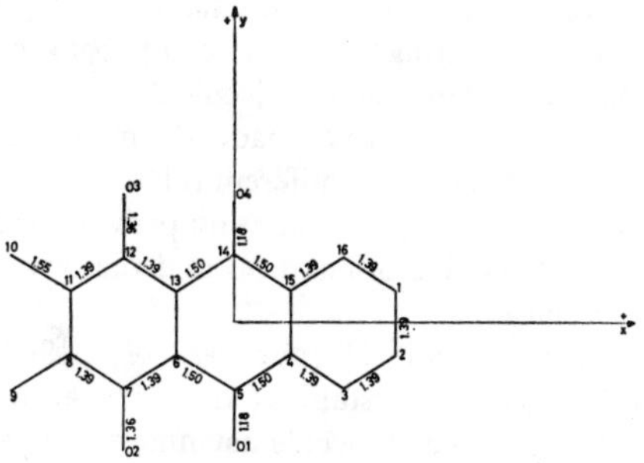

Fig. 2. Model for CM calculations of the γ-Rhodomycinon structure.

ψ	0– 90°
θ	0–180°
φ	0– 90°

Fig. 3 shows the results of the orientational search which showed only one dominant minimum. This result means that both molecules have either an identical orientation or orientations which differ from one another by a rotation of 180° about the z-axis of the model (Fig. 2), as the model symmetry is lower than the *CM* symmetry. The translational search with a mixed *CM* (Fig. 4) showed two minima arising from the solutions of the two independent molecules. The problem of the relative orientation of the two molecules mentioned above and the origin correlation could be

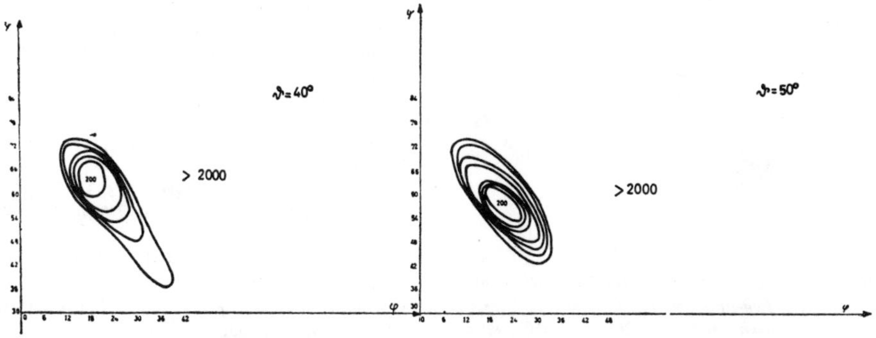

Fig. 3. Orientation determination with the CM of γ-Rhodomycinon. Two sections through the three-dimensional **R** *(ψ, θ, φ) function containing the deepest minimum (height 200) are shown. The mean background is higher than 2000. Scale in degrees.*

solved by a translational search using a *CM* representing the set of vectors between the two independent molecules. Two such calculations have to be made, the molecules arranged in the two different relative orientations. The deeper minimum provides the correct relative orientation and the origin correlation.

Neo-Phorbol (Hoppe *et al.*, 1967) ($C_{13}H_{35}O_9Br$) crystallizes in space group $P2_1$ with one molecule/asymmetric unit. It contains a *p*-bromo-benzoate group. The bromine-bromine vector was clearly visible in the Patterson synthesis. A Fourier synthesis based on the bromine positions alone, which form a centrosymmetric configuration, would show the structure and its centrosymmetric image. We, therefore, made orientational and translational *CM* calculations using the bromobenzoate group. Phasing with this group, which forms a noncentrosymmetric model, leads directly to the structure by successive Fourier syntheses. Fig. 5 represents the translation calculation which showed a subsidiary minimum, as the Br–Br vector dominates in the *CM*.

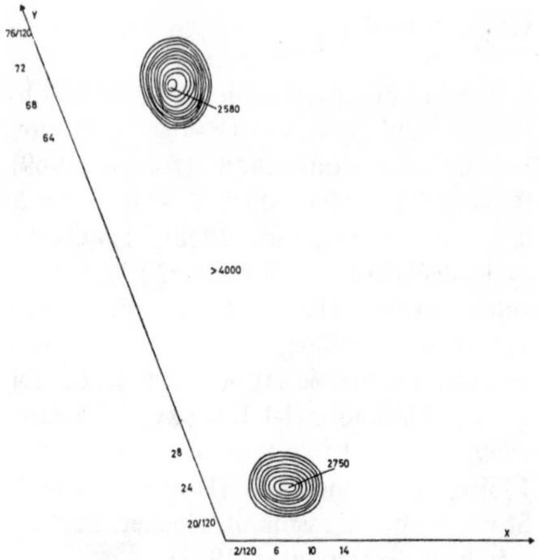

Fig. 5. Translation determination of the p-bromobenzoate group in Neo-Phorbol. The two-dimensional **R** $(x,y,\frac{1}{2})$ *function shows the correct solution* (2580) *and a subsidiary minimum, arising from the dominating* Br–Br *vector* (*Space group* $P2_1$, *unique axis z*).

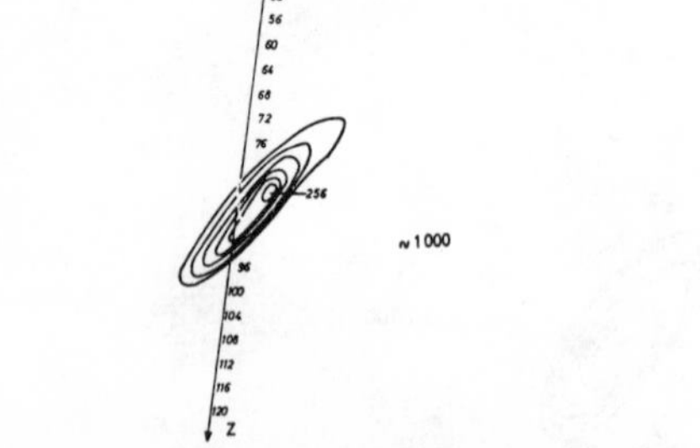

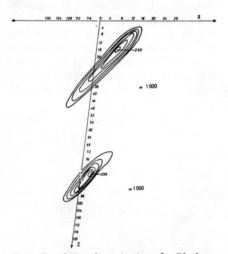

Fig. 4. Translation determination of γ-Rhodomycinon. The two-dimensional function **R** $(x,\frac{1}{2},z)$ *has two minima* (*of height* 260 *and* 256) *representing solutions for the two independent molecules* (*average background about* 1000). *Scale in* $\frac{1}{120}$ *of cell constant* (*Space group* $P2_1$, *unique axis y*).

References

Amit, A., Huber, R. & Hoppe, W. (1968). *Acta Cryst.* **B24**, 865.

Braun, P. B., Hornstra, J. & Leenhouts, J. I. (1969). *Philips Res. Rep.* **24**, 85.

Brodherr, N. (1969). Diss. TH München.

Crowther, R. A. & Blow, D. M. (1967). *Acta Cryst.* **23**, 544.

Dammeier, B. (1969). Diss. TH München.

Hoppe, W. (1957). *Elektrochem.* **61**, 1076.

Hoppe, W., Brandl, F., Strell, I., Röhrl, M., Gassmann, J., Hecker, E., Bartsch, H. & Szczepanski, Ch. (1967). *Angew. Chem.* **79**, 824.

Hoppe, W. & Paulus, E. F. (1967). *Acta Cryst.* **23**, 339.

Huber, R. (1965). *Acta Cryst.* **19**, 353.

Huber, R. & Hoppe, W. (1965). *Chem. Ber.* **98**, 2403.

Lipson, H. & Cochran, W. (1957). *The Determination of Crystal Structures.* London: Bell.

Nordman, C. E. & Nakatsu, K. (1963). *J. Amer. Chem. Soc.* **85**, 353.

Preuss, L. (1969). Diss. TH München.

Qasba, R., Brandl, F., Hoppe, W. & Huber, R. (1969). *Acta Cryst.* **B25**, 1198.

Röhrl, M. (1969). Diss. TH München.
Rossmann, M. G. & Blow, D. M. (1962). *Acta Cryst.* **15**, 24.
Steigemann, W. (1968). Diplomarbeit TH München.
Tollin, P. & Cochran, W. (1964). *Acta Cryst.* **17**, 1322.
Tollin, P., Main, P. & Rossmann, M. G. (1966). *Acta Cryst.* **20**, 404.
Will, G. (1964). *United States Army Electronics Research and Development Laboratories.* Fort Monmouth, N. J., USA ELRDL Technical Report 2436.

Discussion

BURNETT: Do you refine your model at any stage in the determination or orientation and translation?

R. HUBER: No. We have not found that these methods are very dependent on the accuracy of the model used.

THE FAST ROTATION FUNCTION

R. A. Crowther

M.R.C. Laboratory of Molecular Biology,

Hills Road, Cambridge, England

The rotation function (Rossmann and Blow, 1962) remains, despite various attempts to increase its speed (Tollin and Rossmann, 1966; Lattman and Love, 1970), a very time consuming computation. In this short note we outline a radically new approach to computing the rotation function, which is both much faster than existing methods and also potentially more accurate because the approximations introduced in other methods become unnecessary.

The rotation function is generally used to correlate a spherical volume of a given Patterson density with rotated versions of either itself or another Patterson density. Since we are dealing with rotations of spherical volumes, it is likely that a more natural form for the rotation function than that given by Rossmann and Blow (1962) should be derivable if, instead of working with the Cartesian Fourier components $|F_{\underset{\sim}{h}}|^2$ of the crystal, we expand the Patterson density within the sphere in terms of more appropriate functions, namely spherical harmonics.

We use spherical polar coordinates (r, θ, φ) and define normalised expansion functions:

$$S_{lmn}(r,\theta,\varphi) = \hat{j}_l(k_{ln}r)\,\hat{Y}_l^m(\theta,\varphi)$$

Here $\hat{j}_l$ is a normalised spherical Bessel function of order $\underline{l}$ and k_{ln} is such that $\hat{j}_l(k_{ln}a) = 0$, $(n = 1, 2 \ldots)$ where $\underset{\sim}{a}$ is the radius of the sphere of Patterson density. The normalised spherical harmonics $\hat{Y}_l^m(\theta,\varphi)$ are given in terms of the associated Legendre polynomials P_l^m by:

$$\hat{Y}_l^m(\theta,\varphi) = i^{|m|-m}\sqrt{\frac{(2l+1)}{4\pi}\,\frac{(l-|m|)!}{(l+|m|)!}}\;P_l^m(\cos\theta)\,e^{im\varphi}.$$

hen integrated throughout the sphere of radius $\underline{a}$, the $S_{\ell mn}$ hen satisfy the orthogonality relation:

$$\int_{\varphi=0}^{2\pi}\int_{\theta=0}^{\pi}\int_{r=0}^{a} S^*_{\ell mn}\, S_{\ell' m' n'}\, r^2 \sin\theta\, dr\, d\theta\, d\varphi = \delta_{\ell\ell'}\,\delta_{mm'}\,\delta_{nn'} \qquad (1)$$

If we perform a rotation Ω specified by Eulerian angles α, β, γ), a rotated harmonic $\mathcal{R}\hat{Y}^m_\ell$ of degree $\underline{\ell}$ may be expressed s a weighted sum of the ($2\ell+1$) unrotated harmonics $\hat{Y}^m_\ell$ of egree $\underline{\ell}$ in the form (Hamermesh, 1962):

$$\mathcal{R}\hat{Y}^m_\ell(\theta,\varphi) = \sum_q D^\ell_{qm}(\Omega)\, \hat{Y}^q_\ell(\theta,\varphi) \qquad (2)$$

he $D^\ell_{qm}(\Omega)$ have the form:

$$D^\ell_{qm}(\Omega) = e^{iq\gamma}\, d^\ell_{qm}(\beta)\, e^{im\alpha}$$

he matrix elements $d^\ell_{qm}(\beta)$ of the rotation group can be conveniently alculated by recurrence relations (Altmann and Bradley, 1963). They efer to rotations of spherical harmonics and need therefore be alculated only once for all rotation functions.

If we now have two Patterson densities $P_1(r,\theta,\varphi)$ and $P_2(r,\theta,\varphi)$, we may expand them within the spherical volume $r \leq a$ n the form:

$$P_1(r,\theta,\varphi) = \sum_{\ell mn} a^*_{\ell mn}\, \hat{j}_\ell(k_{\ell n} r)\, \hat{Y}^{m*}_\ell(\theta,\varphi) \qquad (3)$$

$$P_2(r,\theta,\varphi) = \sum_{\ell' m' n'} b_{\ell' m' n'}\, \hat{j}_{\ell'}(k_{\ell' n'} r)\, \hat{Y}^{m'}_{\ell'}(\theta,\varphi) \qquad (4)$$

The rotation function is then defined as:

$$R(\Omega) = \int_{\text{sphere}} P_1(r,\theta,\varphi)\, \mathcal{R}P_2(r,\theta,\varphi)\, r^2 \sin\theta\, dr\, d\theta\, d\varphi$$

where $\mathcal{R}P_2$ is the rotated version of P_2 resulting from the rotation $\Omega(\alpha,\beta,\gamma)$. Substituting from (3) and (4) gives:

$$R(\Omega) = \int_{\text{sphere}} \sum_{lmn} a^*_{lmn} \hat{j}_l(k_{ln}r) \hat{Y}^{m*}_l(\theta,\varphi) \sum_{l'm'n'} b_{l'm'n'} \hat{j}_{l'}(k_{l'n'}r) \mathcal{R}\hat{Y}^{m'}_{l'}(\theta,\varphi)\, d$$

Substituting for the rotated harmonics from (2) we obtain:

$$R(\Omega) = \int_{\text{sphere}} \sum_{lmn} a^*_{lmn} \hat{j}_l(k_{ln}r) \hat{Y}^{m*}_l(\theta,\varphi) \sum_{l'm'n'} b_{l'm'n'} \hat{j}_{l'}(k_{l'n'}r) \sum_q D^{l'}_{qm'} \hat{Y}^q_{l'}(\theta,\varphi)\, d$$

Using the orthogonality relations (1) for the expansion functions this now reduces to:

$$R(\Omega) = \sum_{lmm'n} a^*_{lmn} b_{lm'n} D^l_{m'm}(\Omega)$$

We may perform the radial summation n independently of the rotation Ω and so writing

$$c_{lmm'} = \sum_n a^*_{lmn} b_{lm'n} \qquad (5)$$

we get finally:

$$R(\Omega) = \sum_{lmm'} c_{lmm'} D^l_{m'm}(\Omega)$$

or

$$R(\beta \mid \alpha,\gamma) = \sum_{mm'} \left(\sum_l c_{lmm'} d^l_{m'm}(\beta) \right) e^{im'\gamma + im\alpha} \qquad (6)$$

It is now apparent that by using expansion functions appropriate to the rotation group (rather than the Fourier series appropriate to the translation group of the crystal), the rotation function has been split into two parts. The coefficients $c_{lmm'}$ refer to a particular pair of Patterson densities and are independent of the rotation Ω. The coefficients $D^l_{m'm}(\Omega)$, which contain the whole rotational part of the problem, refer to rotations of spherical harmonics and are independent of the particular Patterson densities. This new form for rotational correlations is comparable with that derived previously for translational correlations (Blow, Rossmann, Harding and Coller, 1964;

Crowther and Blow, 1967), where the same type of separation occurs.

Furthermore, because of the form of the rotation coefficients $\mathcal{D}^{\ell}_{m'm}$, two of the three summations in expression (6), those over $\underline{m}$ and $\underline{m'}$, occur as Fourier series. They may therefore be performed very efficiently by using fast Fourier summing techniques (Cooley and Tukey, 1965).

Computation of the fast rotation function therefore proceeds as follows. We set up and store the elements $d^{\ell}_{m'm}(\beta)$ of the rotation matrices for each β. This need be done once only. We then determine from the crystal intensities, $|F_{\underset{\sim}{h}}|^2$, the expansion coefficients for the two Patterson functions by using an expression of the form:

$$a_{\ell mn} = \sum_{\underset{\sim}{h}} |F_{\underset{\sim}{h}}|^2 \, T_{\ell mn}(\underset{\sim}{h})$$

where $T_{\ell mn}(\underset{\sim}{h})$ is the Fourier transform of the expansion function $S_{\ell mn}$, sampled at the reciprocal lattice point $\underset{\sim}{h}$ of the crystal. From the two sets of expansion coefficients we calculate the coefficients $c_{\ell mm'}$ using equation (5). Then for each β we perform the $\underline{\ell}$ summation in expression (6). The resulting coefficients form the input to a fast Fourier transform program which produces values of the rotation function for all α and γ for each β.

Preliminary studies indicate that this new way of evaluating the rotation function is at least 100 times faster than previous methods. Furthermore, the approximations introduced in previous methods by truncating the interpolation function G and by using only large values of $|F_{\underset{\sim}{h}}|^2$ (Tollin and Rossmann, 1966) need no longer be made. The fast rotation function is therefore potentially more accurate, though whether it will be significantly so in practice remains to be investigated. A more detailed description of the fast rotation function and its applications is in preparation.

References

1. Altmann, S.L. and Bradley, C.J. (1963), Phil. Trans. Roy. Soc. Lond. A255, 193.

2. Blow, D.M., Rossmann, M.G., Harding, M.M. and Coller, E. (1964), Acta Cryst. 17, 338.

3. Cooley, J.W. and Tukey, J.W. (1965), Maths. of Computation 19, 297.

4. Crowther, R.A. and Blow, D.M. (1967), Acta Cryst. 23, 544.

5. Hamermesh, M. (1962), Group Theory and its Application to Physical Problems: Addison-Wesley Publishing Co. Inc., Reading, Mass.

6. Lattman, E.E. and Love, W.E. (1970), Acta Cryst. B26, 1854.

7. Rossmann, M.G. and Blow, D.M. (1962), Acta Cryst. 15, 24.

8. Tollin, P. and Rossmann, M.G. (1966), Acta Cryst. 21, 872.

OPTIMAL SAMPLING OF THE ROTATION FUNCTION

Eaton E. Lattman
Department of Biophysics
Johns Hopkins University
Baltimore, Maryland 21218

INTRODUCTION

The rotation function of Rossmann and Blow (1962) pro-
ides a measure of the similarity or overlap between two
hree-dimensional structures, as a function of their relative
rientation. With minor variations it has had wide applica-
ion in recent years. The function can be written

$$R(\underline{C}) = \int_U P_1(\underline{C}\cdot\underline{x})P_2(\underline{x})dV \qquad (1)$$

n which P_1 and P_2 are known functions (often Patterson func-
ions), $\underline{C}$ is a variable rotation operator and R is the rotation
unction. The integration is taken over a suitable volume U,
sually centered at the origin.*

The matrix $\underline{C}$ is usually expressed in one of two systems
f angular variables. The Eulerian angles θ_1, θ_2, θ_3, ($\underline{\theta}$),
ell-known in classical mechanics, are described by Goldstein
1959) and by Rossmann and Blow. Tollin, Main and Rossmann
1966) have shown that the symmetry of the rotation function
ppears in a particularly simple way through the use of these
ngles.

The second angular system makes use of the theorem that
n arbitrary rotation can be accomplished by an appropriate
pin about a properly chosen axis. The spherical polar angles
 and ψ specify the longitude and co-latitude of this axis, and
he azimuthal angle χ the spin about it. This system is labor
aving whenever the direction or order of a non-crystallographic
xis of symmetry can be anticipated.

Many workers, e.g., Lattman and Love (1970), have evaluated
 on a grid having fixed identical steps in θ_1, θ_2, θ_3. This

*In this paper underlined capital letters ($\underline{C}$) will represent ma-
rices, and underlined small letters ($\underline{x}$) will represent vectors.

grid produces uneven and inefficient sampling which is costly in computer time. In addition, the apparent shape and separation of peaks are strongly dependent on $\underline{\theta}$. Plots of the rotation function are consequently inconvenient and aesthetically displeasing to deal with. Comparable difficulties have arisen when using the angles ϕ, ψ, χ ($\underline{\phi}$). Described herein is a procedure for the efficient selection of sample points using either angular system. The procedure decreases computation time and distortion, and associates approximately equal volumes of angle space with each sample point.

METHODS

Functions defined in a three-dimensional, Euclidean space, such as electron density functions, are customarily evaluated at the nodes of a sampling lattice whose base vectors are roughly equal in length and roughly orthogonal. The volumes associated with all sample points are equal. To extend these notions to the angular space explored in equation (1) I first adopt an intuitively pleasing definition of the "distance" between two orientations, and then show that it leads automatically to orthogonality of small increments in the angular variables.

Since any two orientations of a body are related by a single rotation χ, it seems appropriate to define the "distance" between these orientations as the magnitude of the spin χ which transforms one into the other. More formally, if O_1 and O_2 are two orientations which are related to a standard orientation O by the operators $\underline{C}(\underline{\omega}_1)$ and $\underline{C}(\underline{\omega}_2)$, then the distance between O_1 and O_2 is defined as the magnitude of the angle χ_d which satisfies the equation

$$C(\underline{\omega}_2) = \underline{P}(\phi, \psi, \chi_d)\underline{C}(\underline{\omega}_1) \ . \qquad (2)$$

Here $\underline{\omega}_1$ and $\underline{\omega}_2$ are angular triples, and the operator $\underline{P}$ transforms O_1 into O_2.

Adjacent sample points in the rotation function represent orientations which differ by small changes in the defining angular variables. It is therefore desirable to calculate the distance etween such nearby orientations. Eulerian angles are taken up irst. It happens that the results are most useful if a linear ecombination of the conventional Eulerian angles is defined. We se the quasi-orthogonal Eulerian angles θ_+, θ_2, θ_- ($\underline{\theta}_\pm$), where

$$\theta_+ = \theta_1 + \theta_3 \qquad \theta_- = \theta_1 - \theta_3 . \tag{3}$$

To solve (2) for χ_d one multiplies both sides by $\underline{\tilde{C}}(\underline{\omega}_1)$, the ranspose of $\underline{C}$, to yield

$$\underline{P}(\phi,\psi,\chi_d) = \underline{C}(\theta_+,\theta_2,\theta_-)\cdot\underline{\tilde{C}}(\theta_++\Delta\theta_+,\theta_2+\Delta\theta_2,\theta_-+\Delta\theta_-) \tag{4}$$

ere the quasi-orthogonal angles and the small increments therein ve been specifically inserted. Since (4) is a matrix equation, is true element by element. Equating the sum of the diagonal ements on both sides of (4) one finds

$$\sum_{i=1}^{3} P_{ii} = 1+2\cos(\chi_d) = \sum_{i,j=1}^{3} C_{ij}(\underline{\theta}_\pm)\cdot C_{ij}(\underline{\theta}_\pm+\Delta\underline{\theta}_\pm) \tag{5}$$

ere P_{ij} and C_{ij}, the elements of $\underline{P}$ and $\underline{C}$, are given explicit- by Rossmann and Blow. Inserting these values into (5) and king use of expansions of the form

$$\begin{matrix}\sin\\ \cos\end{matrix}(\omega+\Delta\omega) = \begin{matrix}\sin\\ \cos\end{matrix}(\omega) \pm \Delta\omega\cdot\begin{matrix}\cos\\ \sin\end{matrix}(\omega) - \frac{\Delta\omega^2}{2}\cdot\begin{matrix}\sin\\ \cos\end{matrix}(\omega) \tag{6}$$

follows that

$$\chi_d^2 = \Delta\theta_+^2\cos^2(\theta_2/2) + \Delta\theta_2^2 + \Delta\theta_-^2\sin^2(\theta_2/2) . \tag{7}$$

gher order terms have been ignored.

Thus χ_d^2, the square of the distance between nearby orien- tions, is given by a sum of terms quadratic in the angular in- ements. This Pythagorean form shows that the quasi-orthogonal lerian angles are, in fact, locally orthogonal. Use of the nventional Eulerian angles in equations (4) - (7) would have nerated a term containing $\Delta\theta_1\Delta\theta_3$, demonstrating their non-ortho- nality.

When R is calculated as a function of $\underline{\theta}_{\pm}$, the procedu for uniform sampling is clear. One takes angular steps which keep constant and equal the three terms on the right hand side equation (7). If sections of constant θ_2 are calculated, the steps in θ_+ and θ_- do not vary within a section. The steps between sections are then also constant.

Figures 1a and 1b display the same rotation function section calculated using conventional and quasi-orthogonal Euleria angles. Because of the small value of θ_2 the peak in the conve tional map is greatly elongated in one direction. When plotted using the methods just described, the same peak has a natural a symmetrical shape.

Tollin et al. (1966) elegantly showed that crystallographi symmetry in the functions P_1 and P_2 generates corresponding sym metry in the rotation function. Hence only an asymmetric unit $\underline{\theta}$-space must be explored in calculating the rotation function. When transformed into $\underline{\theta}_{\pm}$-space these regions are not usually re tangular, and must be re-arranged using the equivalent position in $\underline{\theta}$-space to provide convenient display.

For a given angular step D a conventionally sampled map re quired $(2\pi/D)^2$ grid points to explore the range $0-2\pi$ in θ_1 and For orthogonal sampling this number is a function of θ_2, and is given by $(2\pi/D)^2 \cdot \sin(\theta_2)$. The mean value of the sine over half a cycle is $2/\pi$, so that an orthogonally sampled map required on $2/\pi$ times as many sample points as a conventionally sampled one

Orthogonal sampling also ensures that equal volumes will b associated with all sample points. The volume of parallelepipe with edges $\Delta\theta_+$, $\Delta\theta_2$, $\Delta\theta_-$ is

$$\begin{aligned} V &= \sin(\theta_2/2)\cos(\theta_2/2)\Delta\theta_+\Delta\theta_2\Delta\theta_- \\ &= (1/2)\sin(\theta_2)\Delta\theta_+\Delta\theta_2\Delta\theta_- \end{aligned} \tag{8}$$

a quantity which is constant throughout the map.

The situation for the angles ϕ,ψ,χ will be dealt with very briefly. Expressing $\underline{C}$ in equation (4) in terms of these angles one can calculate the distance χ_d as a function of them and their increments. One finds that

$$\chi_d^2 = \Delta\chi^2 + 4\sin^2(\chi/2)\Delta\psi^2 + 4\sin^2(\chi/2)\sin^2(\psi)\Delta\phi^2 \quad . \qquad (9)$$

These variables are therefore also locally orthogonal. Maps calculated as functions of $\underline{\phi}$ are usually plotted on sections of constant χ, with ψ and ϕ being represented on the surface of a sphere. In this way equal areas on the sphere correspond to equal areas in $\underline{\phi}$-space. There is, however, a factor $4\sin^2(\chi/2)$ weighting the different sections. When χ is small, large areas and lengths on the sphere correspond to much smaller quantities in angle space. Thus peaks which appear widely separated may actually be only a small distance apart. Note also that the local orthogonality of ϕ and ψ is preserved on the sphere, so that selection of sample points is straightforward.

In a paper brought to my attention after this work was completed, Burdina (1971) has investigated many of the problems discussed herein. Choosing a metric like that define in (2) he derives an equation like (8) in terms of conventional Eulerian angles. The sampling technique he suggests, however, is not distortion free.

CONCLUSIONS

This paper has presented a method for sampling the rotation function which reduces computation time, yields undistorted maps, and associates equal volumes of angle space with all sample points. It will appear in elaborated form elsewhere (Lattman, 1971).

I should like to thank Drs. Warner Love and Wayne Hendrickson for helpful discussions. This work has been supported by grant AM02528 from the USPHS, and by a grant for computing from the Johns Hopkins University.

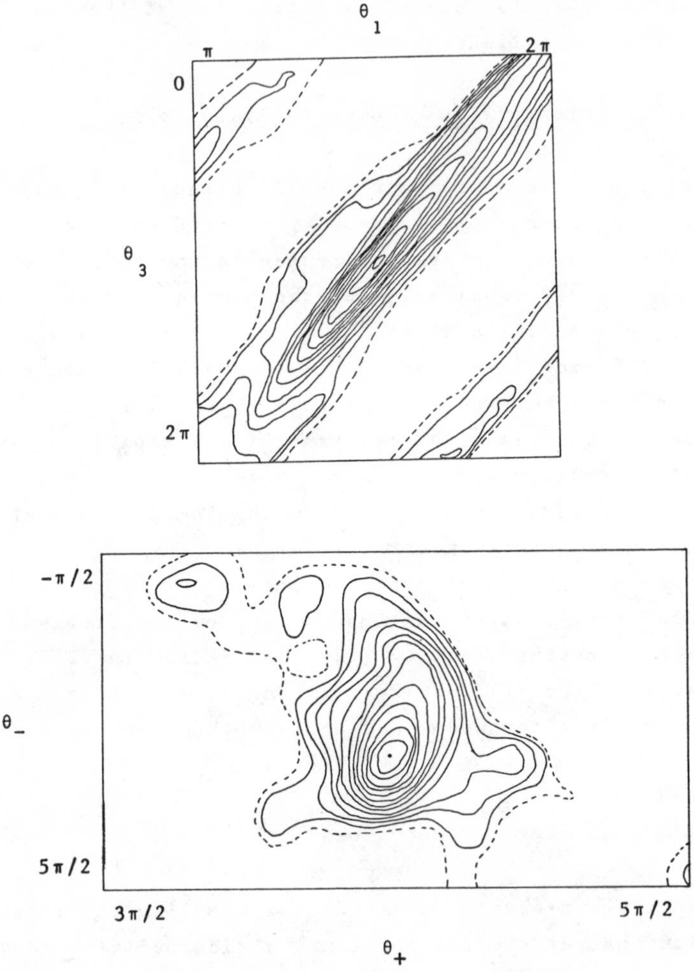

(a)

(b)

Figure 1: (a) a section at $\theta_2 = 15^\circ$ from the rotation function comparing the diffraction patterns from an isolated molecule and crystal of sperm whale myoglobin. Steps of 5° were taken in θ_1 and θ_3. Note the extremely asymmetrical peak. (b) part of the same section calculated with respect to θ_+ and θ_-. The steps in θ_+ were 5°, but 35° in θ_-. The peak is much more symmetrical, an only one seventh as many points were used in the map.

REFERENCES

urdina, V.I. (1971). Soviet Physics - Crystallography, 15, 545.

oldstein, H. (1959). Classical Mechanics, p. 93. Reading: Addison-Wesley.

attman, E.E. (1971). Acta Cryst. In the press.

attman, E.E. & Love, W.E. (1969). Acta Cryst. B26, 1854.

ossmann, M.G. & Blow, D.M. (1962). Acta Cryst. 15, 24.

ollin, P., Main, P. & Rossmann, M.G. (1966). Acta Cryst. 20, 404.

Reprinted from *Acta Crystallographica*, Vol. B 25, Part 12, December 1969

a Cryst. (1969). B25, 2571

The Use of Non-Crystallographic Symmetry for Phase Determination

By R. A. Crowther

Medical Research Council, Laboratory of Molecular Biology, Hills Road, Cambridge, England

(*Received* 13 *January* 1969)

When a crystal contains more than one identical molecule or sub-unit in the crystallographic asymmetric unit, the structure factors must satisfy a set of complex linear equations. Given a set of structure amplitudes for a structure with the postulated non-crystallographic symmetry, the particular nature of the eigenvalue spectrum of the matrix of the equations provides a formal basis for an iterative procedure for generating the phases of the structure factors from the equations. The method has been tested on a number of model structures. An estimate is given of how strong the non-crystallographic symmetry constraints must be in order to generate a unique set of phases.

Introduction

a previous paper (Crowther, 1967) it was shown that structure-factor equations, which may be concted when a crystal contains more than one idenl molecule or sub-unit within the crystallographic mmetric unit (Main & Rossmann, 1966), can be tten in the form

$$\mathbf{HF}=\mathbf{F}. \tag{1}$$

re **F** is a vector whose elements are the complex cture factors out to the resolution to which we are king and **H** is a hermitian matrix ($H_{rs}=H^*_{sr}$, where asterisk denotes complex conjugate) describing the tive geometry of the sub-units. The elements of **H** expressed in terms of the rotations and translations ting the various sub-units, which we assume are wn, so that the elements of **H** can be evaluated nerically for any given arrangement of sub-units. ny eigenvector of the matrix **H** corresponding to nit eigenvalue is a possible solution of (1) and consely the number of independent solutions of (1) is equal to the number of unit eigenvalues of the matrix **H**. The Fourier transform of the particular set of structure factors constituting an eigenvector of **H** will be called an eigendensity. Eigenvectors and eigendensities corresponding to unit eigenvalues will be termed 'allowed'. Any structure with the postulated non-crystallographic symmetry may, to the resolution to which we are working, be expressed as a linear combination of the allowed eigendensities and correspondingly its transform may be expressed as a linear combination of the allowed eigenvectors. The allowed eigendensities form a more appropriate set of functions in which to expand a density with non-crystallographic symmetry than the more normally used Fourier terms.

Turning now to structure determination, let us take an unknown structure with known non-crystallographic symmetry. The question we pose is whether, given a set of measured structure amplitudes, it is possible to use the constraints introduced by non-crystallographic symmetry to solve the structure. For simplicity we take the space group to be $P1$ and let us suppose that $(2N+1)$ reflexions are to be included, that is N independent reflexions plus the N Friedel related reflexions plus the F_0 term. At this resolution the matrix **H** will have m allowed eigenvectors, $(\mathbf{u}_1 \ldots \mathbf{u}_m)$, where $m<N$. The transform, **F**, of the structure must be expressible as a linear combination of the allowed eigenvectors in the form

$$\mathbf{F} = \sum_{j=1}^{m} \mu_j \mathbf{u}_j \qquad (2)$$

where the μ_j are real (Crowther, 1967). The N unknown phases may be eliminated from (2) to give a set of $(N+1)$ simultaneous quadratic equations for the m unknowns μ_j which involve only the measured intensities, namely

$$|F_h|^2 = \sum_{j=1}^{m} \sum_{k=1}^{m} \mu_j \mu_k u^*_{jh} u_{kh}\,, \quad h=0,1,\ldots N \qquad (3)$$

where u_{jh} is the h component of the eigenvector $\mathbf{u}_j$. A plot of the number, m, of unit eigenvalues as ordinate against the number, N, of independent reflexions included, when the equations are truncated at different resolutions, gives a straight line, whose gradient is the fractional decrease in the number of parameters needed to describe the system.

If the gradient of the (m,N) plot were less than unity, the problem should in general be determined, since the number of unknowns is then less than the number of equations. In order for there to be a *unique* solution however, it will be shown that the gradient of the (m,N) plot must be considerably less than unity. In the Appendix it is shown that for space group $P1$ the gradient of the (m,N) plot is less than $(2U/V)$, where U is the volume of a sub-unit and V is the volume of the unit cell. The gradient of the (m,N) plot therefore decreases and the strength of constraint increases as the number of sub-units in the asymmetric unit increases.

Although the above formulation (3) enables a quantitative measure of the constraints introduced by the non-crystallographic symmetry to be given, it is not very useful for structure determination, since there is no simple method of solving a large set of simultaneous quadratic equations. In any case the coefficients $u^*_{jh}u_{kh}$ in (3) become difficult to compute when the number of reflexions included is large. Accordingly a different approach has been used, though still based on the eigenvalue analysis described above. The method, which is iterative, attempts to determine structure factor phases, rather than the coefficients, μ_j, in the expansion of the transform in terms of the allowed eigenvectors.

An iterative method of phase determination

We assume that the iterative phase determination has been initiated in the way described below. Let us suppose that at some stage of phase determination we have an approximate set of phases which, when combined with the observed structure amplitudes, gives a structure factor vector which will be denoted by $\mathbf{F}^{(r)}$.

Since the phases are approximate, the transform c $\mathbf{F}^{(r)}$ will not in general have the required non-crysta logographic symmetry. $\mathbf{F}^{(r)}$ will not be a solution c equations (1) and will therefore contain componen of non-allowed eigenvectors. We may write

$$\mathbf{F}^{(r)} = \sum_{j=1}^{m} \mu_j^{(r)} \mathbf{u}_j + \sum_{j=m+1}^{2N+1} \mu_j^{(r)} \mathbf{u}_j\,,$$

where the summation is split into two parts correspon ing to the allowed and non-allowed components r spectively. In the Appendix to Crowther (1967) it wa proved that the eigenvalues of matrix **H** satisfy th condition $0 \le \lambda_j \le 1$. A better solution of the equatio may therefore be produced by multiplying $\mathbf{F}^{(r)}$ by ma trix **H** giving

$$\mathbf{G}^{(r+1)} = \mathbf{H}\mathbf{F}^{(r)} = \sum_{j=1}^{m} \mu^{(r)} \mathbf{u}_j + \sum_{j=m+1}^{2N+1} \mu_j^{(r)} \lambda_j \mathbf{u}_j\,. \qquad ($$

Multiplication by matrix **H** leaves the allowed com ponents, which have eigenvalue unity, unchanged b reduces the contribution from each non-allowed com ponent by a factor equal to the corresponding eige value. In particular, contributions from eigenvecto with eigenvalue zero will be completely removed. T importance of having an eigenvalue spectrum lyi between 0 and 1 is now apparent.

The moduli of the elements of the resulting vect $\mathbf{G}^{(r+1)}$ will not now be equal to the observed structu amplitudes, so that the modulus of each element mu be individually rescaled. This operation may be wr ten as:

$$\mathbf{F}^{(r+1)} = \mathbf{S}^{(r+1)}\mathbf{G}^{(r+1)} \qquad ($$

where $\mathbf{S}^{(r+1)}$ is the diagonal rescaling matrix. Co bining (4) and (5) we may eliminate $\mathbf{G}^{(r+1)}$ and wr

$$\mathbf{F}^{(r+1)} = \mathbf{S}^{(r+1)}\mathbf{H}\mathbf{F}^{(r)}\,. \qquad ($$

Equation (6) forms the basis for the iterative phasi procedure. Each step of the iteration consists of m tiplying the current approximation vector by the m trix **H** and then rescaling each structure amplitude its observed value. It is important to note that, althou the iterative process is based on the underlying eige value and eigenvector analysis of the matrix **H**, it not necessary to know the eigenvalues or eigenvect explicitly.

For computational purposes the elements of t diagonal rescaling matrix are given by:

$$S_{hh}^{(r+1)} = |F_h| / |G_h^{(r+1)}|\,.$$

However if we wish to investigate the iteration anal ically, we find that the setting up of the rescaling m trix is essentially a non-linear operation, since t elements are given by:

$$S_{hh}^{(r+1)} = |F_h| \left\{ \sum_{j=1}^{2N+1} \sum_{k=1}^{2N+1} \mu_j^{(r)} \mu_k^{(r)} \lambda_j \lambda_k u^*_{jh} u_{kh} \right\}^{-1/2}.$$

Thus rescaling reintroduces or reinforces non-allowed components, so that the next approximation to the solution still has the form:

$$\mathbf{F}^{(r+1)} = \sum_{j=1}^{m} \mu_j^{(r+1)}\mathbf{u}_j + \sum_{j=m+1}^{2N+1} \mu_j^{(r+1)}\mathbf{u}_j \,.$$

A necessary condition for convergence of an iterative process of the type defined by (6) would be that the contribution from the non-allowed components should be smaller at the $(r+1)$th stage than at the rth stage. The contribution from the non-allowed components can be simply expressed, since it follows from the orthonormality of the eigenvectors that at any stage of the iteration the complete set of μ_j must satisfy:

$$\sum_{j=1}^{2N+1} (\mu_j^{(r)})^2 = \sum_{j=1}^{2N+1} (\mu_j^{(r+1)})^2 = \sum_{h=-N}^{N} |F_h|^2 \,.$$

Thus a necessary condition for convergence is:

$$\sum_{j=m+1}^{2N+1} (\mu_j^{(r+1)})^2 < \sum_{j=m+1}^{2N+1} (\mu_j^{(r)})^2 \,.$$

A sufficient condition for convergence would be that

$$\sum_{j=m+1}^{2N+1} (\mu_j^{(r)})^2 \to 0 \quad \text{as} \quad r \to \infty \,.$$

Because of the analytical form of the rescaling matrix any attempt to demonstrate convergence by these means quickly leads to intractable algebra, even if a number of simplifying assumptions are made. It is hoped though that the non-allowed contributions reintroduced by the rescaling will be smaller than the non-allowed contributions removed by multiplying by the matrix **H**, so that the iterative process will converge. The examples discussed below show this to be the case.

An alternative way of considering the phasing procedure is in terms of a complex vector space. The allowed eigenvectors of **H** define a subspace of dimension m in a space of dimension $(2N+1)$. The phasing procedure attempts to find a vector **F** lying in the allowed subspace, the moduli of whose elements are equal to the observed structure amplitudes. Successive applications of the matrix **H** have the effect of projecting into the allowed subspace the vector $\mathbf{F}^{(r)}$ representing an approximate solution. Strictly speaking the condition that **F** lies in a subspace is not quite precise since we have shown that **F** must be a real linear combination of the allowed eigenvectors, whereas the general subspace condition admits of complex linear combinations of the allowed eigenvectors. Granted, however, that the initial approximation is chosen to satisfy the Friedel relation, all subsequent iterates will also satisfy it, since the Friedel character is preserved under transformations of the type considered. Clearly the strength of the geometrical constraint imposed on **F** increases as the relative dimension of the allowed subspace decreases. This relative dimensionality of the allowed subspace is simply one half the gradient of the appropriate (m,N) plot.

We have considered so far the convergence of the phasing process to a solution; we have not considered the uniqueness of this solution. Is it possible for there to be more than one structure which has the given structure amplitudes and which satisfies the particular non-crystallographic symmetry? This is analogous to asking about the existence of homometric structures (Patterson, 1944), though the discussion of these is generally restricted to the case of point atoms, whereas our analysis of non-crystallographic symmetry has not been so restricted. When the density is not restricted to point atoms and the structure amplitudes are in any case subject to error, the question has to be phrased in much vaguer terms; namely do there exist significantly different structures which have the postulated non-crystallographic symmetry and whose structure amplitudes do not differ significantly from the observed values? It will be shown in the next section that for a particular one-dimensional example containing three sub-units there are at least three solutions. A general answer to the uniqueness question can not yet be given. Clearly the more restricted the allowed subspace the more likely the solution is to be unique. However, the restrictedness of the subspace may not be a sufficient criterion for uniqueness, since for given non-crystallographic symmetry it is possible that some permitted sets of structure amplitudes will lead to a unique solution whereas others will not.

Mode of application of the iterative phasing procedure

At the start of the iterative phase determination the only phase which is known is that of the F_0 term, which we assume to be real and positive. The phase determination may proceed in one of two ways. In the first way the initial approximation vector $\mathbf{F}^{(0)}$ has its elements set equal to the corresponding structure amplitudes, all the phases being zero, and we operate from the beginning on a structure factor vector containing all reflexions. The second way is more like the procedure of Main & Rossmann (1966). At first the approximation vector contains only those reflexions close to the origin of reciprocal space, since these are the ones which interact most strongly with the known F_0 term; as before, their phases are initially set to zero. After refining the phases of these reflexions, a new band of reflexions is included and their phases refined, while holding the existing phase estimates fixed. After this partial refinement of the newly introduced reflexions, all reflexions so far included are allowed to refine together. The procedure continues in this way, phase information being gradually extended outwards from the origin of reciprocal space.

In the first method we are working in a space of fixed dimension equal to the total number $(2N_0+1)$ of reflexions included in the structure determination and the initial approximation lies a long way from the solution point. In the second method we are working in a series of subspaces, the dimensions of which eventually increase to $(2N_0+1)$ and where after refinement at any stage we have an approximation to the solution which fits the currently included reflexions as well as possible. The dimension of the allowed subspace into which we are projecting will also increase, but the linearity of the (m, N) plot means that the ratio of the dimension of the currently allowed subspace to the dimension of the subspace spanned by the currently included reflexions remains constant.

Clearly the paths traced by the successive approximation vectors $\mathbf{F}^{(r)}$ are likely to be very different, since in the first method they can lie anywhere in the complete space of dimension $(2N_0+1)$ whereas in the second method they are constrained to lie in a series of subspaces spanned by the reflexions currently included in the refinement. It is possible therefore, if there is more than one solution to a particular problem, that application of these different phasing methods will demonstrate its existence.

The speed of refinement may be followed by observing the mean phase change, $\overline{\delta\theta}$, between successive iterates. The discrepancy, R, between the observed amplitudes and the calculated amplitudes of an iterate before rescaling gives a measure of how far we are from a solution. They are defined formally by:

$$\overline{\delta\theta}=\frac{1}{(2N+1)}\sum_{h=-N}^{N}|\arg F_h^{(r+1)}-\arg F_h^{(r)}|\,,$$

$$R=\Big(\sum_{h=-N}^{N}||F_h|-|G_h^{(r)}||\Big)\Big/\Big(\sum_{h=-N}^{N}|F_h|\Big)\,.$$

The choice of origin for the crystal is determined by the way in which the envelopes around the sub-units are specified. Phases generated during the refinement are referred to the origin chosen for specifying the sub-unit geometry. The enantiomorphy of the final structure will also be fixed by the sub-unit geometry, provided the arrangement of sub-units within the unit cell is enantiomorphic. For suppose we have a problem with matrix $\mathbf{H}$ and solution vector $\mathbf{F}$ so that

$$\mathbf{F}=\mathbf{HF}\,. \qquad (7)$$

The structure factor vector $\mathbf{F}^*$ representing the structure of opposite hand will not in general satisfy these equations. Taking the complex conjugate of (7) we have

$$\mathbf{F}^*=\mathbf{H}^*\mathbf{F}^*\,.$$

Hence $\mathbf{F}^*$ is a solution of (7) if and only if $\mathbf{H}^*=\mathbf{H}$ which implies that $\mathbf{H}$ is real. This means either that the arrangement of envelopes and the structure are centrosymmetric, so that the question of enantiomorphy does not arise, or that the envelopes themselves are centrosymmetric while the structure is not. In the latter case it is clear that a centrosymmetric geometrical constraint can only determine the real parts of structure factors, while the imaginary parts and therefore the enantiomorphy remain undefined. The one further ambiguity, that of distinguishing the positive from the corresponding negative electron density solution, both of which satisfy the phase equations, is overcome by specifying that the F_0 term must be positive. This seems in general sufficient to ensure that the iterative phasing procedure generates the positive rather than the corresponding negative density solution (Rossmann & Blow, 1963).

Application to some one-dimensional examples

It seemed simplest initially to apply the phasing technique to some one-dimensional examples. In particular it was thought to be interesting to try the three sub-unit example published by Main & Rossmann (1966). The fractional sub-unit size is 0·29 with sub-unit centres at 0·2, 0·5 and 0·83; amplitudes and phases of reflexions are given out to $h=44$. The (m, N) plot for this arrange-

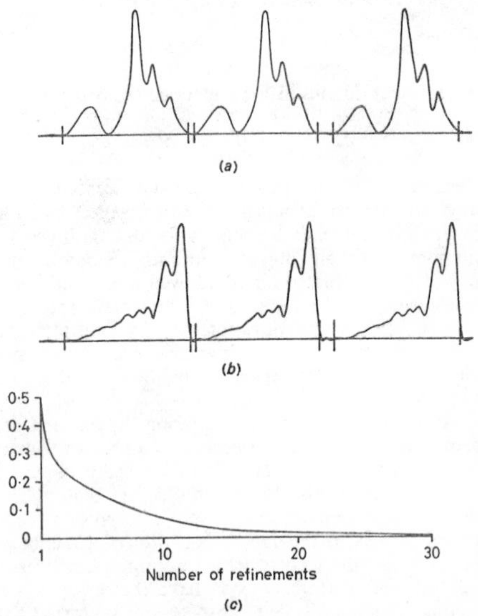

Fig. 1. Phase determination for a one-dimensional example containing three sub-units (Main & Rossmann, 1966). (*a*) postulated structure; (*b*) structure generated by the first phasing procedure; (*c*) behaviour of the R value during refinement.

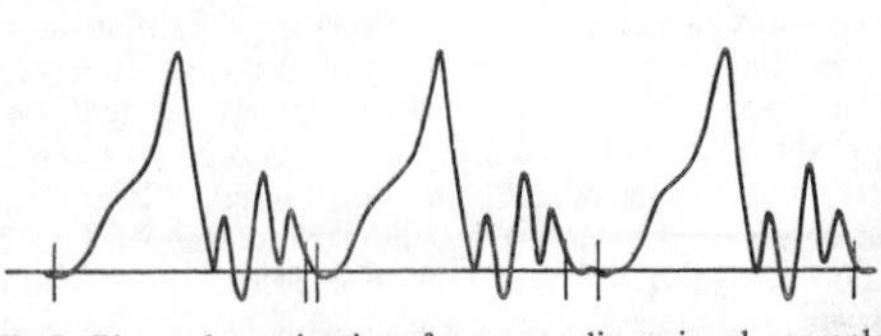

Fig. 2. Phase determination for a one-dimensional example containing three sub-units (Main & Rossmann, 1966): the structure generated by the second phasing procedure.

ment of sub-units has gradient 0·56, so that the problem appears to be well overdetermined. The structure calculated from the given amplitudes and phases is shown in Fig. 1(*a*). The first phasing technique, that is, repeated projection of the vector containing the 45 available independent structure amplitudes, converged well and after 30 iterations the value of R had fallen to 0·008. However the calculated phases were very different from the postulated ones and the structure obtained from the calculated phases and given amplitudes is shown in Fig. 1(*b*). The behaviour of R during the refinement is given in Fig. 1(*c*). Application of the second phasing procedure, in which phase information is extended outwards from the origin, gives yet another structure with $R<0{\cdot}01$ as shown in Fig. 2. Clearly then, the solution to this problem is not unique, since we have generated three structures having the given non-crystallographic symmetry and structure amplitudes. The solution point corresponding to the postulated structure does not seem to be accessible to the projection methods used. However the iterative methods do converge and the suggestion that the different projection methods might generate different solutions, when more than one exists, seems justified.

An example containing four sub-units was tried next, with sub-unit size 0·21 and sub-unit centres at 0, 0·22, 0·46 and 0·72, reflexions out to $h=45$ being included. The gradient of the (m,N) plot is 0·40. The postulated structure is shown in Fig. 3(*a*). Application of the second phasing method gave good results out to $h=34$, at which point the mean phase error was 23°. Beyond this the structure amplitudes are small and phasing breaks down. The structure obtained from the calculated phases [Fig. 3(*b*)] is very similar to the postulated structure. Application of the first phasing method also converged but did not give the postulated structure.

This rather brief discussion of some one-dimensional examples shows that the phasing method does converge. The fact that the answers are not unique is the fault of the problems, not of the phasing method. Accordingly it was decided to study some two-dimensional problems to see whether the constraints introduced by non-crystallographic symmetry would be strong enough to ensure unique solutions.

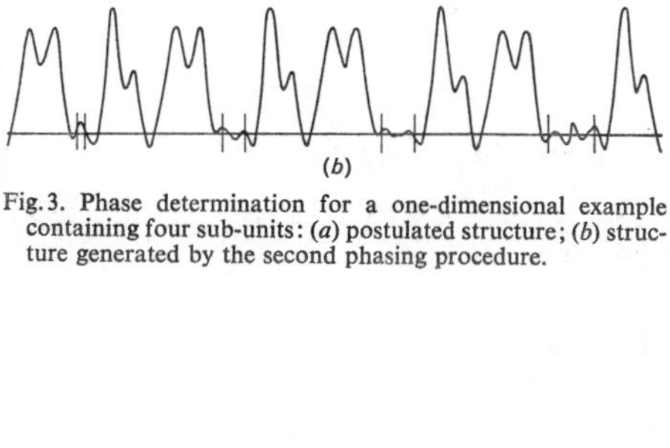

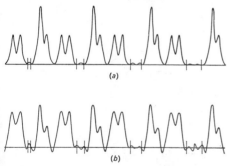

Fig. 3. Phase determination for a one-dimensional example containing four sub-units: (*a*) postulated structure; (*b*) structure generated by the second phasing procedure.

Some two-dimensional examples

Application of the phasing procedures to a two-dimensional example containing two sub-units failed to give good results, despite the fact that the gradient of the corresponding (m,N) plot was 0·36. However the methods did give good results with a three sub-unit example and this will be discussed next.

The model structure was based on the molecule 1,3,5-triamino-2,4,6-trinitrobenzene (Cady & Larson, 1965). The structure of this molecule is shown in Fig. 4, the hydrogen atoms of the amino groups being omitted. The envelope enclosing the reference sub-unit is shown as a dotted rectangle, this shape being chosen for ease of calculation of the matrix **H**. The other two sub-units are generated by threefold rotation of the reference sub-unit about the centre of the cell. The gradient of the (m,N) plot for this arrangement of rectangular sub-units is 0·18. Fig. 5 is a histogram showing the distribution of eigenvalues when the innermost 69 reflexions are included. (Note that this includes only 35 independent reflexions.) It can be seen that the majority of the eigenvalues (50 out of 69) are less than 0·05, so that the application of the matrix **H** will effectively remove a large part of the non-allowed components from the current approximation vector.

The molecule was placed in a square cell of side 9 Å and structure factors were calculated to a resolution of 1·0 Å, with the assumption that all 18 atoms were identical. The result of the Fourier synthesis using these model structure factors is shown in Fig. 6.

The second phasing method was applied to the structure amplitudes. Reflexions were included by bands of 0·10 in $(2\sin\theta/\lambda)$, a new band of reflexions being added when the mean phase change produced by a refinement of the phases already included fell below 0·1°. The phasing procedure converged well and when refinement was terminated the mean phase error, excluding structure factors with very small amplitudes, whose phases are poorly determined, was 22°. The R value at this point was 14%. A Fourier synthesis using the generated phases and postulated structure amplitudes, gave the result shown in Fig. 7. The chief difference between the calculated structure and the postulated one lies in the relative weights of the atoms rather than their positions. The variation of the mean phase error with $(2\sin\theta/\lambda)$ at various stages of refinement is shown in Fig. 8. These plots have a very similar form to those given by Main (1967). In both examples the phase error, which is a rapidly increasing function of $(2\sin\theta/\lambda)$ when reflexions out to $(2\sin\theta/\lambda)=0{\cdot}8$ are included, falls dramatically when reflexions out to 1 Å are included; at this stage only the last band of reflexions to be introduced had bad phase errors.

Application of the first phasing procedure gave very similar results to those already described. The behaviour during refinement of the mean phase error and R value are shown in Fig. 9. After 150 projections of the complete vector, the mean phase change between projections had fallen to less than 0·1°, at which point the R value was 13% and the mean phase error 26°. Refinement was continuing but very slowly.

These results suggest that in this case the constraints introduced by the non-crystallographic symmetry are sufficiently strong to generate a reasonably good set of phases. If we regard the problem as one of generating a set of phases to minimize the value of the R value, we may say that the R value has a single very shallow minimum; that is, the solution is unique but poorly defined. The absolute difference in R values produced by substitution of the postulated structure factors into the equations and by refinement is only 1%. These two sets of phases have nevertheless a mean difference of approximately 20°, although the corresponding structures are very similar. The four sub-unit example considered by Main (1967) clearly had a much sharper minimum, which is to be expected since the maximum gradient of the (m,N) plot for his example, as predicted by the fraction $(2U/V)$, is 0·08 and the actual gradient will be even smaller. The gradient of the (m,N) plot for our example was 0·18.

Extension of the theory to two crystal forms

All discussion has been limited to the case where the independent sub-units occur within a single crystal form. Is it possible to extend the theory to the case where a given sub-unit occurs in more than one crystal form, as done by Main & Rossmann (1966)? The problem is of course that the introduction of a new crystal form produces information at a new set of sampling points, rather than simply increasing the information available at the existing lattice points. Suppose we have two crystal forms with structure factor vectors $\mathbf{F}_1$ and $\mathbf{F}_2$, where, when working to a given resolution, these vectors lie in two spaces of different dimension. The vectors satisfy equations of the form

$$\mathbf{H}_{11}\mathbf{F}_1=\mathbf{F}_1 \qquad (8)$$

$$\mathbf{H}_{22}\mathbf{F}_2=\mathbf{F}_2\,. \qquad (9)$$

Either or both of the crystal forms may contain only a single sub-unit in the asymmetric unit, in which case the corresponding equations arise from exclusion of density only (Main & Woolfson, 1963) and not from non-crystallographic symmetry. Constraints arising from exclusion are of the same form as those coming from non-crystallographic symmetry but are much weaker. If the two crystal forms contain identical sub-units, their transforms must in addition satisfy connecting relations of the form

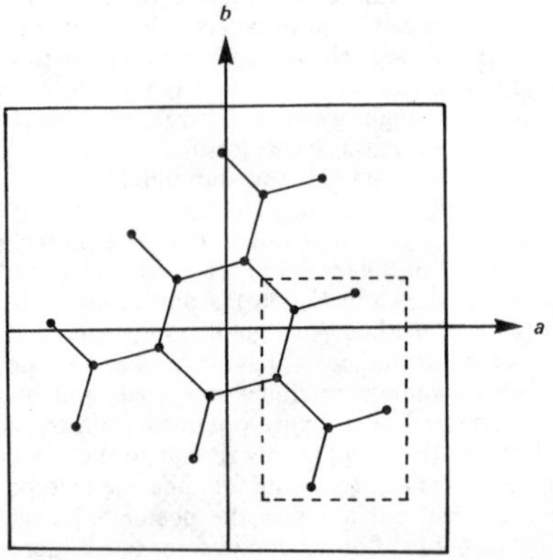

Fig. 4. Model structure based on 1,3,5-triamino-2,4,6-trinitrobenzene. The choice of reference sub-unit is indicated by the dotted rectangle. Other sub-units are generated by threefold rotation about the origin.

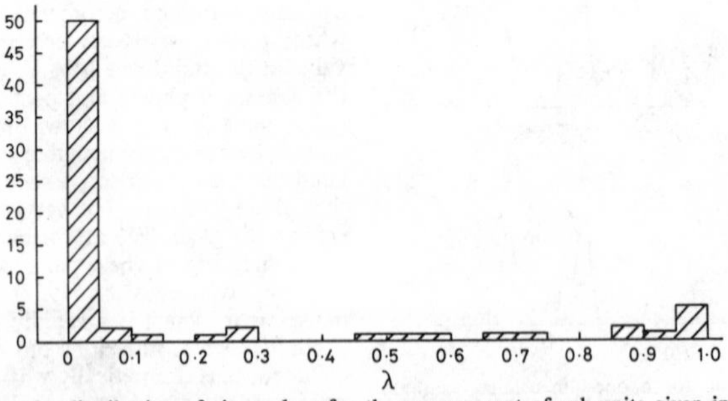

Fig. 5. Histogram showing the distribution of eigenvalues for the arrangement of sub-units given in Fig. 4. The innermost 69 reflexions are included.

$$\mathbf{H}_{12}\mathbf{F}_2 = \mathbf{F}_1$$
$$\mathbf{H}_{21}\mathbf{F}_1 = \mathbf{F}_2 \qquad (10)$$

where $\mathbf{H}_{12}, \mathbf{H}_{21}$ are rectangular matrices representing mappings from a space of one dimension into another space of different dimension. The meaning of equation (10) is that if we take a structure satisfying the postulated non-crystallographic symmetry of crystal 1 and operate on its transform, $\mathbf{F}_1$, with the matrix $\mathbf{H}_{21}$, we generate a new vector $\mathbf{F}_2$ referring to crystal 2. The transform of this vector has sub-units which are identical in structure to the sub-units in crystal 1 but which are arranged according to the non-crystallographic symmetry postulated for crystal 2.

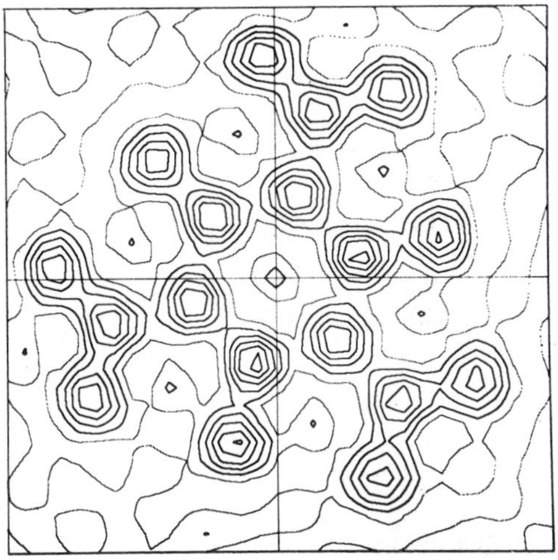

Fig. 6. Fourier synthesis using structure factors computed from the model structure.

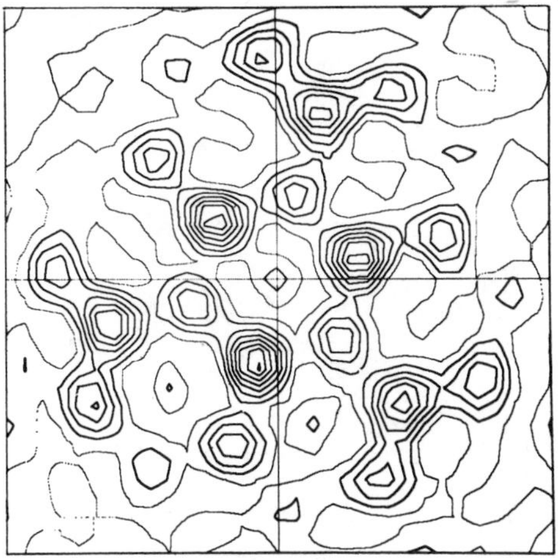

Fig. 7. Fourier synthesis using postulated structure amplitudes and phases generated by the second phasing procedure.

By considering the algebraic form of the connecting equations, which are set up in a similar way to those for a single crystal form with non-crystallographic symmetry (Crowther, 1967), it can be shown that the matrices $\mathbf{H}_{12}, \mathbf{H}_{21}$ of the two sets of connecting equations are related in a rather simple way. In particular it is possible to write the two sets of connecting equations in terms of a single matrix $\mathbf{M}$ in the form

$$\mathbf{MF}_2 = k_2\mathbf{F}_1 \quad (11)$$

$$\mathbf{M}^+\mathbf{F}_1 = k_1\mathbf{F}_2 \quad (12)$$

where $\mathbf{M}^+$ denotes the complex conjugate of the transpose of $\mathbf{M}$ and k_1, k_2 are constants depending on the unit-cell sizes of the two crystals and on the numbers of sub-units in the two asymmetric units. In addition the matrices $\mathbf{M}, \mathbf{M}^+$ can be defined in such a way that they satisfy further relations. To show that this is plausible multiply equation (12) by $\mathbf{M}$ and substitute from equation (11) to give

$$\mathbf{MM}^+\mathbf{F}_1 = k_1k_2\mathbf{F}_1 .$$

Comparing this with (8) we see that it should be possible to make

$$\frac{1}{(k_1k_2)}\mathbf{MM}^+ = \mathbf{H}_{11} . \quad (13)$$

Thus if we perform a mapping $\mathbf{M}^+$ from the first space to the second and then a reverse mapping $\mathbf{M}$ from the second back to the first, the product of these cross mappings is a mapping in the first space, which expresses the constraints arising from the non-crystallographic symmetry in the first crystal. In a similar way we may show

$$\frac{1}{(k_1k_2)}\mathbf{M}^+\mathbf{M} = \mathbf{H}_{22} . \quad (14)$$

The relations imply that if we find vectors $\mathbf{F}_1, \mathbf{F}_2$ whic satisfy (11) and (12), they will also automatically satisf (8) and (9). When we include only a finite numbe of reflexions from the two crystals, the matrix product $\mathbf{MM}^+, \mathbf{M}^+\mathbf{M}$ will suffer truncation effects which mak (13) and (14) only approximately true. However onl those reflexions lying on the edge of the region c reciprocal space being considered will be significantl affected.

We now wish to know whether there is a method c using (11) and (12) for structure determination. Sinc (11) and (12) define mappings between spaces of di ferent dimension, it is not possible to apply the eiger value analysis directly. However by adding respec tively $k_1\mathbf{F}_1, k_2\mathbf{F}_2$ to equations (11) and (12) we obtai

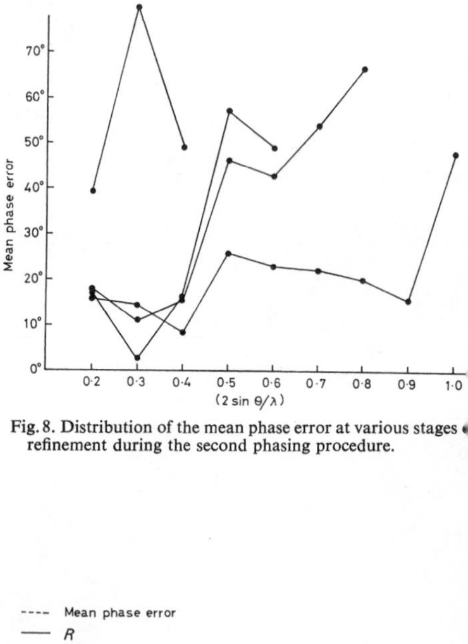

Fig. 8. Distribution of the mean phase error at various stages of refinement during the second phasing procedure.

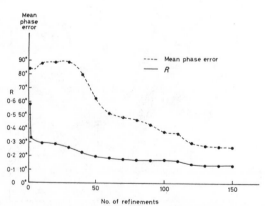

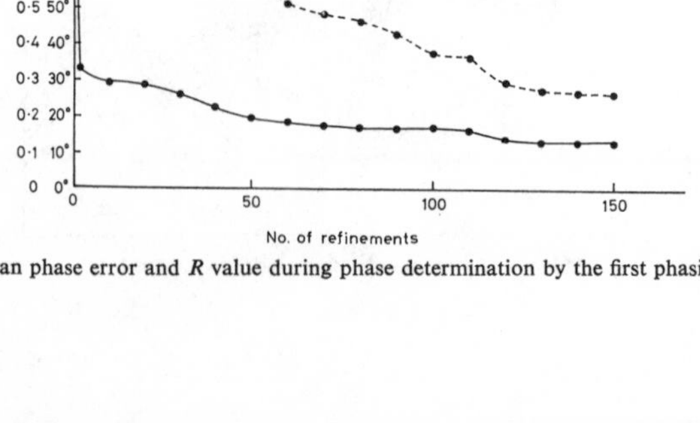

Fig. 9. Behaviour of the mean phase error and R value during phase determination by the first phasing procedure.

$$k_1\mathbf{F}_1+\mathbf{M}\mathbf{F}_2=(k_1+k_2)\mathbf{F}_1\,, \tag{15}$$

$$\mathbf{M}^+\mathbf{F}_1+k_2\mathbf{F}_2=(k_1+k_2)\mathbf{F}_2\,. \tag{16}$$

These may be written in partitioned matrix form as

$$\begin{pmatrix} k_1\mathbf{I} & \mathbf{M} \\ \mathbf{M}^+ & k_2\mathbf{I} \end{pmatrix}\begin{pmatrix} \mathbf{F}_1 \\ \mathbf{F}_2 \end{pmatrix} = (k_1+k_2)\begin{pmatrix} \mathbf{F}_1 \\ \mathbf{F}_2 \end{pmatrix}$$

where $\mathbf{I}$ is the identity matrix. Putting

$$\hat{\mathbf{H}}=\frac{1}{(k_1+k_2)}\begin{pmatrix} k_1\mathbf{I} & \mathbf{M} \\ \mathbf{M}^+ & k_2\mathbf{I} \end{pmatrix}, \quad \hat{\mathbf{F}}=\begin{pmatrix} \mathbf{F}_1 \\ \mathbf{F}_2 \end{pmatrix}$$

this becomes

$$\hat{\mathbf{H}}\hat{\mathbf{F}}=\hat{\mathbf{F}}\,. \tag{17}$$

Thus we can represent the two sets of equations (11) and (12) by a single set of equations in a compound space of dimension equal to the sum of the dimensions of the separate transform spaces. The matrix $\hat{\mathbf{H}}$ is hermitian and can be shown to have an eigenvalue spectrum satisfying $0 \le \lambda_j \le 1$. Equations (20) describing the non-crystallographic symmetry constraints in the two crystal case therefore have an identical form to those arising from non-crystallographic symmetry in a single form.

The strength of constraints introduced by having two crystal forms can now be measured by the gradient of the (m,N) plot for the matrix $\hat{\mathbf{H}}$ in just the same way as for the single crystal case, except that now the number of unit eigenvalues is plotted against the sum of the number of independent reflexions included for each crystal. Similarly (20) can be used as a basis for an iterative phasing procedure, of the same type as that described for a single crystal, except that now between applications of matrix $\hat{\mathbf{H}}$ the two parts of the vector $\hat{\mathbf{F}}$ must be scaled to the structure amplitudes appropriate for the two crystal forms. In practice, because of the special form of $\hat{\mathbf{H}}$, it is convenient to rewrite (17) for the iteration as:

$$\mathbf{G}_1^{(r+1)} = (\mathbf{M}\mathbf{F}_2^{(r)} + k_1\mathbf{F}_1^{(r)})/(k_1+k_2)$$

$$\mathbf{G}_2^{(r+1)} = (\mathbf{M}^+\mathbf{F}_1^{(r)} + k_2\,\mathbf{F}_2^{(r)})/(k_1+k_2),$$

where $\mathbf{G}_1^{(r+1)}, \mathbf{G}_2^{(r+1)}$ are to be rescaled to the structure amplitudes appropriate for the two crystals. A computer program written to perform the iteration need only store the matrix $\mathbf{M}$, which has far fewer elements than $\hat{\mathbf{H}}$.

Summary

The results described in this paper, taken in conjunction with those of Main (1967), are encouraging. They suggest that although the presence of two identical sub-units in the asymmetric unit is not a sufficiently strong constraint to generate reliable phase information, the presence of three or four such sub-units can provide reliable phase information. In particular the gradient of the (m,N) plot, which gives a measure of the strength of the constraints introduced by the non-crystallographic symmetry, must be less than about 0·2 and preferably even smaller.

APPENDIX

The gradient of the (m,N) plot

Although in any given case the gradient of the (m,N) plot can be found by computing the eigenvalue spectrum of the matrix $\mathbf{H}$ when it is truncated at different resolutions, it would be useful if an estimate could be made without going through this tedious computation. The argument given in Crowther (1967), which predicts that the gradient is $1/n$ in the case where the asymmetric unit contains n sub-units, is incorrect and should be replaced by the following.

Let us take n equal sub-units of size U in a one-dimensional unit cell of size V, so that the sub-units occupy a fraction (nU/V) of the unit cell and let us consider reflexions out to $h=N$ say. The Fourier terms corresponding to these reflexions form, to this resolution, a complete set of functions in the mathematical sense. There are $(2N+1)$ such terms, namely $F_0, A_1, B_1, \ldots A_N, B_N$. We may take independent linear combinations of these terms to form eigendensities, of which a fraction (nU/V) will have density only within the sub-units, while the remaining fraction $(1-nU/V)$ will have density only in the gaps between the sub-units. This means that we can construct $(nU/V)(2N+1)$ independent densities which vanish outside the sub-units. By considering the symmetry of these functions, it is clear that only $1/n$ of them can be chosen to give equal densities within the sub-units; that is, only a fraction $1/n$ of them correspond to allowed eigendensities. We therefore have the relation:

$$m=\frac{1}{n}\left(\frac{nU}{V}\right)(2N+1)$$

or

$$m\simeq\left(\frac{2U}{V}\right)N\,.$$

We therefore predict that the gradients of the various (m,N) plots for different numbers of sub-units, shown in Crowther (1967), (Fig. 4), should be given by $(2U/V)$. Table 1 shows this prediction to be very good.

Table 1. *Agreement between observed and predicted gradients of (m,N) plots for some one-dimensional examples*

Number of sub-units	Predicted gradient $(2U/V)$	Observed gradient
2	0·71	0·70
3	0·58	0·56
4	0·42	0·40

In two- and three-dimensional examples the agreement between predicted and observed gradients is not nearly so good. This is for the following reason. We have divided the original set of functions into a set complete on the sub-units and a set complete on the gaps, both sets vanishing on the sub-unit boundaries. Clearly the original set of functions can give non-zero densities on the sub-unit boundaries. In one dimension, where the boundaries are points, this distinction is not important. In two- and three-dimensions where the boundaries become respectively closed curves and surfaces, the effect is significant and means that the observed gradient of the (m, N) plots for two- and three-dimensional examples is always less than $(2U/V)$.

Most of the material described in this paper is taken from a Ph.D. thesis submitted to Cambridge University. The author is grateful to Dr D. M. Blow for helpful discussions during the preparation of this manuscript. The work was undertaken while the author was holder of a Medical Research Council Scholarship.

References

Cady, H. H. & Larson, A. C. (1965). *Acta Cryst.* **18**, 485.
Crowther, R. A. (1967). *Acta Cryst.* **22**, 758.
Main, P. (1967). *Acta Cryst.* **23**, 50.
Main, P. & Rossmann, M. G. (1966). *Acta Cryst.* **21**, 67.
Main, P. & Woolfson, M. M. (1963). *Acta Cryst.* **16**, 1046.
Patterson, A. L. (1944). *Phys. Rev.* **65**, 195.
Rossmann, M. G. & Blow, D. M. (1963). *Acta Cryst.* **16**, 39.

Reprinted from *Acta Crystallographica*, Vol. A 26, Part 6, November 1970

:ta *Cryst.* (1970). **A26**, 692

pplication of Patterson methods to the solution of molecular crystal structures containing a known rigid group. By H.R. Harrison, *Chemical Crystallography Laboratory, South Parks Road, Oxford, England* and M.A. Joynson, *Laboratory of Molecular Biophysics, Dept. of Zoology, Parks Road, Oxford, England*

(*Received* 17 *March* 1970)

The rotational and translational parameters of a known molecular rigid group in an unknown crystal structure have been determined using reciprocal-space methods based on the Patterson function. Various refinements of the rotation function have been introduced in order to increase the speed and sensitivity of this method.

number of methods have been proposed for interpreting .e Patterson function of crystals containing a molecular fragment of known internal geometry, *e.g.* Hoppe (1957) and Nordman & Nakatsu (1963). The rotation function

(Rossmann & Blow, 1962) has been widely used in the investigation of protein structures and its successful applications include horse haemoglobin (Rossmann & Blow, 1962), insulin (Dodson, Harding, Hodgkin & Rossmann, 1966), seal myoglobin (Tollin, 1969) and aldolase (Eagles, Johnson, Joynson, McMurray & Gutfreund, 1969). In the work described here this function, together with the Q-function of Tollin (1966), has been applied to the solution of a 32-atom molecular structure, *i*-cholesteryl chloroacetate (Fig. 1, X=Cl).

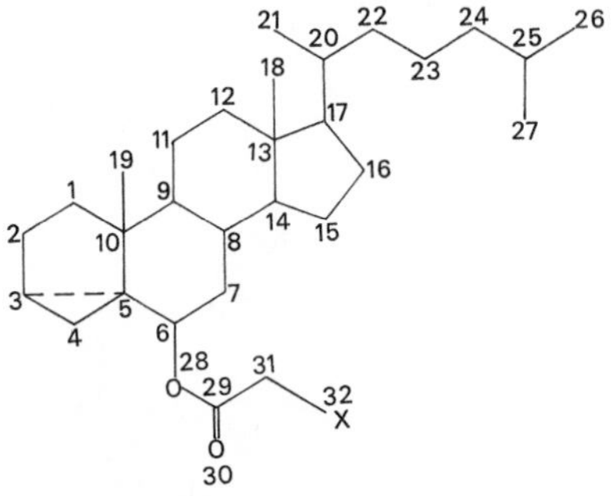

Fig. 1. The 6β-acetyl-*i*-cholesterol skeleton.

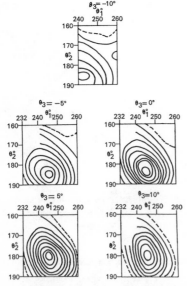

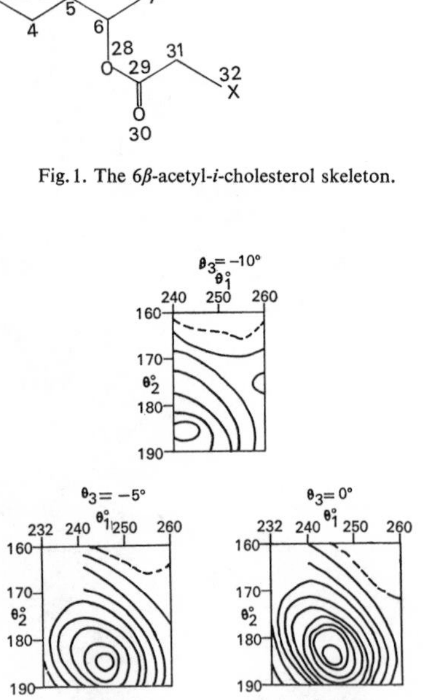

Fig. 2. The rotation function for *i*-cholesteryl chloroacetate in terms of the Cartesian angles θ_1, θ_2, θ_3, in the vicinity of the correct peak.

The rotation function determines the orientation o known structural fragment in an unknown structure measuring the degree of overlap between the arbitrar rotated fragment self-Patterson and the observed Patters function within a volume U centred on the origin. Wh the vector sets of the fragment in both Patterson functic coincide, it is hoped that a rotation function maximum v be produced. In our case, the known fragment is the 21-atc [C(1)–C(20), O(28)] rigid group of *i*-cholesteryl bromoacet (Fig. 1, X=Br), the geometry of which was obtained fr the heavy-atom solution of the full orthorhombic structu (Harrison, Hodgkin, Maslen & Motherwell, 1970). The u known structure, *i*-cholesteryl chloroacetate, space gro $P2_1$, had been solved independently with non-centrosy metric direct methods (Harrison & Motherwell, 1970). obtain well-resolved Patterson peaks and hence good ro tion function resolution, it was found necessary to empl $|E|^2$ (Karle & Karle, 1966) rather than the normal $|F|^2$ both known and unknown. In a previous unsuccessful s lution attempt the use of $|F|^2$ as coefficients gave a ma mum in approximately the desired region, but the peak w quite distorted and packing considerations excluded the c responding rotation. Subsequent structure determinati showed all three rotational parameters to be in error 10–15°.

The expression for the rotation function in recipro space in terms of the $|E|^2$ may now be written as:

$$R=\sum_P |EP|^2\left(\sum_h |E_h|^2 G_{h,h'}\right)$$

where $G_{h,h'}$ is the magnitude of the Fourier transform the volume U. The known Patterson coefficients ($E_h|^2$ we calculated using a hypothetical $P1$ unit cell of consta $a=c=9{\cdot}5$, $b=16$ Å, $\alpha=\beta=\gamma=90°$, with the long dimensi of the fragment made parallel to **b**. Since the rigid gro approximates a rectangular parallelepiped $\sim 4\times 7{\cdot}5\times 4$ this choice of cell dimensions and fragment orientati results in clear separation of the Patterson intramolecu and intermolecular vectors. The volume U reflects t envelope of the rigid group and was therefore taken to a rectangular parallelepiped $9\times 15\times 9$ Å. This volun slightly smaller than that of the hypothetical cell, excluc possible contributions to the rotation function from neig bouring Patterson origins. The unknown Patterson functi was approximated with the largest $350|E_P|^2$, since it w found that they adequately represented the sharpened fu data (1900 reflexion) Patterson without introducing lar series-termination effects.

The program used for the calculation of R was writt in Fortran for the Oxford KDF-9 computer, the inner su mation in (1) being taken over 27 points. Because of t computational time involved, it is desirable to restrict t calculation of R to as small a region of rotation space possible (Tollin, Main & Rossmann, 1966). With the hi resolution available in small molecule work and a know edge of fragment geometry, visual pre-examination of t calculated and observed Pattersons may exclude ma rotations from consideration. In the present work the cha acteristic steroid 1·54, 2·5 and 3 Å multiple vectors we used to predetermine three most likely rotation regio Because they were more easily visualized and directly a plicable to restricted searches, Cartesian, rather than Eu rian, angles were used to describe the rotations of the rig group about the three triclinic axes. Using a 5° grid, three regions of R were calculated and found to conta ngle peaks, indicating the strength of the multiple regular ctors. The correct peak (Fig. 2) was the sharpest of the ree and, after subtraction of mean background, was 25% rger than the other two. The exact rotational parameters ere determined with a 1° grid and these were then used to lculate the relative fractional coordinates of the fragment the unknown ($P2_1$) cell.

The absolute position of the correctly orientated rigid oup was found using the $Q(X_0Z_0)$ function (Tollin, 1966) th the 350 largest $|E_p|^2$ (Fig. 3). This function uses a odified sum function (Buerger, 1959) to express the cor- ation of the cross vectors between symmetry related olecular fragments with the observed Patterson. For a ucture containing a 2_1 axis, a spurious peak will occur if ere is a pair of atoms in the known group whose y coor- nates differ by $\frac{1}{2}$. Seven such false peaks were expected d are marked with an 'X' in Fig. 3. The correct peak, hich fixes the position of the fragment relative to the ystallographic 2_1 axis, is marked with a '+'.

The resulting atomic position were compared with those tained from least-squares refinement and found to be in ror by from 0·03 to 0·23 Å. Calculation of an $|F_{obs}|$ nthesis using the trial coordinates clearly revealed the sitions of C(29), O(30), C(31), Cl(32), C(21), C(22), and 23), virtually completing the structure solution.

We wish to thank the Marshall Aid commemoration mmission, the Medical Research Council and the Royal ciety for financial support.

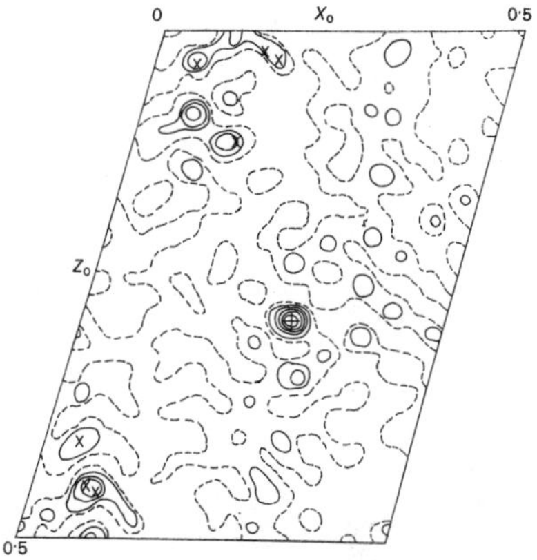

Fig. 3. $Q(X_0Z_0)$ for *i*-cholesteryl chloroacetate. × indicates the false peaks. + indicates the correct peak.

References

UERGER, M. J. (1959). *Vector Space*. New York: John Wiley.

ODSON, E., HARDING, M. M., HODGKIN, D. C. & ROSS- MANN, M. G. (1966). *J. Mol. Biol.* **16**, 227.

AGLES, P. A. M., JOHNSON, L. N., JOYNSON, M. A., MCMURRAY, C. W. & GUTFREUND, H. (1969). *J. Mol. Biol.* **45**, 533.

HARRISON, H. R., HODGKIN, D. C., MASLEN, E. N. & MOTHERWELL, W. D. S. (1970). In preparation.

HARRISON, H. R. & MOTHERWELL, W. D. S. (1970). In preparation.

HOPPE, W. (1957). *Z. Elektrochem.* **61**, 1076.

KARLE, J. & KARLE, I. L. (1966). *Acta Cryst.* **21**, 849.

NORDMAN, C. E. & NAKATSU, K. (1963). *J. Amer. Chem. Soc.* **85**, 353.

ROSSMANN, M. G. & BLOW, D. M. (1962). *Acta Cryst.* **15**, 24.

TOLLIN, P. (1966). *Acta Cryst.* **21**, 613.

TOLLIN, P. (1969). *J. Mol. Biol.* **45**, 481.

TOLLIN, P., MAIN, P. & ROSSMANN, M. G. (1966). *Acta Cryst.* **20**, 407.

Reprinted from *Acta Chrystallographica*, Vol. B 27, Part 7, July 1971

Acta Cryst. (1971). B**27**, 1378

The Determination of the Crystal Structure of *trans*-2,4-Dihydroxy-2,4-Dimethylcyclohexane-*trans*-l-Acetic Acid γ-Lactone, $C_{10}H_{16}O_3$, using Rotation and Translation Functions in Reciprocal Space.

By Roger M. Burnett* and Michael G. Rossmann

Department of Biological Sciences, Purdue University, Lafayette, Indiana 47907, *U.S.A.*

(*Received* 23 *April* 1970)

Crystals of *trans*-2,4-dihydroxy-2,4-dimethylcyclohexane-*trans*-1-acetic acid γ-lactone, $C_{10}H_{16}O_3$, have an orthorhombic unit cell with $a = 10{\cdot}09_6$, $b = 14{\cdot}02_8$, $c = 7{\cdot}03_9$ Å. The space group is $P2_12_12_1$ and there are four molecules per unit cell. The structure was solved using a known grouping of atoms to calculate a search Patterson function. The rotation function of Rossmann & Blow was used to obtain the relative orientation of the known and unknown Patterson functions. The *Q*-functions of Tollin were used to obtain the translational parameters of the known group relative to the 2_1 axes present in the crystal structure. The 988 observed reflections, collected on a Picker four-circle automatic diffractometer were used to refine the structure to give a conventional *R* value of 0·068. The molecular structure consists of a lactone ring fused to a cyclohexane ring distorted by the closeness of the $-CH_3$ and $-OH$ groups attached to C(2) and C(4). The lactone ring is non-planar with one atom, C(1), lying 0·55 Å from the least-squares plane through the other four atoms. The C–O bond lengths in the lactone ring differ by 0·130 Å, the shorter bond being adjacent to the carbonyl group.

Introduction

The rotation function (Rossmann & Blow, 1962) has been used to evaluate the degree of superposition of two sets of Patterson vectors when one set is rotated with respect to the other. A fuller account of this method has been given by Tollin (1970) and by Rossmann (1971). Tollin & Rossmann (1966) suggest the use of this method in the solution of the following problems:

(*A*) Determining the relative orientation of identical groups of atoms within the same crystallographic asymmetric unit.

(*B*) Determining the absolute orientation of a rigid group with known chemical structure in a molecular crystal.

(*C*) Determining the relative orientations of identical groups in different crystal forms, when the chemical structure is unknown.

* Present address: Biophysics Research Division, Institute of Science and Technology, University of Michigan, Ann Arbor, Michigan 48104 U.S.A.

The method has been successful in the investigation of several protein structures; that of hemoglobin (Rossmann & Blow, 1962), insulin (Dodson, Harding, Hodgkin & Rossmann, 1966), and α-chymotrypsin (Blow, Rossmann & Jeffery, 1964) illustrate problems of type (*A*) while the comparison of horse oxyhemoglobin with seal myoglobin (Lattman & Love, 1970) illustrates type (*C*) problems. We report here the solution of a small molecular crystal structure, for part of which the configuration was known, representing an application of the rotation function to a problem of type (*B*).

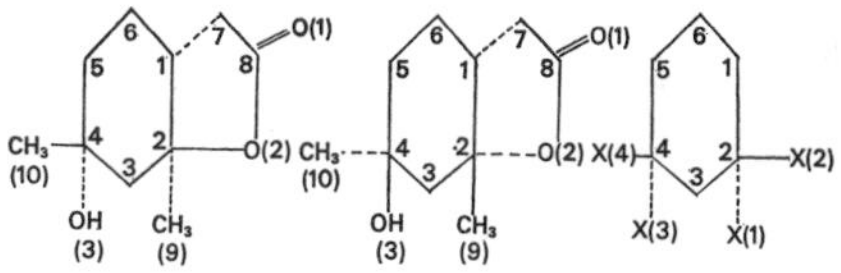

(I) (II) (III)

In a chemical study Wolinsky & Chan (1966) indicated the configuration of *trans*-2,4-dihydroxy-2,4-

Table 1. *Observed and calculated structure factors*

L	FO	FC	A
0 0 L			
2	368	367	0
4	147	141	180
6	185	180	0
8	7	0	180
0 1 L			
1	111	108	270
2	416	426	90
3	97	97	90
4	152	147	90
5	48	50	90
6	68	72	270
7	66	64	270
8	13	20	90
0 2 L			
0	539	561	180
1	80	81	180
2	48	34	180
3	183	187	180
4	71	69	0
5	124	121	180
6	86	82	180
7	0	7	360
8	34	34	0
0 3 L			
1	145	151	90
2	232	235	270
3	413	404	90
4	9	10	270
5	50	50	270
6	0	14	270
7	0	9	90
8	39	38	270
0 4 L			
0	334	344	180
1	74	72	180
2	112	107	0
3	266	252	0
4	177	169	0
5	52	52	0
6	5	19	180
7	0	3	180
0 5 L			
1	152	153	90
2	9	10	270
3	68	62	270
4	0	6	270
5	23	20	90
6	63	62	90
7	114	107	90
0 6 L			
0	682	682	0
1	248	748	180
2	109	108	0
3	11	13	180
4	72	75	180
5	30	31	360
6	89	88	0
7	36	37	180
0 7 L			
1	22	15	270
2	115	110	90
3	126	126	90
4	39	37	270
5	103	103	90
6	0	6	270
7	15	23	270
0 8 L			
0	546	533	180
1	249	238	0
2	161	161	180
3	39	42	0
4	84	81	180
5	83	81	180
6	41	45	180
7	0	5	0
0 9 L			
1	80	80	270
2	0	9	90
3	194	187	90
4	119	118	270
5	64	59	90
6	0	7	90
0 10 L			
0	52	53	180
1	88	83	0
2	7	22	0
3	111	108	0
4	32	36	360
5	0	0	180
6	24	20	180
0 11 L			
1	25	26	270
2	64	67	270
3	138	135	270
4	107	97	90
5	7	24	90
6	15	20	90
0 12 L			
0	42	38	0
1	23	20	180
2	39	37	180
3	94	85	180
4	32	40	180
5	0	2	0
0 13 L			
1	47	47	90
2	0	13	90
3	0	7	90
4	12	16	270
0 14 L			
0	49	48	180
1	0	12	180
2	73	65	180
3	15	27	180
4	5	11	180
0 15 L			
1	24	26	270
2	10	20	270
3	0	4	90
0 16 L			
0	0	14	180
1	0	2	180
1 0 L			
1	299	301	270
2	165	168	180
3	34	29	90
4	197	189	180
5	195	191	90
6	187	187	180
7	32	31	90
8	45	49	180
1 1 L			
0	283	283	80
1	754	783	275
2	94	97	128
3	392	388	348
4	96	102	68
5	173	171	73
6	30	35	49
7	8	14	253
8	3	15	166
1 2 L			
0	685	709	90
1	422	429	156
2	436	432	3
3	135	134	187
4	63	53	281
5	127	128	325
6	148	150	22
7	4	16	251
8	31	32	359
1 3 L			
0	360	360	270
1	354	359	323
2	333	332	233
3	269	260	213
4	50	43	147
5	58	51	258
6	32	34	316
7	54	54	22
8	27	32	255
1 4 L			
0	256	261	90
1	150	149	92
2	158	158	92
3	57	53	39
4	118	115	42
5	67	71	306
6	0	12	302
7	39	45	167
1 5 L			
0	57	60	90
1	96	95	143
2	164	163	47
3	129	121	42
4	87	92	161
5	74	79	334
6	64	64	79
7	0	13	70
1 6 L			
0	60	60	90
1	267	253	240
2	157	161	95
3	76	75	211
4	105	105	108
5	90	93	87
6	136	138	181
7	25	31	66
1 7 L			
0	257	255	270
1	258	249	236
2	104	96	68
3	69	71	327
4	25	28	70
5	46	52	76
6	40	42	243
7	42	44	187
1 8 L			
0	179	181	90
1	82	79	227
2	113	114	15
3	88	87	190
4	46	52	5
5	10	23	314
6	84	81	45
7	24	26	250
1 9 L			
0	68	69	270
1	58	51	124
2	137	136	222
3	150	150	205
4	56	55	307
5	58	57	207
6	0	6	244
1 10 L			
0	14	8	270
1	79	78	114
2	160	157	171
3	151	156	24
4	0	14	228
5	50	50	205
6	5	18	201
1 11 L			
0	111	112	90
1	43	42	77
2	80	81	71
3	49	51	149
4	54	48	269
5	34	34	118
6	9	16	283
1 12 L			
0	54	51	270
1	0	13	137
2	5	12	133
3	31	31	178
4	36	42	172
5	4	14	360
1 13 L			
0	24	34	90
1	39	41	211
2	33	37	271
3	45	49	280
4	15	26	237
1 14 L			
0	3	10	90
1	0	9	227
2	7	18	314
3	0	14	233
4	18	20	270
1 15 L			
0	0	13	270
1	0	16	220
2	36	37	229
3	2	8	185
1 16 L			
0	0	2	270
1	0	11	73
2 0 L			
0	821	837	180
1	665	676	90
2	61	55	0
3	331	329	90
4	20	18	0
5	14	15	90
6	30	32	180
7	33	36	90
8	40	40	0
2 1 L			
0	298	293	0
1	410	412	159
2	134	131	88
3	248	240	121
4	149	152	237
5	96	99	278
6	28	30	28
7	2	15	97
8	0	7	28
2 2 L			
0	455	458	0
1	220	219	13
2	327	326	40
3	104	99	280
4	192	186	309
5	70	71	237
6	115	111	321
7	49	47	26
8	15	19	166
2 3 L			
0	357	368	180
1	156	159	83
2	343	341	259
3	106	99	314
4	141	137	120
5	70	69	85
6	75	73	97
7	35	38	2
2 4 L			
0	117	121	180
1	100	99	206
2	141	138	321
3	212	204	157
4	64	63	22
5	38	40	42
6	98	104	96
7	20	26	207
2 5 L			
0	284	285	180
1	276	276	70
2	45	40	67
3	49	43	58
4	31	29	346
5	96	99	109
6	35	41	231
7	33	33	211
2 6 L			
0	214	200	180
1	91	86	94
2	137	132	167
3	69	71	114
4	47	44	189
5	100	97	85
6	13	21	184
7	0	15	17
2 7 L			
0	94	87	0
1	144	146	95
2	101	94	107
3	71	72	117
4	105	106	215
5	52	54	301
6	31	37	210
7	26	31	114
2 8 L			
0	228	220	0
1	95	93	251
2	139	135	102
3	182	182	269
4	26	22	66
5	30	31	251
6	80	76	295
7	0	1	267
2 9 L			
0	81	78	0
1	56	56	359
2	132	135	248
3	10	25	279
4	142	144	127
5	0	12	23
6	9	18	139
2 10 L			
0	135	136	180
1	14	16	208
2	51	52	151
3	62	62	149
4	35	42	144
5	0	9	216
6	50	49	177
2 11 L			
0	68	67	0
1	36	35	97
2	67	73	82
3	51	56	93
4	52	55	307
5	22	25	191
2 12 L			
0	12	14	180
1	57	60	204
2	57	53	251
2 12 L			
3	21	26	24
4	30	31	162
5	15	21	349
2 13 L			
0	43	41	180
1	21	28	226
2	30	34	126
3	48	48	276
4	20	22	333
2 14 L			
0	25	21	0
1	11	29	306
2	0	12	320
3	24	27	288
4	0	18	236
2 15 L			
0	0	6	0
1	17	23	269
2	8	14	296
2 16 L			
0	2	13	180
1	14	16	326
3 0 L			
1	292	287	270
2	42	45	180
3	115	120	270
4	95	95	180
5	108	107	270
6	111	112	0
7	83	83	270
3 1 L			
0	294	291	90
1	137	149	51
2	285	277	127
3	175	169	254
4	125	119	9
5	62	68	285
6	43	43	211
7	51	50	88
3 2 L			
0	346	350	270
1	333	326	171
2	183	184	206
3	249	241	50
4	64	64	50
5	82	83	79
6	84	84	146
7	47	47	126
3 3 L			
0	129	128	90
1	355	353	343
2	158	152	29
3	117	110	353
4	86	87	355
5	111	115	30
6	77	78	115
7	0	8	310
3 4 L			
0	6	8	90
1	181	179	99
2	247	246	75
3	207	199	175
4	88	88	89
5	73	71	202
6	0	11	182
7	12	23	52
3 5 L			
0	28	20	270
1	58	56	109
2	66	64	7
3	83	75	158
4	50	44	151
5	88	90	186
6	58	59	202
7	0	15	241
3 6 L			
0	66	67	270
1	31	31	166
2	60	61	75
3	130	128	209
4	25	24	112
5	47	51	214
6	61	60	29
7	50	55	266
3 7 L			
0	77	73	270
1	114	113	121
2	104	99	224
3	28	33	329
4	39	39	22
5	72	76	209
6	0	11	62
7	20	25	24
3 8 L			
0	3	5	90
1	115	117	133
2	26	23	306
3	90	92	39
4	16	18	38
5	57	63	134
6	53	55	186
3 9 L			
0	77	78	270
1	38	37	300
2	56	59	343
3	61	61	76
4	28	30	238
5	55	52	54
6	14	19	312
3 10 L			
0	98	93	90
1	67	67	0
2	7	23	349
3	141	145	220
4	31	35	127
5	44	46	258
6	24	24	30
3 11 L			
0	26	29	90
1	115	122	172
2	65	60	293
3	22	29	196
4	70	69	212
5	27	30	257
3 12 L			
0	33	42	270
1	67	69	262
2	57	61	202
3	32	37	306
4	6	14	58
5	16	25	88
3 13 L			
0	54	55	270
1	0	12	190
2	4	16	349
3	0	12	250
4	18	23	0
3 14 L			
0	7	21	270
1	0	13	221
2	45	43	325
3	39	38	33
3 15 L			
0	21	25	270
1	8	20	328
2	0	1	157
4 0 L			
0	172	168	0
1	252	245	270
2	225	214	180
3	214	203	270
4	24	18	360
5	107	106	90
6	120	122	0
7	0	8	90
4 1 L			
0	6	4	0
1	278	268	333
2	98	90	242
3	79	79	359
4	67	67	222
5	98	92	93
6	34	36	131
7	0	15	258
4 2 L			
0	200	195	180
1	346	339	56
2	145	139	0
3	291	280	76
4	115	115	61
5	81	80	89
6	61	63	145
7	6	8	280
4 3 L			
0	34	27	360
1	107	103	220
2	186	173	150
3	168	166	140
4	66	76	87
5	23	21	143
6	13	15	320
7	6	14	150
4 4 L			
0	65	56	0
1	50	50	108
2	148	143	291
3	39	41	72
4	61	59	254
5	10	29	151
6	65	68	250
7	9	25	145
4 5 L			
0	291	280	180
1	121	119	86
2	195	195	169
3	93	86	319
4	0	6	111
5	10	16	41
6	32	32	214
7	18	23	102
4 6 L			
0	162	155	0
1	187	182	256
2	103	99	205
3	93	92	276
4	74	75	146
5	41	42	289
6	24	31	6
7	13	17	157
4 7 L			
0	52	48	180
1	17	10	316
2	51	52	195
3	54	54	19
4	57	50	152
5	31	37	128
6	0	16	199
4 8 L			
0	67	61	180
1	74	74	59
2	26	31	352
3	119	124	110
4	30	30	286
5	30	31	227
6	51	49	133
4 9 L			
0	69	67	180
1	114	112	163
2	39	40	95
3	69	72	133
4	34	38	330
5	57	57	268
6	11	14	11
4 10 L			
0	38	38	180
1	106	106	227
2	61	54	240
3	89	85	262
4	32	33	289
5	31	38	282
4 11 L			
0	136	135	180
1	50	50	41
2	86	80	266
3	54	56	283
4	0	3	192
5	0	5	30
4 12 L			
0	29	29	180
1	27	25	336
2	31	39	124
3	50	45	292
4	0	9	239
4 13 L			
0	81	79	0
1	52	52	272
2	44	46	5
3	31	32	118
4	7	21	236
4 14 L			
0	0	3	180
1	28	31	58
2	0	12	8
3	7	15	351
4 15 L			
0	0	3	360
1	0	11	204
5 0 L			
1	102	100	270
2	25	23	180
3	83	77	90
4	70	136	0
5	148	150	90
6	0	5	0
7	24	26	90
5 1 L			
0	91	95	90
1	121	116	235
2	88	91	92
3	153	148	24
4	45	41	146
5	59	61	83
6	52	56	30
7	33	34	265
5 2 L			
0	391	384	90
1	72	65	26
2	20	13	305
3	171	168	253
4	83	84	219
5	94	97	228
6	30	38	118
7	0	14	110
5 3 L			
0	121	124	90
1	174	166	122
2	138	131	119
3	146	141	168
4	104	110	92
5	16	27	265
6	2	17	127
7	15	23	14
5 4 L			
0	213	202	270
1	130	126	177
2	116	112	242
3	67	64	178
4	52	55	97
5	57	60	173
6	0	8	206
7	0	3	57
5 5 L			
0	79	80	90
1	100	95	35
2	88	88	339
3	53	54	329
4	48	59	234
5	34	37	282
6	7	12	326
7	0	10	192
5 6 L			
0	8	14	90
1	97	97	195
2	42	42	91
3	114	110	99
4	0	6	51
5	42	52	120
6	51	53	303
5 7 L			
0	20	22	90
1	89	87	284
2	74	70	208
3	13	4	294
4	58	63	220
5	30	41	80
6	22	26	324
5 8 L			
0	212	209	90
1	46	49	262
2	7	4	239
3	82	86	220
4	97	96	232
5	39	44	284
6	33	30	69
5 9 L			
0	0	6	90
1	39	42	148
2	120	122	204
3	28	37	184
4	15	29	43
5	22	28	252
5 10 L			
0	115	111	270
1	30	33	179
2	11	16	44
3	27	35	86
4	37	41	359
5	17	21	118
5 11 L			
0	121	117	270
1	51	56	341
2	45	46	308
3	0	5	119
4	12	21	325
5 12 L			
0	0	3	270
1	40	43	49
2	46	44	17
3	0	14	148
4	0	7	320
5 13 L			
0	0	12	270
1	7	20	217
2	0	11	228
3	22	26	31
5 14 L			
0	0	16	90
1	25	29	347
2	16	21	190
6 0 L			
0	212	205	0
1	127	126	90
2	66	63	360
3	233	226	90
4	10	20	0
5	25	27	90
6	0	9	360
7	6	11	90
6 1 L			
0	133	125	0
1	140	139	241
2	105	102	109
3	147	145	89
4	13	20	150
5	18	25	292
6	11	21	326
7	21	22	217
6 2 L			
0	4	10	180
1	114	108	13
2	180	171	141
3	85	83	310
4	83	78	212
5	111	109	168
6	32	37	263
7	43	38	145
6 3 L			
0	93	87	180
1	72	72	332
2	100	91	258
3	29	29	63
4	84	87	154
5	27	32	189
6	59	54	204
6 4 L			
0	120	111	180
1	117	109	147
2	29	28	41
3	26	23	75
4	53	57	76
5	81	79	340
6	35	40	141
6 5 L			
0	14	17	180
1	46	43	204
2	20	21	123
3	116	114	236
4	71	72	189
5	23	27	278
6	33	38	124
6 6 L			
0	46	46	0
1	74	75	127
2	77	80	12
3	20	25	96
4	36	38	305
5	0	8	254
6	15	18	328
6 7 L			
0	48	43	180
1	76	80	219
2	114	114	119
3	50	55	135
4	52	51	266
5	29	28	354
6	0	3	6
6 8 L			
0	7	9	0
1	104	96	322
2	56	54	200
3	114	112	290
4	59	62	188
5	43	48	184
6 9 L			
0	70	68	180
1	99	101	357
2	64	60	234
3	29	33	12
4	0	12	179
5	35	37	129
6 10 L			
0	30	35	180
1	62	60	314
2	50	51	352
3	31	29	120
4	34	38	351
6 11 L			
0	75	72	0
1	12	21	223
2	1	18	306
3	33	40	298
4	0	1	239
6 12 L			
0	0	5	0
1	45	48	243
2	0	4	308
3	0	14	212
6 13 L			
0	0	4	180
1	24	27	88
2	0	7	242
6 14 L			
0	25	23	0
7 0 L			
1	17	9	90
2	133	129	0
3	0	12	90
4	133	129	180
5	6	16	90
6	66	66	180
7 1 L			
0	22	19	270
1	20	22	181
2	223	225	169
3	23	22	156
4	133	130	67
5	47	51	169
6	23	27	69
7 2 L			
0	100	100	90
1	106	101	188
2	30	32	317
3	50	46	105
4	95	98	309
5	17	25	148
6	26	28	348
7 3 L			
0	62	55	90
1	83	79	254
2	42	40	251
3	44	48	178
4	78	76	256
5	0	16	7
6	19	22	3
7 4 L			
0	71	72	270
1	73	72	59
2	66	60	199
3	40	47	184
4	0	9	10
5	53	53	289
6	11	17	315
7 5 L			
0	14	13	90
1	0	4	16
2	122	125	24
3	31	35	144
4	42	45	135
5	0	11	247
6	33	32	162
7 6 L			
0	76	72	270
1	73	73	224
2	23	24	279
3	68	69	215
4	38	44	171
5	12	29	81
7 7 L			
0	72	71	270
1	42	50	180
2	59	62	153
3	65	66	335
4	22	29	17
5	0	15	268
7 8 L			
0	52	52	270
1	100	97	204
2	5	14	267
3	28	33	351
4	45	50	351
5	21	23	128
7 9 L			
0	45	47	270
1	55	55	296
2	31	37	316
3	44	51	258
4	56	59	285
7 10 L			
0	20	24	90
1	55	54	96
2	27	37	229
3	16	23	27
4	0	9	199
7 11 L			
0	31	33	90
1	47	50	36
2	19	22	335
3	0	2	325
7 12 L			
0	14	22	270
1	0	12	294
2	13	23	63
7 13 L			
0	3	21	270
1	6	18	102
8 0 L			
0	95	94	180
1	187	186	90
2	142	142	180
3	124	123	270
4	99	93	180
5	0	0	90
6	6	9	180
8 1 L			
0	64	59	180
1	51	53	183
2	24	26	126
3	37	38	188
4	41	38	211
5	0	6	13
6	0	4	9
8 2 L			
0	21	21	180
1	65	65	308
2	64	62	358
3	95	95	106
4	50	53	288
5	0	4	314
8 3 L			
0	33	33	0
1	46	50	350
2	37	38	272
3	71	71	323
4	28	30	152
5	34	36	252
8 4 L			
0	62	63	180
1	67	65	229
2	31	32	110
3	81	80	145
4	16	25	26
5	14	27	111
8 5 L			
0	74	71	180
1	35	36	85
2	54	55	284
3	55	56	254
4	29	29	342
5	9	20	212
8 6 L			
0	26	26	180
1	76	80	94
2	99	101	217
3	72	72	269
4	0	11	141
5	10	20	338
8 7 L			
0	42	42	180
1	40	40	261
2	21	26	223
3	25	30	221
4	6	19	196
8 8 L			
0	69	73	0
1	37	40	301
2	60	58	24
3	0	11	70
4	44	48	317
8 9 L			
0	82	74	0
1	50	46	250
2	23	23	133
3	17	22	19
4	28	31	141
8 10 L			
0	7	19	0
1	34	36	213
2	0	14	95
3	0	6	30
8 11 L			
0	20	28	180
1	45	42	47
2	0	11	27
8 12 L			
0	23	26	0
9 0 L			
1	53	57	270
2	26	38	0
3	21	22	90
4	7	22	0
5	6	19	270
9 1 L			
0	13	25	270
1	51	51	222
2	77	77	17
3	35	40	194
4	0	20	194
5	13	17	168
9 2 L			
0	23	22	270
1	42	45	99
2	76	78	211
3	43	42	22
4	44	43	208
5	0	2	110
9 3 L			
0	107	108	90
1	28	37	1
2	36	39	166
3	26	29	220
4	32	34	311
5	0	14	107
9 4 L			
0	15	26	270
1	40	43	195
2	41	40	148
3	9	20	215
4	6	19	311
9 5 L			
0	32	36	270
1	63	66	148
2	48	47	208
3	7	18	325
4	0	8	153
9 6 L			
0	55	51	270
1	35	39	344
2	67	65	347
3	20	28	221
4	22	24	309
9 7 L			
0	50	46	270
1	0	11	76
2	51	53	348
3	25	27	87
9 8 L			
0	0	5	90
1	37	36	61
2	46	48	273
3	0	4	17
9 9 L			
0	43	48	90
1	34	36	357
2	0	4	304
9 10 L			
0	34	34	270
1	4	16	235
10 0 L			
0	27	33	0
1	37	41	270
2	0	3	360
3	0	12	270
4	0	12	180
10 1 L			
0	29	33	0
1	3	21	218
2	25	34	170
3	19	22	204
4	15	20	353
10 2 L			
0	40	45	180
1	36	47	112
2	37	37	181
3	12	20	231
4	0	16	183
10 3 L			
0	20	25	180
1	45	46	343
2	0	3	251
3	0	5	289
4	15	22	26
10 4 L			
0	0	1	180
1	22	30	315
2	54	57	268
3	33	37	42
10 5 L			
0	0	11	180
1	34	39	268
2	15	22	120
3	4	21	317
10 6 L			
0	27	31	0
1	44	46	269
2	5	20	14
3	0	6	352
10 7 L			
0	22	22	0
1	30	35	214
2	0	2	272
10 8 L			
0	22	27	180
1	19	26	94
11 0 L			
1	0	2	90
2	0	0	180
11 1 L			
0	0	7	270
1	27	30	194
2	12	18	197
11 2 L			
0	11	17	270
1	9	16	253
2	0	8	225
11 3 L			
0	0	4	270
1	17	20	193
2	19	24	2
11 4 L			
0	0	5	270
1	11	20	98
2	29	33	270
11 5 L			
0	0	12	270
1	2	18	351

dimethylcyclohexane-*trans*-1-acetic acid γ-lactone (I) to be preferred to that of *trans*-2,4-dihydroxy-2,4-dimethylcyclohexane-*cis*-1-acetic acid γ-lactone (II). These two possible structures both have cyclohexane rings and two groups attached at both the C(2) and C(4) positions. The common atoms could be approximately represented by (III) which has mirror symmetry. The orientation of the vector set derived from this arrangement of atoms was determined with the rotation function. Subsequently, the position of the known fragment relative to the crystallographic symmetry elements was found using the *Q*-functions (Tollin, 1966). Our results have verified the assignment of Wolinsky & Chan.

Experimental

Crystal data

Name:	*trans*-2,4-Dihydroxy-2,4-dimethylcyclohexane-*trans*-1-acetic acid γ-lactone.
Molecular formula:	$C_{10}H_{16}O_3$
Molecular weight:	184·2
Melting point:	145·5 ± 0·5 °C
Growth solvent:	Methylene chloride–diethyl ether
Crystal shape:	Hexagonal prisms
System:	Orthorhombic
Space group:	$P2_12_12_1$
Systematic absences:	$h00$ when h is odd; $0k0$ when k is odd; $00l$ when l is odd
Cell dimensions:	$a = 10{\cdot}09_6$, $b = 14{\cdot}02_8$, $c = 7{\cdot}03_9$ Å; $\alpha = \beta = \gamma = 90°$
Volume of unit cell:	996·9 Å^3
Density, measured:	$1{\cdot}2_5$ g.cm^{-3} (Flotation in ammonium sulphate solution)
Density, calculated:	1·23 g.cm^{-3}

Number of molecules per unit cell: 4

Linear absorption coefficient, calculated: 7·4 cm^{-1}

F_{000}: 400.

Preliminary investigations of Laue symmetry and systematic absences were made with a Buerger precession camera. A Picker four-circle diffractometer was used to collect all available reflections in the *hkl* and $\bar{h}kl$ octants from a single crystal at room temperature. The intensities were measured in blocks of 25 pairs of symmetry-related reflections. Two intense reference reflections (002 and 200) were measured after each block. A decay of 5·5% was observed in both intensities at the end of the 48 hours of exposure required for the total data collection. Errors were estimated entirely on the basis of counting statistics, and reflections with negative corrected intensities were assigned a value of zero. Other details of diffractometer technique were:

Radiation:	Cu *Kα*
Crystal size:	0·4 mm long × 0·1 mm thick
Mosaicity:	0·1°
Crystal–counter distance:	200 mm
Crystal–source distance:	146 mm
Counter aperture:	2·5 mm high × 2·3 mm wide

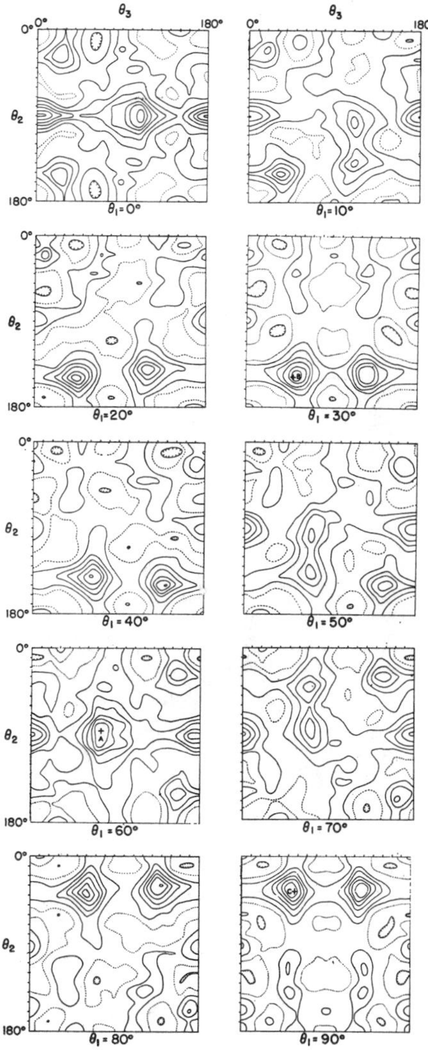

Fig. 1. The rotation function of the model structure against the unknown structure. The corresponding Pattersons were in space group *P2/m* and *Pmmm*, respectively, producing the Eulerian space group *Pbab*.

Take-off angle:	4°
Attenuators:	not necessary owing to the small size of the crystal
Scan type:	moving-crystal, moving-counter (2θ scan)
Scan limits:	$2\theta° - (0{\cdot}55 + 0{\cdot}4 \tan \theta)°$ to $2\theta° + 0{\cdot}55(1 + \tan \theta)°$
Scan rates:	30 sec per degree
Background:	10 sec at each end of the range of 2θ

An allowance was made for decay of the crystal due to X-ray damage by multiplying each reflection by a factor found from the normalized plot of the reference reflection intensities. The pairs of reflections were corrected for Lorentz and polarization effects but no correction was made for absorption. The pairs were then averaged to give a set of 988 independent reflections (Table 1).

A Wilson (1942) plot yielded an initial overall B value of 5·0 Å^2, and allowed the data to be placed on an approximately absolute scale. For the purposes of the rotation and Q-functions, the data were sharpened to be representative of those obtained from point atoms, with an effective B value of 4·0 Å^2 to reduce series termination effects.

Table 2. *Atomic positional coordinates and temperature parameters*

The estimated standard deviations in parentheses refer to the last decimal positions of the corresponding values. The temperature factor expression used was $\exp[-(h^2\beta_{11}+k^2\beta_{22}+l^2\beta_{33}+2hk\beta_{12}+2hl\beta_{13}+2kl\beta_{23})]$. The β_{ij} in the Table have been multiplied by 10^4.

	x	y	z	β_{11}	β_{22}	β_{33}	β_{12}	β_{13}	β_{23}
C(1)	0·2211 (4)	0·1701 (3)	0·3591 (5)	124 (5)	56 (2)	154 (7)	−3 (3)	3 (6)	12 (4)
C(2)	0·2762 (4)	0·2116 (3)	0·1750 (5)	97 (4)	56 (2)	147 (7)	3 (3)	−8 (5)	0 (4)
C(3)	0·2699 (4)	0·3193 (3)	0·1870 (5)	112 (5)	56 (2)	182 (8)	2 (3)	−13 (6)	10 (4)
C(4)	0·3426 (4)	0·3572 (3)	0·3654 (6)	108 (5)	60 (2)	194 (9)	3 (3)	0 (6)	−11 (4)
C(5)	0·3088 (5)	0·3018 (3)	0·5466 (6)	144 (6)	78 (3)	164 (8)	−9 (4)	9 (7)	−8 (4)
C(6)	0·3127 (5)	0·1925 (3)	0·5252 (5)	176 (6)	69 (3)	147 (8)	−18 (4)	−16 (7)	15 (4)
C(7)	0·1799 (4)	0·0702 (3)	0·2976 (6)	146 (5)	56 (2)	224 (10)	−4 (3)	−16 (7)	18 (4)
C(8)	0·1287 (4)	0·0918 (3)	0·1000 (6)	106 (5)	56 (2)	241 (10)	11 (3)	4 (6)	−7 (5)
C(9)	0·4094 (4)	0·1731 (3)	0·1103 (6)	97 (4)	80 (3)	252 (10)	7 (3)	25 (6)	−27 (5)
C(10)	0·3105 (5)	0·4634 (3)	0·3910 (7)	162 (6)	61 (2)	342 (13)	5 (3)	−15 (9)	−32 (5)
O(1)	0·0513 (3)	0·0463 (2)	0·0039 (4)	131 (3)	68 (2)	294 (8)	−7 (2)	−41 (5)	−17 (4)
O(2)	0·1781 (3)	0·1754 (2)	0·0360 (3)	113 (3)	62 (2)	179 (6)	−4 (2)	−33 (4)	2 (3)
O(3)	0·4839 (2)	0·3470 (2)	0·3431 (4)	98 (3)	80 (2)	208 (6)	−4 (2)	−12 (4)	0 (3)
				B					
H(1)	0·129 (3)	0 203 (2)	0 391 (5)	2 2 (8)					
H(2)	0 103 (4)	0 036 (3)	0·383 (6)	4·5 (10)					
H(3)	0·249 (4)	0·023 (2)	0·289 (5)	2·3 (8)					
H(4)	0·414 (3)	0·097 (2)	0·105 (5)	3·1 (9)					
H(5)	0·436 (4)	0·188 (3)	0·998 (6)	3·6 (9)					
H(6)	0·484 (4)	0·199 (2)	0·188 (5)	3·3 (9)					
H(7)	0·308 (3)	0·347 (2)	0·075 (5)	2·7 (8)					
H(8)	0·171 (3)	0·343 (2)	0·193 (5)	2·5 (8)					
H(9)	0·502 (5)	0·382 (3)	0·257 (7)	5·4 (12)					
H(10)	0·344 (4)	0·508 (3)	0·269 (6)	6·2 (12)					
H(11)	0·359 (4)	0·483 (3)	0·509 (6)	3·9 (10)					
H(12)	0·207 (4)	0·471 (3)	0·395 (6)	5·3 (12)					
H(13)	0·379 (4)	0·324 (3)	0·647 (6)	4·1 (10)					
H(14)	0·210 (4)	0·321 (3)	0·598 (5)	3·3 (9)					
H(15)	0·271 (3)	0·163 (2)	0·640 (5)	3·4 (9)					
H(16)	0·416 (4)	0·166 (3)	0·503 (6)	3·8 (10)					

Table 3. *Distances in* Å *between the model atoms and their final refined positions*

	Results from rotation function		Results from rigid body refinement
	10° search	0·5° search	
	(50°, 88°, 72°)	(61·0°, 85·0°, 74·5°)	(57·70°, 78·59°, 77·68°)
C(1)	0·12	0·08	0·14
C(2)	0·04	0·07	0·06
C(3)	0·05	0·07	0·19
C(4)	0·08	0·08	0·03
C(5)	0·37	0·31	0·11
C(6)	0·36	0·27	0·07
X(1)–C(9)	0·43	0·39	0·29
X(2)–O(2)	0·32	0·26	0·15
X(3)–O(3)	0·33	0·26	0·24
X(4)–C(10)	0·40	0·33	0·16
Average distance	0·25 Å	0·21 Å	0·14 Å

Structure determination

e search model (III), used in this determination, nsisted of tetrahedral carbon atoms separated by nd lengths of 1·54 Å in the cyclohexane ring and by mean, 1·47 Å, of a C–O and C–C bond elsewhere. is molecule was placed in a monoclinic unit cell of ace group *Pm* and cell dimensions $a=8{\cdot}0$, $b=12{\cdot}0$, 6·0 Å, $\alpha=\beta=\gamma=90°$. The local mirror plane, ough atoms (6) and (3) (III), was made coincident th the mirror plane of the chosen space group, and pseudo molecular $\bar{3}$ axis was oriented parallel to **c**. e utilization in the model crystal structure of the rch model's symmetry avoided the generation of nlinear symmetry in the rotation function. Additi-nally, the unit cell was chosen to be of sufficient size prevent the overlap of intramolecular vectors from jacent origins (Tollin & Rossmann, 1966). Structure tors were calculated for this model at all reciprocal tice points within the copper sphere and were sharp-ed in the same manner as the observed data.

In the large terms version of the rotation function ogram (Tollin & Rossmann, 1966), the largest ucture factors are used to define one of the vector s. Since a partial data set of given size will define the l structure more accurately than the model structure ie to the absence of electron density in a large pro-rtion of the model cell), the one hundred largest served reflections were chosen to define the vector to be rotated.

The rotation function, *R*,

$$= \sum_p |F_p|^2 \sum_h |F_h|^2 G_{h,h'} \quad \text{(Rossmann \& Blow, 1962)}$$

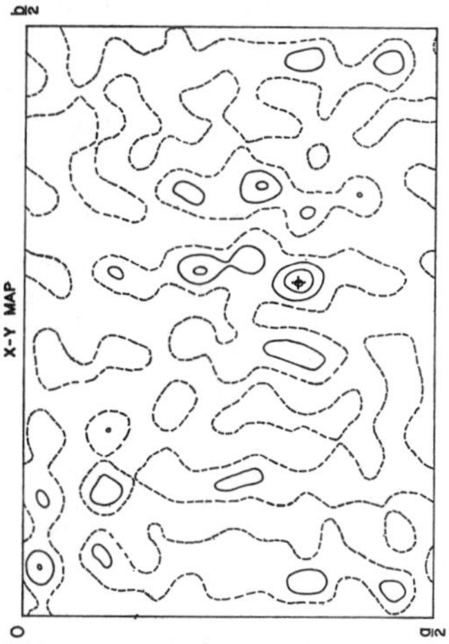

. 2. *Q*-functions calculated parallel to the three mutually erpendicular 2_1 axes in the unknown structure, computed vith sharpened $|F|$ values.

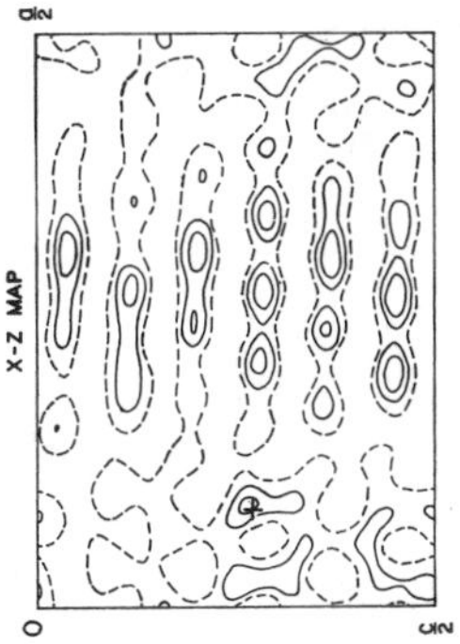

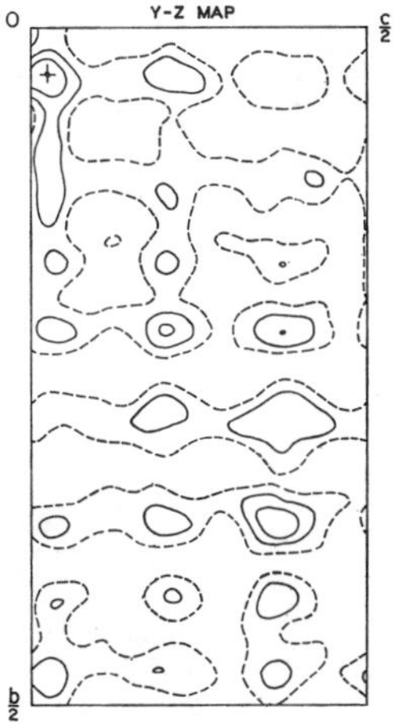

Fig. 2 (*cont.*)

is the result of a double summation. The summation over **h** is around the non-integral lattice points **h′** obtained by rotating the lattice points **p** through a set of known angles. The function $G_{h,h'}$ is determined by the distance, **H**, between the points **h** and **h′** and the radius of integration, *r*, within which the two Patterson functions are to be compared. Since for a sphere

$$G_{h,h'} = \frac{3(\sin 2\pi Hr - 2\pi Hr \cos 2\pi Hr)}{(2\pi Hr)^3},$$

its value can be considered negligible when $|Hr| > 1{\cdot}0$ (Tollin & Rossmann, 1966). Therefore if we express **H** as n/d, where *n* is an integer and **d** is the cell dimension in a particular direction, *n* need be no greater than $\pm(d/r-1)$ in that direction. In this investigation a sphere of radius of 5·5 Å was used, giving values of $|n| \leq 1$ and a range of integration of $-1 \leq n \leq +1$ along each axis.

The superposition of the *Pmmm* Patterson of the unknown structure on the $P2/m$ symmetry of the model Patterson gives a rotation function of space group *Pbab* (Tollin, Main & Rossmann, 1966) with angles defined

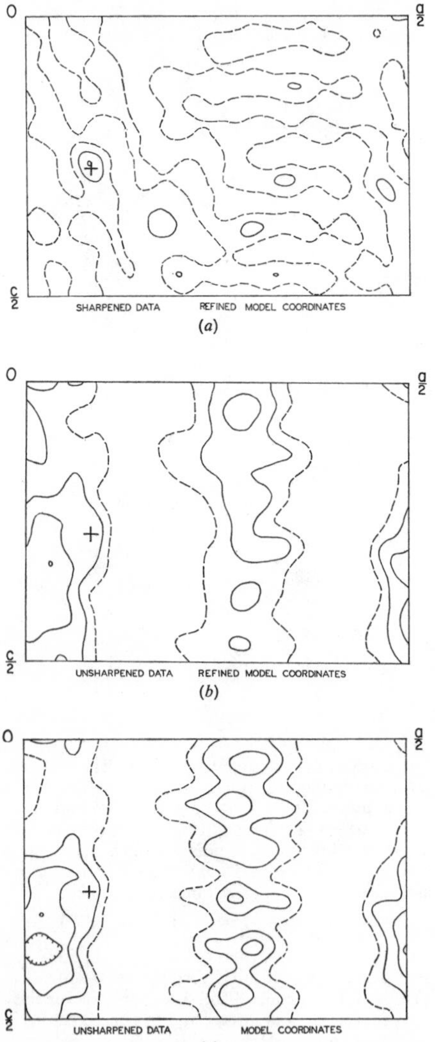

Fig. 3. The $(x-z)$ Q-function calculated using final refined and unsharpened coordinates for the model atoms with sharpened data (*a*, *b*), and the original model coordinates with unsharpened data (*c*).

according to the convention of Rossmann & Bl (1962). An asymmetric unit of this space group, fined by the limits $(0 \leq \theta_1 \leq \pi/2,\ 0 \leq \theta_2 < \pi,\ 0 \leq \theta_3 <$ was explored at 10° intervals of θ_1, θ_2, θ_3.

The rotation function is shown in Fig. 1. The pseu $\bar{3}m$ symmetry of the cyclohexane ring in the kno structure generates a corresponding higher pseu symmetry within the Eulerian space group. The thr fold axis parallel to **c** gives rise to the symmetry ope tion $(\theta_1, \theta_2, \theta_3) \rightarrow (-2\pi/3+\theta_1, \theta_2, \theta_3)$ which represe a complete repetition of the *Pbab* symmetry ev 120° along θ_1. Thus the twofold axes at levels $\theta_1 = 0$ $\theta_1 = \pi/2$ will occur additionally at $\theta_1 = \pm\pi/3$ $\theta_1 = \pm\pi/6$ respectively, giving rise to the pseudo t fold axes

$$(\theta_1\theta_2\theta_3) \rightarrow \frac{\pi}{3} - \theta_1, \qquad \theta_2, \pi - \theta_3$$

and

$$(\theta_1\theta_2\theta_3) \rightarrow \frac{2\pi}{3} - \theta_1, \pi - \theta_2, \qquad \theta_3$$

within the true asymmetric unit. The pseudo asym tric unit is now contained within the limits $0 \leq \theta_1 \leq$ $0 \leq \theta_2 < \pi$, $0 \leq \theta_3 < \pi$. These pseudo-symmetry ope tions are easily visible in Fig. 1, which shows the asymmetric unit and illustrates the importance placing even a pseudo-symmetry operation along, normal to, a crystallographic axis. If this had not b done fortuitously in the present case, interpretat would have been more difficult. The rotation funct was explored at 0·5° intervals around the th pseudo-symmetry related, major peaks (*A*, *B*, *C* Fig. 1). Each represented an orientation closely rela to that given by the other two (*i.e.* the molecular fra work was in a different orientation but the vector had much in common with that from the other orie tions of the model). The peak *A* (61·0°, 85·0°, 74 giving the largest value was used to compute ato coordinates relative to an arbitrary origin.

The position of a known group of atoms relative symmetry operation may be determined with the functions (Tollin, 1966), which are multiple th dimensional sum functions of the Patterson funct on each of the atomic positions calculated from rela coordinates and arbitrary origin displacements. A function was calculated for each of the three mutu perpendicular 2_1 axes and the resulting set of th maps (Fig. 2) should have given consistent tran tional parameters, noting the shift of origin by $\frac{1}{4}$ of unit cell from one map to the next. The x–y m which explored the position of the model struct relative to the 2_1 axis parallel to z, gave the clea results, with the y coordinate of its largest peak c sistent with the y coordinate of the largest peak on y–z map. This was in agreement with a minor peak the x–z map.

Structure factors based on these rotational and tra lational parameters were used to phase an elect density map which not only revealed the positions he remaining three atoms, but also distinguished between the carbon and oxygen atoms. The conventional R value at this stage was 0·56.

A modified version of the Busing, Martin & Levy 1962) full-matrix least-squares program, *ORFLS*, was sed to minimize the expression $\sum\omega(|F_o|-|F_c|)^2$; the tomic form factors were taken from *International Tables for X-ray Crystallography* (1962). The initial veighting scheme was based on estimates of the standard deviations derived from the counting statistics of each intensity measurement. Refinement using isotropic temperature factors ceased at a residual of 0·16. No significant improvement, measured by the tests of Hamilton (1965), was obtained by introducing anisotropic temperature factors.

A plot of $\sum\omega(|F_o|-|F_c|)^2$ for different ranges of F_o revealed a strong dependence on F_o, apparently due to underestimating the errors in the large intensities.

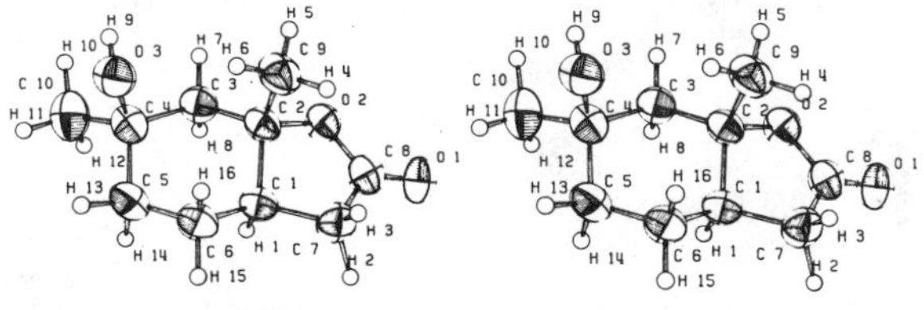

ig. 4. Stereoscopic pair showing the cyclohexane lactone in an arbitrary orientation to illustrate the thermal ellipsoids of the atoms.

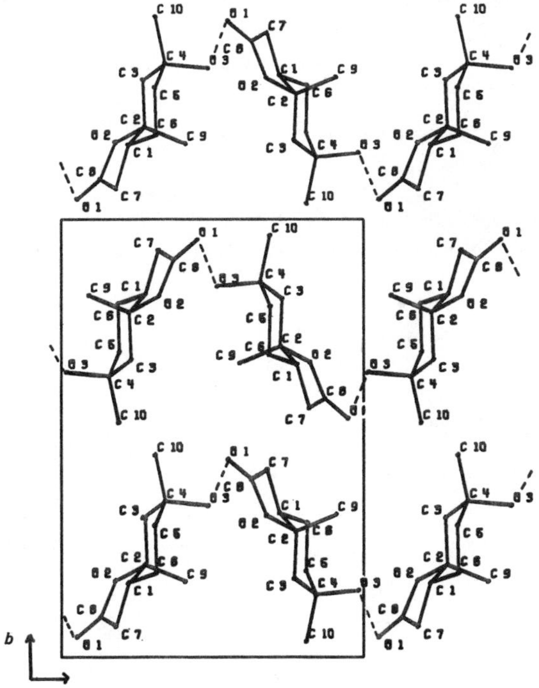

ig. 5. View of part of the crystal structure, looking down the z axis, illustrating the packing arrangement of the molecnle.

Unitary weights were then assigned to all but the weakest reflections and refinement then progressed with the introduction of anisotropic thermal parameters to a residual of 0·12. A difference map at this stage yielded the positions of 15 of the 16 hydrogen atoms and the refinement was continued with alternating blocks of nonhydrogen and hydrogen atom refinement due to the large number of variables. A further difference map gave three possible positions of the undetected hydrogen of the hydroxyl group. An occupancy of $\frac{1}{3}$ was assigned to each position and a further cycle gave an occupancy–standard deviation ratio of less than one for two positions and greater than two for the third, thus establishing the position of the missing hydrogen. Refinement was then continued with all atoms present to give a final residual of 0·068, calculated for all intensities, and 0·054 without including the zero terms.

The final atomic positional and thermal parameters are shown in Table 2, and these were used to calculate the F_{calc} values and phase angles listed in Table 1.

Discussion of structure determination

Some difficulty was experienced in the solution of this structure because of the inconsistency of the translational parameters taken from the maps shown in Fig. 2. To determine the cause of this difficulty, the distance between the positions, $\mathbf{x}_i$, of each of the model atoms and their final refined positions, $\mathbf{x}'_i$, was calculated fo various orientations of the model. Table 3 shows thes values for the peak positions found in the 10° search and the 0·5° search. A rigid body refinement of th model against the final parameters was performed b varying the Eulerian angles and translational param eters in order to minimize the sum $\sum_{i=1}^{n}(\mathbf{x}_i-\mathbf{x}'_i)^2$. It ca be seen that each atom except X(1) was within 0·35 Å o its final position when the angles obtained from the 0·5 search were used. Comparing the results of the trans lation functions calculated from the final refined atomi positions showed that the Q-function maps can b sensitive to relatively small errors in the model [com pare Fig. 3(*a*) and the corresponding map of Fig. 2]

Table 4.

	Refined model	Original model
Sharpened	Fig. 3(*a*)	Fig. 2
Unsharpened	Fig. 3(*b*)	Fig. 3(*c*)

The accurate location of the peak maximum in th rotation function may thus be useful. (*cf.* Table 3). Th rotation function itself appears relatively insensitive t small errors of the search model.

Q-functions have been computed for the four com binations of original and refined model parameters

Table 5. *Bond lengths* (Å) *and angles* (°) *for the non-hydrogen atoms*

Lengths	
C(1)–C(2)	1·525 (5)
C(1)–C(6)	1·523 (6)
C(1)–C(7)	1 524 (6)
C(2)–C(3)	1·514 (5)
C(2)–C(9)	1·519 (5)
C(3)–C(4)	1·549 (5)
C(4)–C(5)	1·532 (6)
C(4)–C(10)	1·535 (6)
C(5)–C(6)	1·541 (6)
C(7)–C(8)	1·515 (6)
(Average C–C	1·528° (6))
C(2)–O(2)	1·482 (5)
C(8)–O(2)	1·352 (5)
C(4)–O(3)	1·443 (5)
C(8)=O(1)	1·214 (5)

Angles*	
C(2)—C(1)–C(6)	110·6°
C(1)—C(2)–C(3)	108·6
C(2)—C(3)–C(4)	111·6
C(3)—C(4)–C(5)	113·3
C(4)—C(5)–C(6)	114·7
C(1)—C(6)–C(5)	105·4
(Average cyclohexane C–C–C 110·7°)	
C(2)—C(1)–C(7)	102·1
C(6)—C(1)–C(7)	125·0
C(1)—C(7)–C(8)	99·8
C(1)—C(2)–C(9)	116·2
C(3)—C(2)–C(9)	114·1
C(3)—C(4)–C(10)	109·2
C(5)—C(4)–C(10)	110·4
(Average C–C–C	111·0°)
C(1)—C(2)–O(2)	100·8
C(3)—C(2)–O(2)	110·5
C(9)—C(2)–O(2)	105·8
C(3)—C(4)–O(3)	110·3
C(5)—C(4)–O(3)	105·1
C(10)–C(4)–O(3)	108·5
C(7)—C(8)–O(2)	110·7
(Average C–C–O	107·4°)
C(2)—O(2)–C(8)	108·9
O(2)—C(8)=O(1)	120·5
C(7)–C(8)=O(1)	128·8

* The root mean square estimated standard deviation of the angles is 0·3°.

vith sharpened and unsharpened data. A key to the our x–z maps illustrated here (as this was the poorest ection) is given in Table 4. These maps indicate the dvantage to be gained from sharpening the data when n accurate model is available. Since the accuracy of he search model is not usually known at the outset f an investigation, a useful procedure could be to calulate Q-functions both with sharpened and unsharpned data. The correct position should be marked by a eak common to both maps.

Our experience with this structure has shown that of he rotational and translational problems, the latter is he more intractable. The major advantage of the vecor space search employed by Nordman & Nakatsu 1963) is that the correctly orientated vector set may be efined to give the best fit with the observed Patterson unction before proceeding with the translational earch. The principal disadvantage of a vector space earch is that the whole Patterson function must be tored in the computer. The ability to refine the vector et should therefore be set against the storage capacity f the available computing facilities.

Discussion of the structure

At the end of the refinement the root mean square value or the ratio of shift to error for all parameters was less han 20%. Standard errors were then computed by inversion of the least-squares matrix using the Busing, Martin & Levy program *ORFFE* (1964). The errors computed for the hydrogen atoms were necessarily low due to the separate refinement of the nonhydrogen and hydrogen atoms.

The principal axes of the thermal ellipsoids are illustrated in a stereoscopic pair drawing (Fig. 4) (Johnson, 1965). Tables 5 and 6 contain intramolecular bond lengths and angles.

The molecule consists of a slightly flattened cyclohexane ring fused to a lactone ring. The distortion of the cyclohexane ring is due to the overcrowding between the –OH and $-CH_3$ groups at C(4) and C(2). The separation of O(3) and C(9) is 3·03 Å, which is somewhat shorter than the van der Waals separation of 3·4 Å for an oxygen atom and a methyl group. It is therefore of some interest that H(6) is inclined towards O(3) [the angle O(3)–H(6)–C(9) is $125 \pm 3°$] suggesting an interaction between H(6) and O(3). These two atoms are 2·34 Å apart.

Several planes were fitted to the atoms in the lactone group and ring using a program written by Pippy & Ahmed (1968) utilizing the least-squares procedure of Blow (1960). The best fit was obtained with a plane of equation $0{\cdot}7701X - 0{\cdot}4936Y - 0{\cdot}4041Z - 0{\cdot}0693 = 0$ (X, Y, Z are coordinates in Å measured along the crystallographic axes and referred to the cell origin) passing through C(7), C(8), O(1) and O(2) of the lactone group.

Table 6. *Bond lengths* (Å) *and angles* (°) *involving hydrogen atoms*

Lengths

C(1)—H(1)	1·06 (3)
C(3)—H(7)	0·9 (4)
C(3)—H(8)	1·06 (4)
C(5)—H(13)	1·05 (4)
C(5)—H(14)	1·10 (4)
C(6)—H(15)	1·00 (4)
C(6)—H(16)	1·12 (4)
C(7)—H(2)	1·09 (4)
C(7)—H(3)	0·96 (4)
C(9)—H(4)	1·07 (4)
C(9)—H(5)	0·86 (4)
C(9)—H(6)	0·99 (4)
C(10)–H(10)	1·11 (5)
C(10)–H(11)	1·00 (5)
C(10)–H(12)	1·05 (5)
(Average C–H	1·03 Å)
O(3)—H(9)	0·80 (5)

Angles*

H(13)–C(5)–H(14)	109°
H(15)–C(6)–H(16)	112
H(2)—C(7)–H(3)	104
H(4)—C(9)–H(5)	101
H(4)—C(9)–H(6)	110
H(5)—C(9)–H(6)	100
H(11)–C(10)–H(10)	110
H(11)–C(10)–H(12)	115
H(12)–C(10)–H(10)	106
(Average H–C–H	108°)

Angles*

C(2)–C(1)—H(1)	109°
C(6)–C(1)—H(1)	106
C(7)–C(1)–H(1)	103
C(2)–C(3)–H(7)	110
C(4)–C(3)—H(7)	110
C(2)–C(3)—H(8)	110
C(4)–C(3)—H(8)	108
C(4)–C(5)—H(13)	105
C(6)–C(5)—H(13)	110
C(4)–C(5)—H(14)	111
C(6)–C(5)—H(14)	107
C(1)–C(6)—H(15)	106
C(5)–C(6)—H(15)	109
C(1)–C(6)—H(16)	113
C(5)–C(6)—H(16)	111
C(1)–C(7)—H(2)	117
C(8)–C(7)—H(2)	110
C(1)–C(7)—H(3)	117
C(8)–C(7)—H(3)	109
C(2)–C(9)—H(4)	114
C(2)–C(9)—H(5)	118
C(2)–C(9)—H(6)	112
C(4)–C(10)–H(10)	113
C(4)–C(10)–H(11)	105
C(4)–C(10)–H(12)	108
(Average C–C–H	110°)
C(4)–O(3)—H(9)	105° (4)

* The r.m.s. estimated standard deviations of the angles involving one, and two, hydrogen atoms are respectively 2° and 3°.

C(1) and C(2) are displaced by −0·55 Å and +0·12 Å from this plane; the average r.m.s. for the displacement of the remaining four atoms was 0·006 Å. The bonds C(8)–O(2) and O(2)–C(2) are of interest since there is a difference of 0·130 Å between them, the shorter bond being adjacent to the carbonyl group. This shortening is connected with the planarity of the lactone group. The average angle in the lactone ring is 104·5 ± 0·3°. The displacement of one atom from the plane through the remaining atoms in the lactone ring, the shortening of the bond adjacent to the carbonyl group, and the average angle within the ring observed here are consistent with previous observations (Kim, Jeffrey, Rosenstein & Corfield, 1967; Jeffrey, Rosenstein & Vlasse, 1967).

The shortest intermolecular contact is 2·154 Å between O(1) and H(9) and this is due to hydrogen bonding between the hydroxyl hydrogen and the oxygen of the carboxyl group. The angle C(8)=O(1)···H(9) is 112° and the angle O(3)–H(9)···O(1) is 169°. The hydrogen bond distance O(1)–O(3) is rather long at 2·944 Å but since the hydrogen bonding is approximately collinear with the O(3)–H(9) bond some interaction would appear likely. Fig. 5 illustrates the packing arrangement of the molecules in the crystal structure from which it can be seen that the hydrogen bonding links chains of molecules along the direction of the crystallographic *a* axis.

We thank Dr P. Tollin for guidance in the application of *Q*-functions, Dr A. Wonacott for instruction in the use of the four-circle diffractometer, and Drs Adams, Ford, Main, and Schevitz for many helpful discussions. We are grateful to Dr J. Wolinsky for contributing the crystals and details of their probable molecular structure, as well as to NSF and NIH in giving financial support (Grants GB-5477X and 2 R01 GM10704 respectively).

References

Blow, D. M. (1960). *Acta Cryst.* **13**, 168.
Blow, D. M., Rossmann, M. G. & Jeffery, B. A. (1964). *J. Mol. Biol.* **8**, 65.
Busing, W. R., Martin, K. O. & Levy, H. A. (1962). Report ORNL-TM-305, Oak Ridge National Laboratory, Tennessee.
Busing, W. R., Martin, K. O. & Levy, H. A. (1964). Report ORNL-TM-306, Oak Ridge National Laboratory, Tennessee.
Dodson, E., Harding, M. M., Hodgkin, D. C. & Rossmann, M. G. (1966). *J. Mol. Biol.* **16**, 227.
Hamilton, W. C. (1965). *Acta Cryst.* **18**, 502.
International Tables for X-ray Crystallography (1962) Vol. III, Table 3.3.1A, p. 202. Birmingham: Kynoch Press.
Jeffrey, G. A., Rosenstein, R. D. & Vlasse, M. (1967). *Acta Cryst.* **22**, 725.
Johnson, C. K. (1965). Report 3794, Oak Ridge National Laboratory, Tennessee.
Kim, S. H., Jeffrey, G. A., Rosenstein, R. D. & Corfield, P. W. R. (1967). *Acta Cryst.* **22**, 733.
Lattman, E. E. & Love, W. (1970). *Acta Cryst.* B **26**, 1854.
Nordman, C. E. & Nakatsu, K. (1963). *J. Amer. Chem. Soc.* **85**, 353.
Pippy, M. E. & Ahmed, F. R. (1968). Program NRC-22, National Research Council of Canada, Ottawa, Canada.
Rossmann, M. G. (1971). *The Molecular Replacement Method*. New York: Gordon & Breach.
Rossmann, M. G. & Blow, D. M. (1962). *Acta Cryst.* **15**, 24.
Tollin, P. (1966). *Acta Cryst.* **21**, 613.
Tollin, P. (1970). In *Crystallographic Computing*. Copenhagen: Munksgaard.
Tollin, P., Main, P. & Rossmann, M. G. (1966). *Acta Cryst.* **20**, 404.
Tollin, P. & Rossmann, M. G. (1966). *Acta Cryst.* **21**, 872.
Wilson, A. J. C. (1942). *Nature, Lond.* **150**, 152.
Wolinsky, J. & Chan, D. (1966). *J. Org. Chem.* **31**, 2471

J. Mol. Biol. (1969) **45**, 481–490

Determination of the Orientation and Position of the Myoglobin Molecule in the Crystal of Seal Myoglobin

Patrick Tollin

Department of Biological Sciences, Purdue University, Lafayette, Indiana, U.S.A.
and
Carnegie Laboratory of Physics, The University, Dundee, Scotland

(*Received 21 May 1969*)

The orientation of the myoglobin molecule in the crystal of seal myoglobin has been determined, by using the rotation function (Rossmann & Blow, 1962) to compare the 5·8 Å resolution data from sperm whale myoglobin with the 5 Å data from seal myoglobin obtained by Scouloudi (1969). The position of the molecule in the unit cell has been found using the Q-functions defined by Tollin (1966*a*). The position of the haem group obtained in this way is in good agreement with that obtained by Scouloudi (1969) from a 5 Å resolution electron density map obtained using the isomorphous replacement map. A three-dimensional electron density map has been obtained by calculating phases for a whale myoglobin molecule correctly located in the seal myoglobin cell and applying these to the observed seal structure amplitudes. This map has been compared with Scouloudi's published results and indicates a good agreement between the two investigations.

1. Introduction

Once the structure of one member of a group of structurally related proteins has been solved by the multiple isomorphous replacement technique, it is of some interest to see how much information about the structure of the other members of the group can be found from X-ray diffraction data for the native protein crystals alone. Assuming that the members of the group of related proteins, each of which crystallizes in a different unit cell and with a different space group, have approximately the same tertiary structure, one approach to this problem would use the known structure as a model to calculate phases for the diffraction data from a second member of the group. By examining the electron density map obtained by applying these calculated phases to the observed intensities, it may be possible to derive useful information about the similarities and differences between the two related molecules. In order to be able to perform such a calculation it is first necessary to determine the orientation and position of the protein molecule with respect to the crystal axes of the second member of the group. As a test of some methods of determining the orientation and position of a known molecule in an unknown crystal, these parameters have been determined for the molecule of myoglobin in the crystal structure of seal myoglobin at 5·8 Å resolution. In this series of experiments the known molecule is the molecule of sperm whale myoglobin, whose structure has been determined by the isomorphous replacement technique (Bodo, Dintzis, Kendrew & Wyckoff,

1959). The orientation of this molecule with respect to the crystal axes of seal myoglobin has been determined using the rotation function of Rossmann & Blow (1962). Once the orientation of the molecule had been found, its position in the unit cell of seal myoglobin was determined using the Q-functions by Tollin (1966*a*). Finally, an electron density map has been calculated using the correctly oriented and positioned whale myoglobin molecule to provide phases for the structure amplitudes of the seal myoglobin. This map has been compared with the illustrations from the 5 Å map obtained using the isomorphous replacement technique. This comparison indicates that the orientation and position obtained for the molecule are in agreement with those obtained by Scouloudi (1969). How much useful information about structural differences between the molecules can be found from this comparison will require a more careful analysis. It seems likely that for such a comparison diffraction data at higher resolution would be more useful. However, this present work at least indicates that the techniques work and their extension to higher resolution should be possible.

A preliminary account of these results has been given previously (Tollin, 1966*b*); the full publication has been delayed until a comparison with the isomorphous replacement results became possible.

2. The Molecular Orientation

The orientation of the myoglobin molecule with respect to the crystal axes of seal myoglobin has been determined from the rotation function calculated using the 5·8 Å resolution data from sperm whale myoglobin and the 5 Å resolution data from seal myoglobin. The data for sperm whale myoglobin were kindly supplied by Dr J. C. Kendrew and Dr H. C. Watson and those for seal myoglobin by Dr H. Scouloudi.

The rotation function is defined (Rossmann & Blow, 1962) as

$$R = \int_u P_2(\boldsymbol{x}_2) P_1(\boldsymbol{x}_1) \mathrm{d}\boldsymbol{x}_1.$$

It measures the degree of coincidence within the volume u when the Patterson P_1 is rotated on the Patterson function P_2. Any point $\boldsymbol{x}_1$ in P_1 is related to any other point $\boldsymbol{x}_2$ in P_2 through the rotation matrix [C] by the relationship

$$\boldsymbol{x}_2 = [\mathrm{C}]\boldsymbol{x}_1.$$

The above integral has been shown to reduce to the double summation

$$R = \sum_p |\mathrm{F}_p|^2 \sum_h |\mathrm{F}_h|^2 \, \mathrm{G}_{h\cdot h'}$$

where $|\mathrm{F}_p|$ and $|\mathrm{F}_h|$ are the structure amplitudes corresponding to the Patterson functions P_2 and P_1, respectively. $\mathrm{G}_{h\,h'}$ is an interference function whose magnitude depends on the reciprocal lattice vectors $\mathbf{h}$ and $\mathbf{h}'$ and on the volume u. The non-integral reciprocal lattice vector $\mathbf{h}'$ is given by

$$\mathbf{h}' = \boldsymbol{p}\,[\mathrm{C}].$$

The rotation of the Patterson function is described here in terms of the Eulerian angles θ_1 θ_2 θ_3. The definition of these angles is that given by Rossmann & Blow (1962). Since seal myoglobin crystallizes in the space group $A2$ and whale myoglobin crystallizes in the space group $P2_1$, both Patterson functions belong to the proper rotation group 2 as defined by Tollin, Main & Rossmann (1966), and therefore the rotation function belongs to the space group Pbnb and the asymmetric unit is $0 \leqslant \theta_1 \leqslant 2\pi$, $0 \leqslant \theta_2 \leqslant \pi$, $0 \leqslant \theta_3 \leqslant \pi/2$.

The calculation of the rotation function was performed using the programs described by Tollin & Rossmann (1966). The seal myoglobin data were used as the data $|F_p|^2$ for the Patterson function $P_2(\boldsymbol{x}_2)$, that is (within the program) the reciprocal lattice which is rotated is that of the seal myoglobin crystal. Because the seal myoglobin crystal possesses a centred cell, and hence general systematic absences, the use of the seal $|F|^2$ values as the coefficients of the stationary reciprocal lattice, that is the $|F_h|^2$ values, would have led to difficulties in the interpolation in the $G_{h\,h'}$ table. Because of the centring, the reciprocal lattice points are closer together than they would be in a primitive cell and hence the cut-off on the $G_{h\,h'}$ table occurs at a smaller value of $H.R$ in some directions in reciprocal space. In addition, time would be wasted in including in the sum over the index h, points which must make zero contribution to the rotation function.

Although an isolated myoglobin molecule has dimensions of about 45 × 35 × 25 Å (Bodo *et al.*, 1959), because both the seal and whale myoglobin crystals have cell dimensions of the order of 30 Å the volume of integration u was chosen as a sphere of radius 25 Å. At a resolution of about 6 Å the origin peak in the Patterson function extends out to approximately 6 Å from the origin. The choice of a radius much more than 25 Å would have led to the possibility of false peaks in the rotation function, due to the overlap of some high region in one Patterson function with the origin peak one unit cell away from the origin of rotation, in the other Patterson function. This is exactly analogous to the observed false peaks in the application of the $I(\theta\phi)$ function (Tollin & Cochran, 1964), to the structure determination of deoxyadenosine (Watson, Sutor & Tollin, 1965).

Initially the largest 47 $|F|^2$ values for seal myoglobin were used with the Large Terms program (Tollin & Rossmann, 1966), to survey the whole of the asymmetric unit in the rotation function at 10° intervals in the three angles θ_1, θ_2 and θ_3. The angular interval suggested by the formula $\frac{1}{2}\, d_{\min}/r_o$ (Tollin & Rossmann, 1966), is 7°. The largest peak found in this calculation occurs at $\theta_1 = 90°$, $\theta_2 = 150°$, $\theta_3 = 90°$. The height of this peak on an arbitrary scale was 92, the next highest peak had a height of 76 and the average value of the rotation function was about 50 on the same scale. Since the rotation function has a large positive value everywhere, it is perhaps more reasonable to compare the height of this largest peak with the positive and negative excursions of the function away from the average value over the rest of the asymmetric unit. Relative to the average value of 50, the excursions in both senses are of the order of 20 where the largest peak has a height of about 40 above the average value. The section through the rotation function at $\theta_1 = 90°$ is shown in Figure 1. A region around this largest peak was then explored at 5° intervals in each angular variable using the general rotation function program and all the observed data for both crystals within the 5·8 Å sphere. The peak is still at $\theta_1 = 90°$, $\theta_2 = 150°$, $\theta_3 = 90°$. In all of these calculations the 27 nearest neighbours to the point h' were used for interpolation in the G table. The effect of varying the number of interpolation points is discussed by Tollin & Rossmann (1966).

It seems likely that the rotation function has given a particularly large peak in this case because of a fortunate orientation of the molecule. The required rotation is defined by Eulerian angles which have $\theta_1 = 90°$, $\theta_3 = 90°$. Since the line $\theta_1 = 90°$,

32

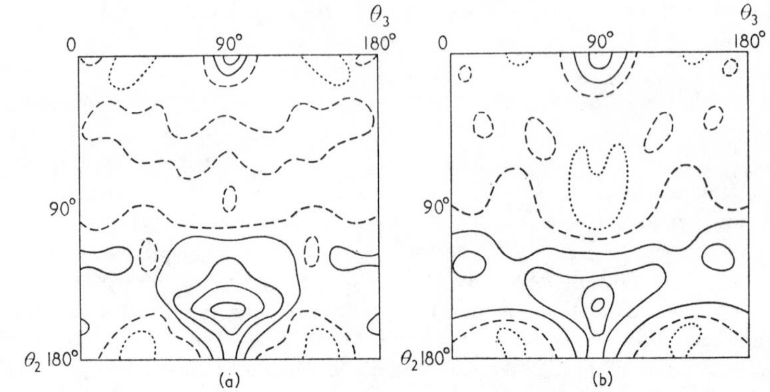

FIG. 1. (a) The section through the rotation function at $\theta_1 = 90°$ calculated with the Larg Terms program.

(b) The section at $\theta_1 = 90°$ through the composite rotation function map formed by operatin with a twofold axis on the rotation function calculated with the transform of a single molecul

$\theta_3 = 90°$ in Eulerian angle space is a twofold axis, a second symmetry related pea occurs close to this line. This peak overlaps the original peak, thus enhancing i This suggestion has been tested by calculating the molecular transform of a singl whale myoglobin molecule and rotating this on the seal diffraction data. This rotatio function does not possess the twofold axis at $\theta_1 = 90°$, $\theta_3 = 90°$ and it now show a peak near the correct orientation but comparable in height with the second larges peak in the original calculation. If this rotation function is operated on by a twofol axis and combined with itself, the shape of the original rotation function can b reproduced. Figure 1(b) shows the result of the combination of the section at $\theta_1 = 90$ with itself after the operation of the twofold axis.

The molecular transform was calculated approximately by using the positions c the atoms N, Cα, Cβ, C and O of 151 amino acid residues of the polypeptide chai and the haem group obtained from the 2 Å resolution refinement of sperm whal myoglobin but not including the molecule related by the 2_1-axis.

These results suggest that, at least at low resolution, the rotation function ma give ambiguous results in the general case. This must in part be due to the fact tha on rotation a protein molecule will often find regions of coincidence with itsel Because the rotation function calculates the product of two Patterson functions such coincidences will lead to large peaks. Work is at present in progress on function, related to the function $I(\theta, \phi, \psi)$ defined by Tollin & Cochran (1964), whic uses the sums of Patterson functions in a manner analogous to the Q-function discussed in a subsequent section of this paper, and which should therefore sho fewer false maxima. It should, however, be noted that the rotation function ca often give useful results. The rotation function has been successfully used to deter mine the structure of a number of molecular crystals (Tollin & Munns, 1969; Munns Tollin, Wilson & Young, to be published).

Although the overlap of the correct peaks produced an enhancement, it make the determination of the precise Eulerian angles required to define the orientatio more difficult. From the shape of the peak around $\theta_1 = 90°$, $\theta_2 = 150°$, $\theta_3 = 90$ the true maximum was assumed to lie at $\theta_1 = 95°$, $\theta_2 = 150°$ and $\theta_3 = 100°$. Th overlap of the peaks does not confuse the determination of the angle θ_2 and fortunately changes in the angles θ_1 and θ_3 of up to 10° about the value of 90° produce only a small change in the orientation of the molecule. For example, an atom at the outside of the molecule is moved by only about 2 Å for a shift of 10° in θ_3. From the angles $\theta_1 = 95°$, $\theta_2 = 150°$ and $\theta_3 = 100°$ the matrix describing the transformation which rotates the whale molecule into the orientation of the myoglobin molecule in the seal unit cell can be calculated.

3. Determination of the Position of the Molecule

Once the orientation of the myoglobin molecule in the seal cell is known, it remains to determine its position in the unit cell. If the orientation with respect to the crystal axis of a group of n atoms is known, then the co-ordinates $\boldsymbol{r}_j$ with respect to an arbitrary origin can be found. The problem of finding the position of a molecule in the unit cell can then be stated as the problem of finding the vector $\mathbf{R}_o$ which relates the arbitrary origin to one of the symmetry operations of the space group. It has been shown that the function

$$Q(\mathbf{R}_o) = \sum_{\boldsymbol{h}} |F(\boldsymbol{h})|^2 \sum_{j, j' = 1}^{n} \cos 2\pi \boldsymbol{h} \cdot (\boldsymbol{r}_j + \mathbf{R}_o - T(\boldsymbol{r}_{j'} + \mathbf{R}_o))$$

(Tollin, 1966*a*), will have a large value when $\mathbf{R}_o$ is this vector. This function has been used successfully in the determination of the structure of a number of organic molecular crystals (Young, Tollin & Sutherland, 1968; Young, Tollin & Wilson, 1969), and the relation of the Q-function to the translation function of Crowther & Blow (1967) has been discussed by Tollin (1969).

In the case of the determination of the position of the myoglobin molecule in the seal cell, since the space group is $A2$, the function $Q(X_oZ_o)$ which defines the position of the molecule relative to the 2_1 axis was used.

As has been noted before, if there are pairs of atoms in the known group which would give rise to non-Harker peaks in the appropriate Harker section (Lipson & Cochran, 1957), there will arise in the Q-function false peaks whose position can be predicted *a priori*. In the case of a protein molecule there will often be very many pairs of atoms which will satisfy these conditions and many false peaks will occur. Because of the number of such peaks it is impractical to attempt to allow for their effect. The alternative method for avoiding the difficulty, suggested previously (Tollin, 1966*a*), is therefore necessary. This method requires the removal of the origin peak from the Patterson function before the Q-functions are calculated. In other words, the coefficients $|F(\mathbf{h})|^2$ used in the summation for $Q(\mathbf{R}_o)$ must be modified to

$$(|F(\mathbf{h})|^2 - \sum_{j=1}^{n} f_j^2).$$

In order to be able so to modify the coefficients it would appear that an accurate knowledge of the absolute scale of the observed structure amplitudes would be required. However, by calculating the origin peak in the Patterson it is possible to test certain approximations. It was found that by using a scale factor which made $\sum_{\mathbf{h}} \sum_{j=1}^{n} f_j^2$ equal to the $\sum_{\mathbf{h}} F(\mathbf{h})^2$, a reasonable approximation to the origin peak could be obtained. Even going one step further and noting that, since data only out to a resolution of 6 Å were to be used, the curve of f_j is relatively flat, the approximation that $\sum_{j=1}^{n} f_j^2$ was uniform over the whole 6 Å sphere was found to be satisfactory. Approximate removal of the origin peak was then obtained by using the coefficients $(|F(\mathbf{h})|^2 - k)$ where k is defined by $\sum_{\mathbf{h}} F(\mathbf{h})^2 = \sum_{\mathbf{h}} k$. Figure 2 shows the spherically

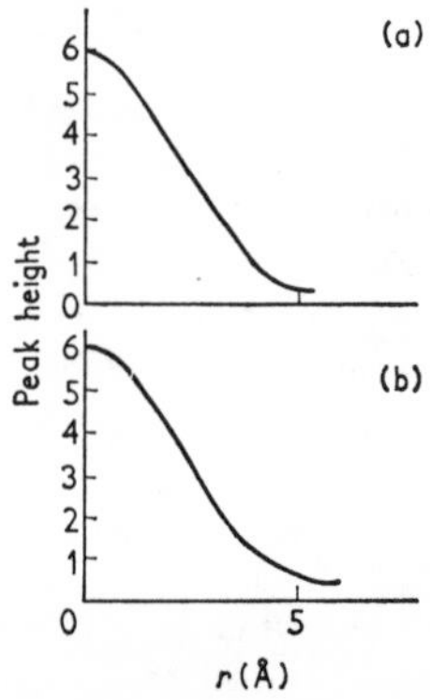

FIG. 2. (a) The section through the spherically averaged Patterson origin peak.
(b) The calculated Patterson origin peak obtained using the coefficients $(|F(\mathbf{h})|^2 - k)$. The vertical scale is arbitrary.

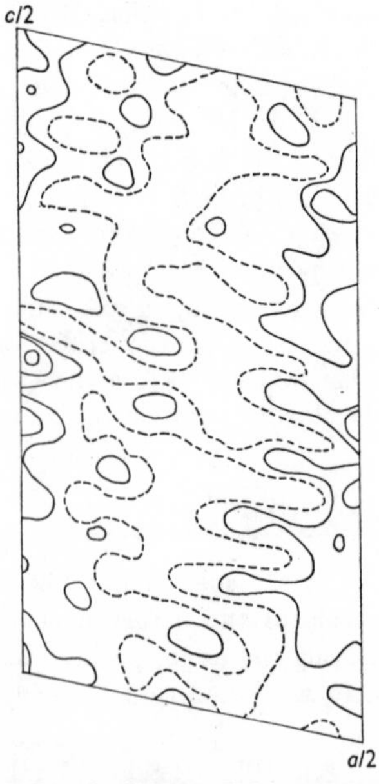

FIG. 3. The function $Q(X_0, Z_0)$; the largest peak occurs at $X_0 = 0{\cdot}008$, $Z_0 = 0{\cdot}246$.

averaged Patterson origin peak for seal myoglobin and the origin peak produced by the approximation that $\sum_{j=1}^{n} f_j^2 = k$.

The model of the myoglobin molecule used in the calculation of the Q-function consisted of the atoms N, Cα, Cβ, C and O of 151 amino acid residues and 27 atoms of the haem group of sperm whale myoglobin obtained from the refined sperm whale structure.

The fractional co-ordinates of those atoms were rotated into the correct orientation in the seal cell and used as the relative fractional co-ordinates $\boldsymbol{r}_j$ in the inner summations of the function $Q(X_0Z_0)$. Figure 3 shows the map of the function $Q(X_0Z_0)$. The largest peak on the map occurs at $X_0 = 0{\cdot}008$, $Z_0 = 0{\cdot}246$, and these must be added to the relative fractional co-ordinates to position the myoglobin molecule correctly in the seal unit cell.

4. Calculation of the Electron Density Map

The electron density representing a single molecule of myoglobin was cut out of the published 6 Å resolution electron density map (Bodo *et al.*, 1959). The centre of the haem group belonging to this particular molecule had approximate fraction co-ordinates $x = 0{\cdot}251$, $y = 0{\cdot}912$, $z = 0{\cdot}144$. The electron density was estimated at 2 Å intervals from this contour map, giving a set of values $\rho_w(\boldsymbol{r}')$. The value attached to each $\rho_w(\boldsymbol{r}')$ was the contour level in the 6 Å map; there was therefore an arbitrary scale factor introduced. The quantities F_{calc} were calculated by assuming that

$$F_{calc}(\mathbf{h}) = \int \rho_w(\boldsymbol{r}) \exp 2\pi i\, \mathbf{h}.\boldsymbol{r}\, d\boldsymbol{r}$$

could be replaced by

$$F_{calc}(\mathbf{h}) = \sum \rho_w(\boldsymbol{r}) \exp 2\pi i\, \mathbf{h}.\boldsymbol{r}$$

where $\boldsymbol{r}_{seal} = [C]\, \boldsymbol{r}'_{whale} + \mathbf{t}$. [C] is the matrix which rotates the myoglobin molecule into its correct orientation in the seal cell, and $\mathbf{t}$ is the translation vector obtained from the Q-function. The elements of [C] and $\mathbf{t}$ are given in Table 1. The summation

TABLE 1

The transformation from whale to seal

The matrix [C]	0·801	−0·054	0·303
	−0·084	−1·045	−0·102
	0·524	0·007	−0·248
The vector **t**			
	0·008	0·000	0·246

was performed over all the points within the molecular boundary. This had the effect of filling the space between the molecules with material of uniform electron density equal to the average electron density in the whale myoglobin structure. The phases of the $F_{calc}(\mathbf{h})$ were then applied to the observed seal structure factors and an electron density map at 5·8 Å resolution was calculated. It is obviously possible to calculate more accurately the phases from the electron density and it is hoped to investigate the effect of a more accurate estimation of the electron density and of changes in the interpolation interval on the calculated phases. However, it was hoped that this approximate calculation would produce a good enough map to allow a comparison with the results of the application of the isomorphous replacement technique, and would show any gross structural differences between the seal and sperm whale myoglobin molecules. The results discussed in the next section appear to justify this hope.

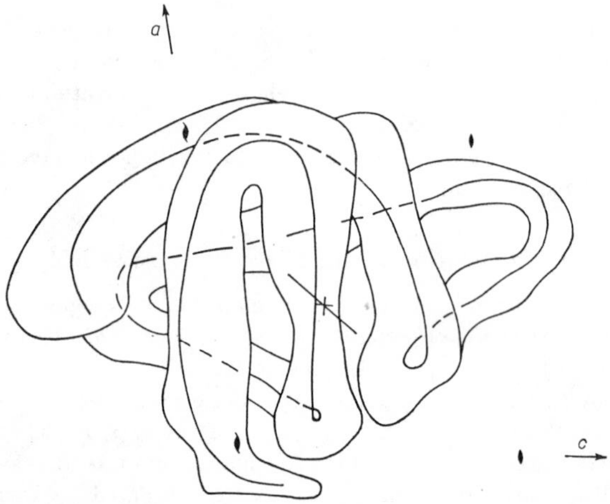

FIG. 4. Diagram indicating the path of the polypeptide chain in the seal myoglobin molecule obtained from the three-dimensional electron density map calculated as described in the text. This is to be compared with Scouloudi (1969, Fig. 3).

5. Comparison with the Isomorphous Replacement Results

While this work was in progress, Dr H. Scouloudi obtained electron density maps at both 6 and 5 Å resolution using the multiple isomorphous replacement technique (Scouloudi, 1969). That the orientation obtained from the rotation function is in good agreement with the results from the isomorphous replacement technique can be seen by comparing Figure 4, the projection of the polypeptide chain down the b-axis obtained in the present investigation, with that shown in Scouloudi (1969, Fig. 3). The position obtained from the Q-function can be checked by comparing the positions of the haem group obtained by both methods. From the Q-function the iron atom of the haem group has fractional co-ordinates, with respect to the origin of the unit cell chosen on the 2_1-axis, of $x = 0{\cdot}202$, $y = 0{\cdot}012$, $z = 0{\cdot}098$, while Scouloudi obtains co-ordinates of $x = 0{\cdot}203$, $y = 0{\cdot}348$, $z = 0{\cdot}096$. The difference in the y-co-ordinates is due to the fact that in the space group $A2$ the origin can be chosen anywhere along the twofold or 2_1-axes.

The similarity between the results of the two investigations is clearly demonstrated by the sections through the electron density map obtained in this study. Figure 5(a) shows the section at $z = 0$ and Figure 5(b) shows the section at $z = 0{\cdot}094$; these should be compared with the sections shown in Figure 4 (Scouloudi, 1969). The paths of the helices G and H, and the positions of the haem group and the sections through the helices, A, E and F, are in good agreement with those obtained by Scouloudi (1969).

It is hoped, in the near future, to compare in detail the electron density map obtained in this investigation with that from the isomorphous replacement technique. From our experience with the application of the techniques to molecular crystals, it seems likely that a similar analysis at higher resolution is possible and likely to

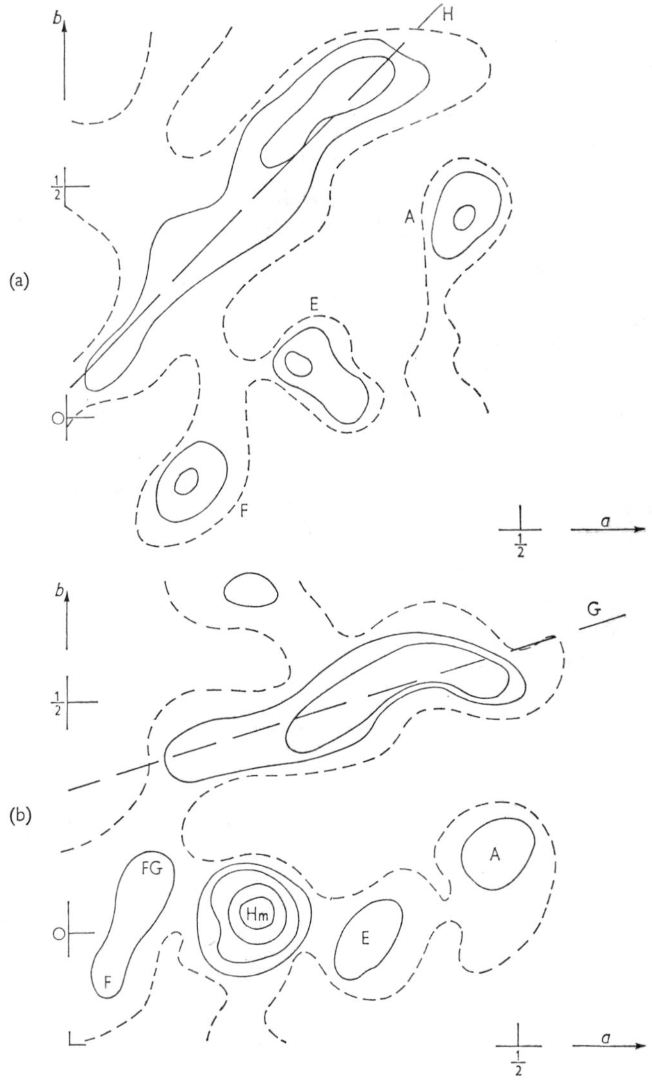

FIG. 5. The sections through the eletron density map obtained in this investigation at (a) $z = 0$ and (b) $z = 0{\cdot}94$. These should be compared with Scouloudi (1969, Fig. 4).

show in more detail any differences between the seal and sperm whale myoglobin molecules.

I wish to thank Dr H. Scouloudi for making available the 5 Å native seal myoglobin data and Dr J. C. Kendrew and Professor H. C. Watson for supplying the 5·8 Å resolution data and the co-ordinates of the backbone atoms for sperm whale myoglobin. I am grateful to Professor M. G. Rossmann for suggesting the problem and for his advice and assistance. Thanks are also due to Drs H. R. Wilson and D. W. Young for useful discussions, to Mrs J. Roberts, Mrs A. Brydie, Miss P. Hendry and Mrs E. M. Millar for technical and clerical assistance.

This work was supported by National Science Foundation grant no. GB 5477X and by National Institutes of Health grant no. 5 R01–Gmi 0704.

REFERENCES

Bodo, G., Dintzis, H. M., Kendrew, J. C. & Wyckoff, H. W. (1959). *Proc. Roy. Soc.* A, **253**, 70.

Crowther, R. A. & Blow, D. M. (1967). *Acta Cryst.* **23**, 544.

Lipson, H. & Cochran, W. (1957). *The Determination of Crystal Structure.* p. 170. London: Bell.

Rossmann, M. G. & Blow, D. M. (1962). *Acta Cryst.* **15**, 24.

Scouloudi, H. (1969). *J. Mol. Biol.* **40**, 353.

Tollin, P. (1966*a*). *Acta Cryst.* **21**, 613.

Tollin, P. (1966*b*). *Acta Cryst.* **21**, A165.

Tollin, P. (1969). *Acta Cryst.* A, **25**, 376.

Tollin, P. & Cochran, W. (1964). *Acta Cryst.* **17**, 1332.

Tollin, P., Main, P. & Rossmann, M. G. (1966). *Acta Cryst.* **20**, 404.

Tollin, P. & Munns, A. R. I. (1969). *Nature*, **222**, 1170.

Tollin, P. & Rossmann, M. G. (1966). *Acta Cryst.* **21**, 872.

Watson, D. C., Sutor, D. J. & Tollin, P. (1965). *Acta Cryst.* **19**, 111.

Young, D. W., Tollin, P. & Sutherland, H. (1968). *Acta Cryst.* B, **24**, 161.

Young, D. W., Tollin, P. & Wilson, H. R. (1969). *Acta Cryst.* B, **25**, 1423.

Reprinted from *Acta Crystallographica*, Vol. B 26, Part 11, November 1970

Acta Cryst. (1970). **B26**, 1854

A Rotational Search Procedure for Detecting A Known Molecule In a Crystal*

BY EATON E. LATTMAN AND WARNER E. LOVE

Thomas C. Jenkins Department of Biophysics, Johns Hopkins University, Charles and 34th Streets, Baltimore, Maryland 21218, *U.S.A.*

(*Received* 20 *August* 1969)

A computationally swift modification of the Rossmann–Blow rotation function has been developed. With the use of this function the single chains present in the D2 crystals of hemoglobin from the sea lamprey, *Petromyzon marinus*, have been shown to resemble the sperm-whale metmyoglobin molecule, and the orientation of the lamprey hemoglobin molecules in the unit cell of this crystal has been found. The results are confirmed by the crystal structure analysis of lamprey hemoglobin.

Introduction

The oxygen-carrying heme proteins from a variety of sources have similar tertiary structures, but occur in widely differing crystal forms. In particular, the α- and β-chains of horse and human hemoglobin (Cullis, Muirhead, Perutz, Rossmann & North, 1962; Muirhead, Cox, Mazzarella & Perutz, 1967), the single chains of the hemoglobins from the common bloodworm, *Glycera dibranchiata* (Padlan & Love, 1968) and from the larval form of the fly, *Chironomus thummi*, (Huber, Formanek & Epp, 1968), and the single chains of seal and sperm-whale myoglobin (Scouloudi, 1969; Bodo, Dintzis, Kendrew & Wyckoff, 1959) all appear to have essentially the same topology when viewed at low resolution, although the crystallographic arrangements in which they are found are quite diverse. The α- and β-chains of horse methemoglobin, for example, are nearly identical with those of human deoxyhemoglobin (Muirhead *et al.*, 1967), but the assembly into tetramers is somewhat different in the two cases, and the packing of these tetramers into their unit cells is very different indeed.

Situations like the above, in which a known molecular structure occurs in a variety of interesting crystallographic arrangements, are likely to arise for many large and important biological molecules. Much labor would be saved in these cases if the relevant crystal structures were determined starting from the known molecular structure, rather than *ab initio*. To piece together a structure in this way one must be able to find the orientation and location of each molecule in the unit cell. The problem of fixing the translations has been attacked by Nordman & Nakatsu (1963), Rossmann, Blow, Harding & Coller (1964), Tollin (1966) and Crowther & Blow (1967). The fundamental work on determining the orientations is that of Rossmann & Blow (1962). Tollin (1969) has combined these techniques to effect a complete protein structure determination.

* A portion of this work was presented in the Ph. D. thesis submitted (by EEL) to the Thomas C. Jenkins Department of Biophysics, The Johns Hopkins University.

In what follows a 'Patterson function' denotes the convolution of a structure with its centrosymmetric image, and may be periodic or aperiodic as the case warrants. A 'self-Patterson function' is one containing only intramolecular vectors, whereas a 'cross-Patterson function' contains only intermolecular vectors.

Let P_1 and P_2 be Patterson functions. Rossmann & Blow (1962) compare P_1 and P_2 as a function of their relative orientation. Their measure of agreement, R, is large whenever a self-Patterson function in P_1 lies parallel to an identical or similar function in P_2. The Fourier coefficients of P_1 and P_2 are required for the calculation, which is done in reciprocal space for convenience. We discuss here a computationally swift version of the Rossmann–Blow approach which we have used to compare the Patterson function of an isolated molecule of sperm-whale metmyoglobin (SWMb) with the Patterson function of the D2 crystals of lamprey hemoglobin (Hendrickson, Love & Murray, 1968), and also for other experiments.

Nordman & Nakatsu (1963) have used a minimum function to compare directly the Patterson functions of a crystal and of a known, isolated molecule. More recently Nordman (1969) has used a modified minimum function to find the directions of the heme normal and of the axes of the α-helical sections in the SWMb molecule. Technical details are given by Nordman (1966) and Schilling (1968).

Zwick (1969), using a reciprocal space approach similar to ours, has also determined the direction of the heme normal and the helix axes. In addition he has found the orientation about the helix axis, and the position, of one of the helical segments.

Sarma (1969) at Oxford has investigated the triclinic form of lysozyme by forming the usual crystallographic R value between the squared transform of one molecule and the diffraction pattern from the crystal as a function of their relative orientation.

What happens to these methods when differences between the known molecule and the molecules in the crystal cannot be ignored? A trial structure can be obtained, as outlined above, by finding the orientation and position at which a known molecule fits best in the unit cell of a crystal. But some type of refinement is then required in order to achieve an accurate structure determination. For proteins only two possibilities suggest themselves: direct methods, which have not yet been fully tested on macromolecules, and methods using non-crystallographic symmetry (Main & Rossmann, 1966; Muirhead *et al.*, 1967; Maslen, 1968), which are not always applicable. Clearly the technique of assembling accurate crystal structures from the known structures of the constituent molecules is far from complete.

Methods

Rossmann & Blow (1962) studied a rotational correlation function, R, which can be written

$$R(\mathbf{C})=\int_{-\infty}^{\infty} P_1(\mathbf{x})U(\mathbf{x})P_2(\mathbf{Cx})\mathrm{d}V\,. \qquad (1)$$

Here P_1 and P_2 are Patterson functions, $\mathbf{C}$ is a variable rotation matrix, and U is a shape function having value one within a chosen volume (usually a sphere) and value zero outside. By Fourier transformation of the right-hand side they showed that, apart from constants of proportionality,

$$R(\mathbf{C})=\sum_{\mathbf{p}}\sum_{\mathbf{h}} F_2^2(\mathbf{p})F_1^2(\mathbf{h})G(\mathbf{h}+\mathbf{h}')\,. \qquad (2)$$

The summations extend over all values of $\mathbf{h}$ and $\mathbf{p}$, the reciprocal lattice vectors of P_1 and P_2; F_1^2 and F_2^2 are the corresponding intensities. The non-integral reciprocal lattice vector $\mathbf{h}'$ is given by $\tilde{\mathbf{C}}\mathbf{p}$, where $\tilde{\mathbf{C}}$ is the transpose of the matrix $\mathbf{C}$, and G is the Fourier transform of U.

In the Rossmann–Blow formulation P_1 and P_2 are periodic. As they point out, however, no operational limitation arises, since (2) applies to any Patterson function when properly 'crystallized'.

The sum over $\mathbf{h}$ in (2) is, in fact, a convolution whose value is the Fourier transform of P_1U, which we term F_U^2. We can therefore write that

$$R(\mathbf{C})=\sum_{\mathbf{p}} F_2^2(\mathbf{p})F_U^2(\tilde{\mathbf{C}}\mathbf{p})\,, \qquad (3)$$

in which the summation need extend only over one hemisphere of reciprocal space. In the special case in which P_1 is the Patterson function P_M of an isolated molecule M, the shape function U is no longer necessary since M itself is bounded. Letting F_M^2 represent the intensity transform of M, and rotating P_1 instead of P_2, we have

$$R(\mathbf{C})=\sum_{\mathbf{p}} F_M^2(\mathbf{Cp})F_2^2(\mathbf{p})\,, \qquad (4)$$

which is the equation for the rotation function that we have used.

Considering the fast Fourier transform programs (Cooley & Tuckey, 1965; Cooley, Lewis & Welch, 1967) now available to evaluate the quantities F_U^2 or F_M^2 we believe that equation (3) or (4) will usually require less computation time than (2). The choice between direct and reciprocal space calculation, however, must be made individually for each problem. The integral in (1) will always be evaluated digitally; the relevant consideration is the number of sample points required for this evaluation *versus* the number of terms occurring in the summation in (3) or (4).

In order to improve clarity or speed of computation we have made a number of modifications in equation (4). As suggested by Rossmann & Blow we have generally omitted the low-order reflections when comparing proteins. This technique can substantially reduce the number of extraneous peaks in the rotation function, no doubt because these near-in reflections are strongly contaminated by scattering from the intermolecular mother liquor.

It is clear from (1) that, if the molecular Patterson function P_M overlaps the large values at adjacent origins of P_2, strong but physically meaningless contributions will be made to R. When such overlap occurs removal of the origin in P_2 can improve the clarity of the results. We have particularly noted this effect (Lattman, 1969) in a comparison involving 6-azidopurine, a planar molecule whose length is several times greater than that of the b axis of the crystal in which it occurs (Glusker, van der Helm, Love, Minkin & Patterson, 1968). When the possibility of overlap is present we replace the values of F_2^2 in (4) by the Fourier coefficients of P_2 with its origin removed. For proteins we have used only reflections with Bragg spacings larger than 6Å–'within the 6Å sphere'. At this resolution we can employ the relation (Lipson & Cochran, 1966)

$$F'^2 = F_2^2 - \overline{F_2^2}\,, \tag{5}$$

where $F_2'^2$ is the desired coefficient and $\overline{F_2^2}$ is the mean value of F_2^2 within the sphere of data used.

Again following Rossmann & Blow we have omitted terms in (4) for which the magnitude of $F_2'^2$ (or F_2^2) is small, effecting a considerable reduction in computing time. When removal of the origin is not necessary, we have found that only 15–20% of the reflections are required to produce clear maps.

In order to assess the significance of peaks in R we have found it useful to compute Δ, the root-mean-square fluctuation of R, which is given by

$$\Delta^2 = \frac{1}{V}\int_V [R(\boldsymbol{\theta}) - \bar{R}]^2 dV\,. \tag{6}$$

Here $\bar{R}$ is the mean value of R, and $\boldsymbol{\theta}$ $(=\theta_1, \theta_2, \theta_3)$ is the triple of Eulerian angles (Goldstein, 1959) defining **C**. We have found (Lattman, 1969) in all our trials that a peak whose height exceeds that of all other peaks by at least Δ corresponds to an actual alignment of the self-Patterson functions of interest. All our maps are scaled to a maximum value of 150 for ease in contouring. At this level typical values of Δ are between 20 and 25, while the minimum value of R is in the range -20 to 20.

The computation of R is carried out on a grid in $\boldsymbol{\theta}$ which spans the appropriate angular ranges (Tollin, Main & Rossmann, 1966). The grids we have used take fixed increments in each of the three Eulerian angles, producing uneven and inefficient sampling of R. A better sampling technique has been devised by Tollin & Cochran (1964). For every $\boldsymbol{\theta}$ each of the vectors **Ch** is computed in turn, and the value of $F_M^2(\mathbf{Ch})$ is obtained by three-dimensional, linear interpolation. The program when running on the IBM-7094 computer takes about 1 millisecond per reflection to compute one value of $R(\boldsymbol{\theta})$.

Most of our searches were done using the intensity transform of a molecule of SWMb (Bodo *et al.*, 1959; Kendrew, Dickerson, Strandberg, Hart, Davies, Phillips & Shore, 1960) which was computed by Fourier transformation of its calculated electron density function ϱ_W. We computed ϱ_W using structure factors derived from the atomic positions given by Watson (1969). In these calculations an overall, isotropic temperature factor of 20Å² was applied; structure factors were calculated to 6Å resolution; ϱ_W was evaluated at the nodes of a 2Å cubic lattice; the intensity transform was similarly sampled, at intervals of (1/128) Å^{-1}. The resultant transform has about 25,000 unique sample points within the 6Å sphere. The computation of the transform directly by structure factor calculation alone would have taken too long. Problems of correct sampling encountered in this calculation are discussed by Goodman (1968).

Results

We have investigated the D2 crystals of cyanide-methemoglobin from the sea lamprey, *Petromyzon marinus*, with the rotation function, using SWMb as a test molecule. The resultant map of R displays only one significant peak. It is higher than any other by at least $1{\cdot}2\Delta$. A portion of the map including the peak is shown in Fig. 1. In this calculation, for which the origin of the Patterson function was retained, we used about one quarter of the reflections within the 7Å hemisphere, or some 200 data. Reflections with Bragg spacings larger than 12Å were not used. We explored each Eulerian angle in the range 0–180 degrees, using 15 degree steps. A similar calculation in which the

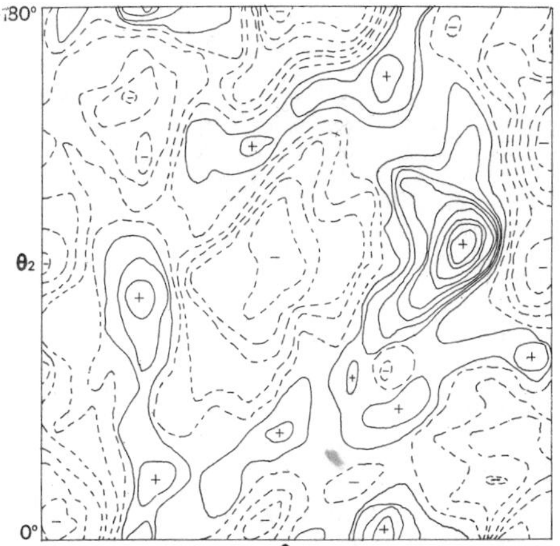

Fig. 1. Section through $R(\boldsymbol{\theta})$ for the SWMb/Lamprey hemoglobin comparison: the major peak in R is on the right, at $\theta_1 = -132$, $\theta_2 = -100$, $\theta_3 = -10°$. In order to better display the peak, unconventional limits on θ_3 have been chosen. The space group of this rotation function is $P2_1ab$, retaining the order θ_1, θ_2, θ_3. The unit cell is defined by $0 \le \theta_1 < 2\pi$, $0 \le \theta_2 < 2\pi$, $0 \le \theta_3 < \pi$. This section was calculated on a 5° grid for clarity. Contours below the mean are hatched.

Patterson function origin was deleted did not yield significantly different results.

While this paper was being revised the structure of these D2 crystals was determined in this laboratory, and it is clear that the predictions of the rotation function are fulfilled: single chains of lamprey hemoglobin do resemble the SWMb molecule, and the orientation of these chains in the unit cell is as indicated by the position of the peak in R.

Lamprey hemoglobin D2 crystals belong to the space group $P2_12_12_1$ and have one molecule weighing about 18000 Daltons in the asymmetric unit. In this case the ratio of the numbers of cross- and self-Patterson functions is 3:1, compared with a 1:1 ratio encountered in various test problems involving monoclinic space groups. The sensitivity of the rotation function may be expected to decline as this ratio increases. We were pleased to see, however, that this decline was not noticeable in going from the 1:1 to the 3:1 ratio.

Of the various test problems studied with the rotation function (Lattman, 1969) only one was of concern. A comparison of a crystalline hemoglobin from the marine annelid, *Glycera dibranchiata*, with a test molecule of SWMb gave three false peaks essentially as high as the correct one. Yet the *Glycera* hemoglobin molecule is known to resemble SWMb (Padlan & Love, 1968). In addition, a control comparison of this crystalline *Glycera* hemoglobin with an isolated molecule of the same material did give a correct and unambiguous result. We have no convincing explanation for these observations.

Conclusions

We have developed a modification of the Rossmann–Blow rotation function in which the squared transform of a molecule is compared with the intensity set from a crystal. It can be rapidly evaluated. We have used it to show that molecules in the D2 crystals of lamprey hemoglobin are closely similar to the sperm-whale metmyoglobin molecule, and to find how they are oriented in the unit cell of this crystal. Using this method, we hope to investigate crystals forms of lamprey hemoglobin having polymeric asymmetric units.

We should like to thank Drs Helen Scouloudi, Herman Watson, Eduardo Padlan and Michael Rossmann for the use of their data. We have had helpful discussions with Drs David Blow, Michael Rossmann, Jon Herriott and Wayne Hendrickson.

One of us (EEL) has been supported by pre-doctoral fellowship GM-15,907 from the USPHS, and by a fellowship from USPHS grant GM-716. The project was supported by grant AM-2528 from the USPHS. Additional funds for computation came from a grant from the Faculty of Arts and Sciences of the Johns Hopkins University, and from USPHS grant GM-716.

References

Bodo, G., Dintzis, H. M., Kendrew, J. C. & Wyckoff, H. W. (1959). *Proc. Roy. Soc.* A**253**, 70.

Cooley, J. W., Lewis, P. A. K. & Welch, P. D. (1967). *The Fast Fourier Transform and its Applications.* IBM research paper RC-1743, Yorktown Heights, N.Y.

Cooley, J. W. & Tuckey, J. W. (1965). *Mathematics of Computation,* **19**, 297.

Crowther, R. A. & Blow, D. M. (1967). *Acta Cryst.* **23**, 544.

Cullis, A. F., Muirhead, H., Perutz, M. F., Rossmann, M. G. & North, A. C. T. (1962). *Proc. Roy. Soc.* A**265**, 161.

Glusker, J. P., Van der Helm, D., Love, W. E., Minkin, J. A. & Patterson, A. L. (1968). *Acta Cryst.* B**24**, 359.

Goldstein, H. (1959). *Classical Mechanics,* p. 93. Reading: Addison-Wesley.

Goodman, J. (1968). *Introduction to Fourier Optics,* p. 21. New York: McGraw-Hill.

Hendrickson, W. A., Love, W. E. & Murray, G. (1968). *J. Mol. Biol.* **33**, 829.

Huber, R., Formanek, H. & Epp, O. (1968). *Naturwissenschaften,* **2**, 75.

Kendrew, J. C., Dickerson, R. E., Strandberg, B. E., Hart, R. G., Davies, D. R., Phillips, D. C. & Shore, V. C. (1960). *Nature, Lond.* **185**, 422.

Lattman, E. (1969). Thesis, Johns Hopkins University.

Lipson, H. & Cochran, W. (1966). *The Determination of Crystal Structures,* p. 170. London: Bell.

Main, P. & Rossmann, M. G. (1966). *Acta Cryst.* **21**, 67.

Maslen, E. N. (1968). *Acta Cryst.* B**24**, 1165.

Muirhead, H., Cox, J. M., Mazzarella, L. & Perutz, M. F. (1967). *J. Mol. Biol.* **28**, 117.

Nordman, C. (1966). *Trans. Amer. Cryst. Assoc.* **2**, 29.

Nordman, C. (1969). Personal communication.

Nordman, C. E. & Nakatsu, K. (1963). *J. Amer. Chem. Soc.* **85**, 353.

Padlan, E. A. & Love, W. E. (1968). *Nature, Lond.* **220**, 376.

Rossmann, M. G. & Blow, D. M. (1962). *Acta Cryst.* **15**, 24.

Rossmann, M. G., Blow, D. M., Harding, M. M. & Coller, E. (1964). *Acta Cryst.* **17**, 338.

Sarma, V. R. (1969). Personal communication.

Schilling, J. C. (1968). Thesis, University of Michigan.

Scouloudi, H. (1969). *J. Mol. Biol.* **40**, 353.

Tollin, P. (1966). *Acta Cryst.* **21**, 613.

Tollin, P. (1969). *J. Mol. Biol.* **45**, 481.

Tollin, P. & Cochran, W. (1964). *Acta Cryst.* **17**, 1322.

Tollin, P. Main, P. & Rossmann, M. G. (1966). *Acta Cryst.* **20**, 404.

Watson, H. C. (1969). In *Progress in Stereochemistry,* **4**, Ed. W. Klyne & P. de la Mare. In the press. New York City: Academic Press.

Zwick, M. (1969). *Abstr. Amer. Cryst. Assoc. Winter Meeting,* p. 74.

Crystallographic Evidence for the Tetrameric Subunit Structure of L-Asparaginase from *Escherichia coli*

Otto Epp, Wolfgang Steigemann, Helmut Formanek, and Robert Huber

Max-Planck-Institut für Eiweiß- und Lederforschung
und Physikalisch-Chemisches Institut der Technischen Universität, München

(Received February 22/April 5, 1971)

The analysis of a monoclinic crystal modification of L-asparaginase from *Escherichia coli* supports the chemical and physico-chemical evidence for a tetrameric subunit structure.

The pseudo-symmetries occurring in the crystal structure provide evidence that the molecules lie on positions with approximate point symmetry 222.

Interest in L-asparaginase arose mainly because of the anti-tumor activity of asparaginases from several sources [1—3]. Of these, asparaginase from *Escherichia coli* appears to be the best characterized by chemical and physico-chemical methods [3a, 4, 5]. The molecular weight is approximately 135000. There was a controversy about the number of subunits. A tetrameric structure, however, with a subunit molecular weight of approximately 35000 seems to clearly established now [6, 5, 7, 7a].

We provide evidence for the tetrameric structure of asparaginase by crystallographic methods. Furthermore, we show that the molecule viewed at 1 nm resolution possesses a high degree of 222 symmetry.

The asparaginase which we used for our investigations was a highly purified preparation from *Escherichia coli* strain ATCC 9637. Its specific activity was 280 U/mg [4]. Prolonged electrophoresis showed that the crystalline material consists of several iso-enzymes [4]. These iso-enzymes, however, showed identical specific activity. Furthermore, cyanogen bromide cleavage of the crystalline material [6], the determination of the N-terminal amino acids of the cyanogen bromide peptides [8] and the determination of the N-terminal amino acid sequences provided no indication of chemical heterogeneity among the polypeptide chains. We may therefore conclude that there are only minor differences between the subunits making up the isoenzymes.

Crystallization and Crystallographic Data

We crystallized our material in analogy to the procedure described by Wagner, Bauer, Irion, Rauenbusch, Kaufmann and Arens [9]. 30 mg of asparaginase was dissolved in 1.5 ml water. 0.5 ml of 50 % polyethylene glycol solution was added. On standing overnight, a small amount of microcrystalline material formed which was removed by centrifugation. Upon addition of small quantities of polyethylene glycol solution crystallization took place within several days. We also obtained suitable crystals by a diffusion procedure. Asparaginase solution in thick-walled capillaries closed with a dialysis membrane was equilibrated with 14 % polyethylene glycol solution. Crystallization took place after approximately a week. The crystals usually grow in needle-like shape with approximate dimensions $0.5 \times 0.2 \times 2.0$ mm. They tend to twin as described later.

Lattice constants and space group are as described by Born and Bauer [10]: $a = 15.44$ nm, $b = 6.29$ nm, $c = 14.29$ nm, $\beta = 62.3°$ (determined by diffractometer measurements), systematic extinctions for hkl: $h + k = 2n + 1$, space group C2, volume of asymmetric unit: 306.9 nm^3. Assuming the most probable value for the solvent content in protein crystals [11] the molecular weight of the asymmetric unit is calculated as 134000 in close agreement with the molecular weight of asparaginase. Furthermore, a closely similar value has been found for the volume occupied by one asparaginase molecule from a different source (*Erwinia carotovora*) crystallized in a different modification [12]. Reflexion intensities were measured with a Siemens diffractometer to 0.75 nm resolution. The 1200 independent reflexions were all measured on one crystal specimen without detectable radiation damage.

RESULTS

A photograph of the $h0l$ plane shows that reflexions at low resolution with $l = 2n + 1$ are all extremely weak. Furthermore, the intensity distribution indicates pseudo-mirror lines along the a^* axis, and by symmetry also perpendicular to a^*. Deviations appear to become appreciable only for reflexions at a resolution higher than about 1 nm.

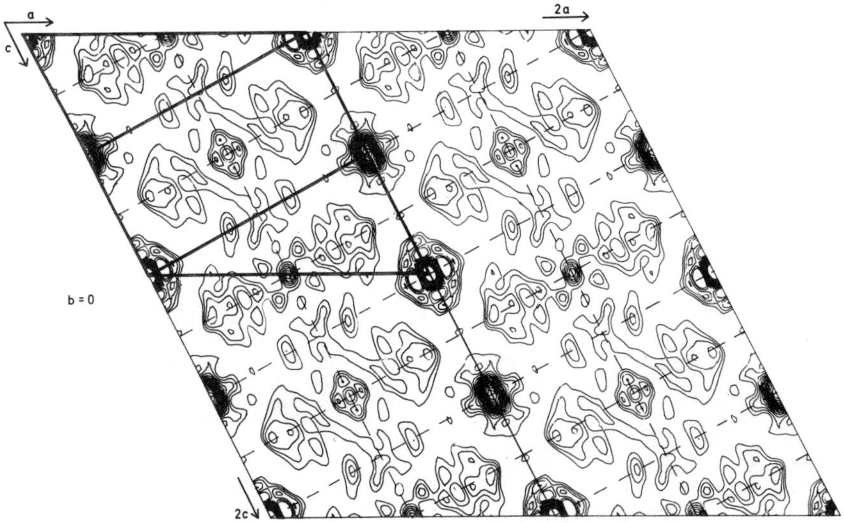

ig. 1. *Patterson map at 1 nm resolution.* Section a, c at $b = 0$. our unit cells are drawn to demonstrate the symmetry roperties. Only positive contour lines are drawn. The first ontour is at 100. The line separation is 100. These are arbirary units. Several contour lines in the immediate vicinity of the zero peak are left out. The pseudo-mirror-lines parallel to c and a^* at $a = 0, 1/2$ and $c = 0, 1/4, 1/2, 3/4$, respectively are dashed. The high peak at 0, 0, 1/2 is the pseudo-origin peak of the orthorhombic pseudo-cell. The true monoclinic cell and the orthorhombic pseudo-cell are heavily out lined

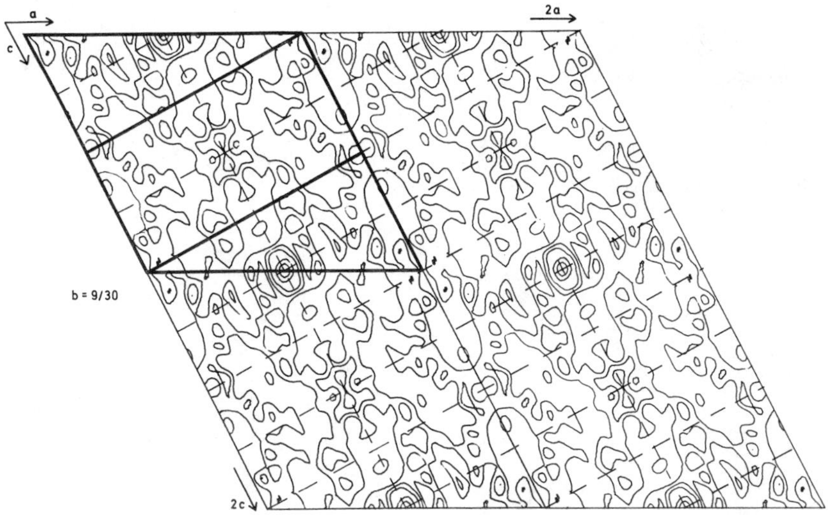

Fig. 2. *Patterson map, section at* b = 9/30. The pseudo-mirror lines are indicated

Other photographs confirmed these observations: low resolution reflexions are generally strong only for even l and their intensity distribution shows pseudo-symmetry planes perpendicular to a^*, and by symmetry also perpendicular to c. Therefore an orthorhombic pseudo-cell in reciprocal space may be defined with $a^{*\prime}$ and $b^{*\prime}$ unchanged with respect to the monoclinic cell and $c^{*\prime}$ perpendicular to a^* and b^* and having a length $2c^* \times \sin\beta$. A pseudo-space-group can be deduced as I222. The volume of the pseudo-cell in real space is one half the volume of the monoclinic cell and contains two molecules. As the pseudo-space-group has eight equivalent general positions the molecules must occupy special positions with point symmetry 222.

In order to confirm these symmetry properties in a more rigorous way, we calculated a Patterson function at 1 nm resolution and explored its pseudo-symmetry using programs devised for the *Faltmolekül* method [13—15].

The Patterson map clearly shows pseudo-symmetry planes perpendicular to c at $c = 0$, 1/4, 1/2, 3/4 and perpendicular to a^* at $a = 0$ and 1/2. Figs. 1 and 2 are sections at heights $b = 0$, and 9/30, respectively, through the threedimensional Patterson map. The pseudo-symmetry planes appear as mirror lines in these sections. They are dashed. The very high peak at 0, 0, 1/2 (Fig. 1) may be regarded as the pseudo origin peak of the orthorhombic cell. This will be discussed later from a different point of view. The Patterson function thus fully confirms the deductions drawn from the inspection of the X-ray photographs.

In order to have a quantitative measure of the pseudo-symmetries, *Faltmolekül* calculations were performed. Such calculations allow one to rotate two structures against one other to determine the degree of similarity as a function of relative orientation. A vector set and a Patterson map or two Patterson maps may, for example, be compared in this way. The pseudo-symmetry of the Patterson map of asparaginase can therefore be explored by rotating it against itself. As we are primarily interested in the symmetry relations between the molecular subunits the calculation was limited to a sphere with a radius of 2 nm centred at the origin of the Patterson map as the intrasubunit vectors should be concentrated here. In order to have reasonable calculation times 500 grid points of the Patterson map were selected for the rotational search. We used the criterion of fit described by one of us [14]. The absolute values of the differences at the grid points of the two maps compared are summed. Orientations where the two maps fit, are therefore characterized by minima of the function.

All significant peaks are concentrated in the plane $\vartheta = 0$. (A definition of the Eulerian angles ψ, ϑ, φ has been given by one of us [14]. ψ is the rotational angle around c^*, ϑ around a, and φ around b.) Fig. 3 is a section through the three-dimensional function at $\vartheta = 0$. To illustrate its symmetry proper-

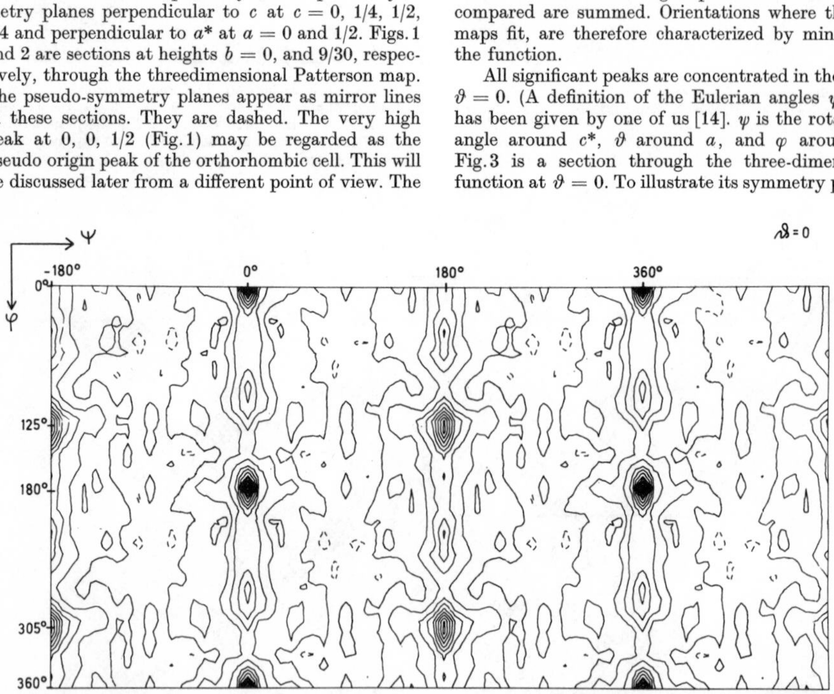

Fig. 3. Faltmolekül *calculation*. Section at $\vartheta = 0$. The contour with a dashed and full line superposed is at height 9470, that is the average value of the function. Contours below this value are drawn out, contours above are dashed. The contour line separation is 809, that is the standard deviation of the function. The minimum at $\varphi = 0°$, $\psi = 0°$ corresponding to no rotation has a height of 185. The minimum at $\varphi = -180°$, $\psi = 125°$ is 2650. It indicates the presence of local diads parallel to c and a^*. More than the asymmetric unit is drawn to demonstrate the symmetry properties of the function

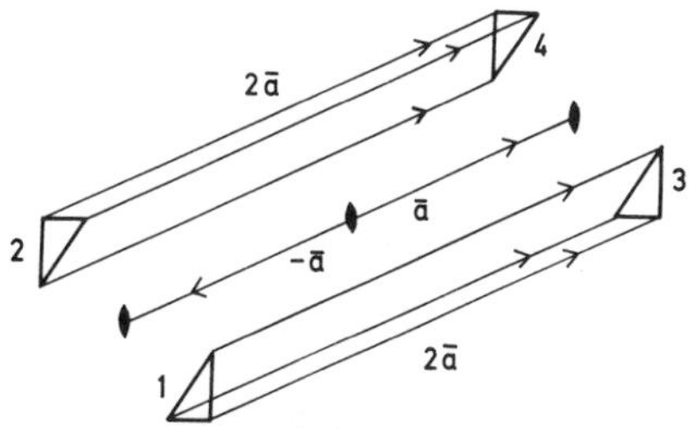

Fig. 4. *Explanation of a peak resulting from a local diad parallel to a crystallographic diad.* The triangles represent model structures consisting of three atoms which lie in the plane of paper. A crystallographic diad and two non-crystallographic diads are perpendicular to the plane of paper. The presence of the non-crystallographic diads parallel to a crystallographic diad gives rise to a maximum in the Patterson map with a height of one half of the zero maximum. If the non-crystallographic diads are at positions $\pm \bar{a}$ from the crystallographic diad, there are 6 identical vectors $2\bar{a}$ between the 12 atoms of the model structure

ties, more than one asymmetric unit is drawn. The average value of the function is 9470, with a standard deviation (σ) of 809. The minimum at $\psi = 0°$, $\varphi = 0°$ corresponding to no rotation has a height of 185. That is 11.5 σ above background. The next lowest value of 2650 is at $\psi = 180°$, $\varphi = 125°$. It is 8.5 σ above background. A further minimum at $\psi = 0°$, $\sigma = 90°$, with a height of 5750 is of doubtful significance being only 4.5 σ above background.

The simultaneous rotations of $\psi = -180°$, $\varphi = 125°$, $\vartheta = 0°$ are equivalent to a two-fold axis lying in the $a\,c$ plane and making an angle of $90° + 62.5°$ with the a axis. It is therefore parallel to the a^* axis. By symmetry there is a second two-fold axis parallel to c. These calculations were confined to a small region of the Patterson map near the origin. Therefore, they strictly provide evidence for local diads only. The Patterson map however clearly showed that the pseudo-symmetry extends through the whole unit cell and does not appear to be stronger near the origin.

The highest peak in the Patterson map is at 0, 0, 1/2. Its height is 2200 compared with 4900 for the zero maximum. It is far higher than any other feature. Fig. 4 explains how such a peak could result from a local diad parallel to a crystallographic diad. If local diads are at $\pm \bar{a}$ a peak should occur at $2\bar{a}$ due to the coincidence of vectors between the triangles 1 and 3 and 2 and 4, respectively. Its height should be one half the height of the origin peak. The peak at 0, 0, 1/2 in the Patterson map is therefore due to a local diad parallel to the b axis at $x = 0$ and $z = 1/4$.

These deductions are in accordance with the symmetry properties derived from inspection of the Patterson map. The molecule possesses a rather high degree of 222 symmetry. We should, however, keep in mind that all calculations were done with data to 1 nm resolution. Our conclusions are therefore only valid within this resolution limit. X-ray photographs and a Patterson map calculated at 0.75 nm resolution clearly show, that the deviation from the high symmetry increases with resolution.

Some considerations can be made concerning the degree and the nature of the deviation of the molecule from 222 symmetry.

Deviation from 222 Symmetry

The *Faltmolekül* calculations showed that the minimum arising from the local diads parallel to a^* and c is much less pronounced than the zero minimum corresponding to no rotation. This must be due to deviations from perfect two-fold symmetry.

The same holds for the pseudo diad parallel to b. The Patterson peak caused by this diad has a height of 2200 compared with the value 4900 it should have on its special position in the Patterson map. Fig. 3 and in particular Fig. 5, however, show that this peak is appreciably elongated in the c-direction. This is probably caused by overlap of two peaks at positions 0, 0, $1/2 + x$, and 0, 0, $1/2 - x$, so that a reduced height might be expected. Nevertheless, the deviation from exact two-fold symmetry appears to be appreciable even at 1 nm resolution.

There is one observation which throws some light on the nature of the distortion of the asparaginase molecule in the crystal lattice. As described before, reflexions on reciprocal lattice planes with l odd are caused by features of the crystal structure deviating from the symmetry required by the pseudo space group. The intensity distribution on plane $hk1$ for example shows that all reflexions on and in the vicinity of the b^* axis are very weak even at high diffraction angles (0.3 nm resolution). This means that the major components of the distortions are in the a and c directions, while the structure is ordered in the b direction in terms of the pseudo-symmetry. Chemical heterogeneity of the four subunits as the sole cause for the deviation from the higher symmetry is therefore improbable, as here the deviations should be observed in the whole reciprocal space. Translational and/or rotational distortions must play an important role. These could be due to packing forces in the crystal lattice even between molecules with identical subunits.

There are two types of diads parallel to b. The exact crystallographic diad at $a = 0$, $c = 0$ and the pseudo-diad at $a = 0, c \simeq 1/4$. The molecule may occupy either position so exhibiting in one case a perfect molecular diad, in the other a pseudo-diad. There is one observation which may be interpreted in favour of the latter possibility. If the elongation

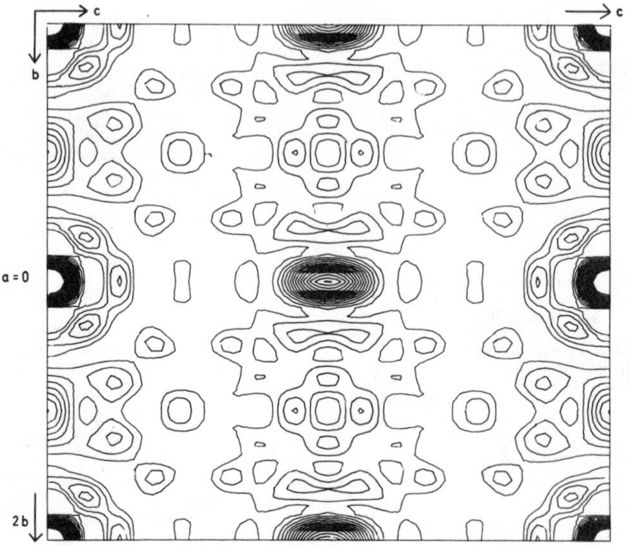

Fig. 5. *Section* b, c *at* a = *0 through the Patterson map.* The pseudo origin peak at 0, 0, 1/2 is appreciably elongated in the c direction. Contours as in Fig. 1

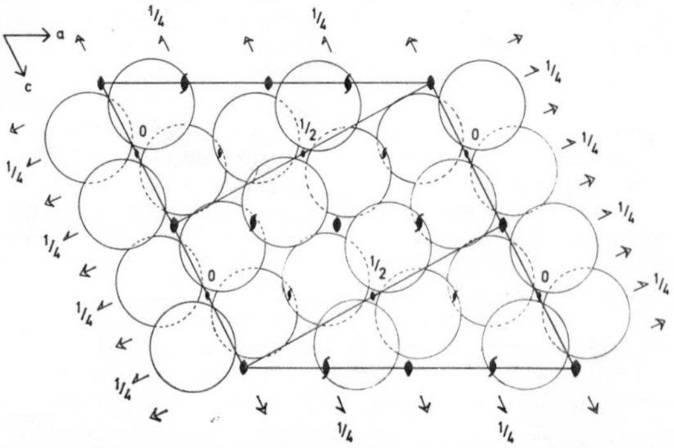

Fig. 6. *Molecular packing as viewed from the* b *direction.* The subunits are assumed to be spheres with a diameter of 4 nm. The crystallographic and the non-crystallographic symmetries are indicated by thick and thin symbols respectively. The monoclinic cell and the orthorhombic pseudo-cell are shown. The molecular centres lie on pseudo-diads parallel to *b*. Their heights are indicated

of the Patterson peak at 0, 0, $\simeq 1/2$ in the *c*-direction is due to overlap of two nearly coincident peaks, the positions of the local diads parallel to *b* should be $a = 0$, $c = 1/4 \pm x/2$ and $a = 0$, $c = 3/4 \mp x/2$. If the molecules lie on the true diads at $c = 0$ and 1/2, it is difficult to explain why the pseudo-diads should deviate from the $c = 1/4$, 3/4 positions. However, if the molecules lie on the pseudo-diads, the deviations would represent small shifts of the molecules in the *c*-direction out of the $c = 1/4$, 3/4 positions, possibly caused by packing forces.

Twinning

Upon examination of X-ray photographs a large proportion of the crystalline material was found to be twinned. The plane of twinning is the *b c* plane. The two individuals are related by the pseudo-diad *c*. Such a twinning scheme can easily be understood in the light of the pseudo-symmetries mentioned above.

DISCUSSION

The crystallographic observations support the chemical and physico-chemical evidence that the asparaginase molecule is a tetramer. Furthermore, it has been shown that the four subunits are structurally similar and assembled according to the 222 pseudo-symmetry of the molecule if viewed at 1 nm resolution. The asparaginase molecules may be packed in the crystal lattice according to the symmetry requirements in a satisfactory way, if we assume tetrahedrally arranged spherical subunits with a diameter of 4 nm (Fig. 6). The measured sedimentation velocity [16] also indicates a spherical shape of the whole molecule, and the electron micrographs show a globular appearance of the molecules [7].

Several other tetrameric protein molecules analysed so far have 222 or pseudo-222 symmetry with their subunits in pseudo-tetrahedral arrangement (haemoglobin [17], lactate dehydrogenase [18], aldolase [19]). This arrangement appears to be favourable also in view of the arguments put forward by Monod, Wyman and Changeaux [20] and Hanson [21] for pseudotetrahedral shell structures.

We thank the Farbenfabriken Bayer AG. for providing us with asparaginase and in particular Drs. E. Rauenbusch and V. Schmidt-Kastner for helpful discussions. We are also indebted to Dr. M. Korekawa, Universität München and Dr. N. Brodherr, Max-Planck-Institut, München, for useful discussions. This work was supported by the Deutsche Forschungsgemeinschaft.

REFERENCES

1. Broome, J. D., *Nature (London)*, 191 (1961) 1114.
2. Mashburn, L. T., and Wriston, J. C., *Arch. Biochem. Biophys.* 105 (1964) 450.
3. Adamson, R. H., and Fabro, S., *Cancer Chemother. Rep.* 52 (1968) 617.
3a. Whelan, H. A., and Wriston, J. C., *Biochemistry*, 8 (1969) 2386.
4. Arens, A., Rauenbusch, E., Irion, E., Wagner, O., Bauer, K., and Kaufmann, W., *Hoppe-Seyler's Z. Physiol. Chem.* 351 (1970) 197.
5. Ho, P. P., Milikan, E. B., Bobitt, J. L., Grinnan, E. L., Burck, P. L., Frank, B. H., Boeck, D., and Squires, R. W., *J. Biol. Chem.* 245 (1970) 3708.
6. Glossmann, H., and Bode, W., *Hoppe-Seyler's Z. Physiol. Chem.* 352 (1971) 132.
7. Irion, E., and Voigt, W. H., *Hoppe-Seyler's Z. Physiol. Chem.* 351 (1970) 1154.
7a. Jackson, R. C., and Handschumacher, R. E., *Biochemistry*, 9 (1970) 3585.
8. Rauenbusch, E., Irion, E., and Arens, A., private communication.
9. Wagner, O., Bauer, K., Irion, E., Rauenbusch, E., Kaufmann, W., and Arens, A., *Angew. Chem.* 81 (1969) 904.
10. Born, L., and Bauer, K., *Naturwissenschaften*, 57 (1970) 545.
11. Matthews, B. W., *J. Mol. Biol.* 33 (1968) 491.
12. North, A. C. T., Wade, H. E., and Cammack, K. A., *Nature (London)*, 224 (1969) 594.
13. Hoppe, W., *Z. Elektrochem.* 61 (1957) 1076.
14. Huber, R., *Acta Cryst.* 19 (1965) 353.
15. Huber, R., in *Crystallographic Computing*, Proc. 1969 Int. Summer School on Crystallographic Computing (edited by F. R. Ahmed), Munksgaard, Copenhagen 1969, p. 96.
16. Frank, B. H., Pekar, A. H., Veros, A. J., and Ho, P. P. K., *J. Biol. Chem.* 245 (1970) 3716.
17. Perutz, M. F., Muirhead, H., Cox, J. M., and Goaman, L. C. G., *Nature (London)*, 219 (1968) 131.
18. Adams, M. J., Mc Pherson, A., Rossmann, M. G., Schevitz, R. W., and Wonacott, A. J., *J. Mol. Biol.* 51 (1970) 31.
19. Eagles, P. A. M., Johnson, L. N., and Joynson, M. A., *J. Mol. Biol.* 45 (1969) 533.
20. Monod, J., Wyman, J., and Changeux, J. P., *J. Mol. Biol.* 12 (1965) 88.
21. Hanson, K. R., *J. Mol. Biol.* 22 (1966) 405.

O. Epp, W. Steigemann, H. Formanek, and R. Huber
Max-Planck-Institut für Eiweiß- und Lederforschung
BRD-8000 München 15, Schillerstraße 46
German Federal Republic

J. Mol. Biol. (1971) **60**, 271–277

Structure of Yellow Fin Tuna Metmyoglobin at 6Å Resolution

Eaton E. Lattman†, Clive E. Nockolds‡, Robert H. Kretsinger‡ and Warner E. Love†

†Thomas C. Jenkins Department of Biophysics Johns Hopkins University, Baltimore, Md. 21218, U.S.A. *and* *‡Department of Biology, University of Virginia Charlottesville, Va. 22903, U.S.A.*

(*Received 22 December 1970, and in revised form 2 June 1971*)

Using Patterson function searches we have shown that myoglobin from the yellow fin tuna (*Neothunnus macropterus*) has, at low resolution, a tertiary structure similar to that of sperm whale myoglobin. The position established for the heme iron by this procedure is in agreement with that independently derived from a Patterson synthesis based on anomalous dispersion.

1. Introduction

In recent years crystallographic studies have shown that myoglobins (Scouloudi, 1969; Bodo, Dintzis, Kendrew & Wyckoff, 1959) and hemoglobin subunits (Cullis, Muirhead, Perutz, Rossmann & North, 1961; Muirhead, Cox, Mazzarella & Perutz, 1967; Padlan & Love, 1968; Huber, Formanek & Epp, 1968; Hendrickson & Love, *Abstr. Amer. Cryst. Ass.* Summer, 1970) from various sources all have similar structures, whose prototype has been termed the "myoglobin fold". We have been interested in the phyletic distribution of this structure. No globins from the bony fishes (Osteichthyes) have been included in these studies, so we have undertaken an investigation of crystals of yellow fin tuna (*Neothunnus macropterus*) metmyoglobin (Brown, Martinez, Johnstone & Olcott, 1962).

2. Materials and Methods

Yellow fin tuna met-Mb crystals (Kretsinger, 1968), grown in 70% saturated ammonium sulfate, have the symmetry of the orthorhombic space group $P2_12_12_1$, with a=44·4 Å, b=72·1 Å, c=52·3 Å. There is one molecule of weight about 17,000 daltons in the asymmetric unit. Reflections with Bragg spacings as small as 2 Å are observed. Using 9 crystals, we recorded a nearly complete, 3-dimensional set of 6 Å data, and about 50% of the remaining data between 6 Å and 2·2 Å, on 15, one-zone precession photographs. With exposure times of 50 to 80 hr we were able to assign non-zero values to 70% of the theoretically available intensities. The crystals were stable in the X-ray beam for 150 hr.

Integrated intensities were measured on a rotating drum desnitometer with a 200 micron raster, and processed using programs described by Nockolds & Kretsinger (1970). The quality of the data can be judged from the statistics given in Table 1. Note particularly the values for R_{equiv} and R_{anom} certainly do not suggest the presence of a significant anomalous scatterer. The data from different planes were placed on a common scale and merged by the procedure of Rae & Blake (1966).

TABLE 1

Residuals describing intensity data

Factor	Definition	Value	Comparison
R_{merge}	$\frac{\sum_{h}\sum_{j=1}^{N(h)} \lvert \bar{I}_j(h) - \bar{I}(h) \rvert}{\sum_{h} N(h)\cdot\bar{I}(h)}$	0·06	Averaged intensitie and individual observations
R_{scale}	$\frac{\sum \lvert I_1 - KI_2 \rvert}{\sum (I_1 + KI_2)}$	0·042 (mean)	Observations within a film pack
R_{equiv}	$\frac{\sum \lvert I_1 - I_2 \rvert}{\sum (I_1 + I_2)}$	0·033 (mean)	Equivalent reflections on the same film
R_{anom}	$\frac{\sum \lvert I_+ - I_- \rvert}{\sum (I_+ + I_-)}$	0·034 (mean)	Bijvoet pairs

R_{merge} : $I_j(\mathbf{h})$ is the scaled intensity at reciprocal lattice point **h** as measured on the jth of th N (**h**) films on which it occurs, and $\bar{I}$ is the final averaged value of the I_j.

R_{scale} : K is the scale factor relating 2 films within a film pack.

3. Structure Determination

The hypothesis that yellow fin tuna met-Mb has the myoglobin fold clearly seemed warranted, so we decided to use Patterson function search methods for the structure determination. Our procedure followed closely that of Tollin (1969). It is a two-step process in which first the orientation and then the position of a test molecule are determined, relative to the unit cell axes. Phases calculated with the test molecule in this proposed configuration are then applied to the observed structure amplitudes to yield approximate Fourier coefficients for the experimental structure of interest

Our test molecule was the backbone, including β-carbons, of the well-studied sperm whale myoglobin molecule (Watson, 1969). To determine the orientation at which it fits best in our met-Mb unit cell, we used a computationally swift version of the Rossmann & Blow (1962) rotation function which has been described by Lattman & Love (1970). In it a dominant peak in the correlation function

$$R(\boldsymbol{\theta}) = \sum_{\mathbf{h}} I(\mathbf{h})\cdot F^2(\mathbf{Ch}) \quad (1)$$

is sought. Here $\boldsymbol{\theta} = (\theta_1, \theta_2, \theta_3)$ is a triple of Eulerian angles, the $I(\mathbf{h})$ are the observed intensities, and F^2 is the continuous Fourier transform of the Patterson function of the test molecule. The matrix **C** is a variable rotation operator which is a function of $\boldsymbol{\theta}$. The index **h** runs through reciprocal lattice points included in the summation. As is customary we deleted all reflections with Bragg spacings larger than 12 Å and used only the strongest fifth of the reflections with spacings between 12 and 6 Å.

To assess the significance of peaks in $R(\boldsymbol{\theta})$ it has been found useful to compute the quantity

$$\Delta^2 = \frac{1}{N}\sum_{i=1}^{N} (R(\boldsymbol{\theta}_i) - \bar{R})^2$$

which is the mean square fluctuation of R. Here, the $\boldsymbol{\theta}_i$ are the N points at which R

was evaluated, and $\bar{R}$ is the mean value of $R(\boldsymbol{\theta})$. Experience has shown that a peak higher than any other by at least Δ is very likely to represent the correct orientation of the test molecule in the crystal. We have found such a peak at $\theta_1 = 189°$, $\theta_2 = 232°$, $\theta_3 = 294°$, where the initial orientation and axial system have been defined by Lattman & Love (1970).

With the values of R scaled to the range 0 to 100, Δ is 14. The second-highest peak on the map has value 85, and there are five peaks in the interval 80 to 85. In the direction of greatest elongation the largest peak falls off by an amount Δ in a true rotational distance of about 10 degrees.

The translation function of Crowther & Blow (1967) is most easily visualized in terms of a comparison between the model and experimental Patterson functions. It can reveal the position of a correctly oriented test molecule, relative to a chosen symmetry element. Crowther & Blow describe several variants of this function. We have chosen the type they term T_1, wherein the intramolecular vectors of the experimental Patterson function are approximately removed to improve the signal-to-noise ratio. Sections of the translation function were calculated at $x = 1/2$, $y = 1/2$ and $z = 1/2$, utilizing separately the symmetry of three mutually perpendicular screw axes. The procedure is a straightforward extension of that described by Crowther & Blow

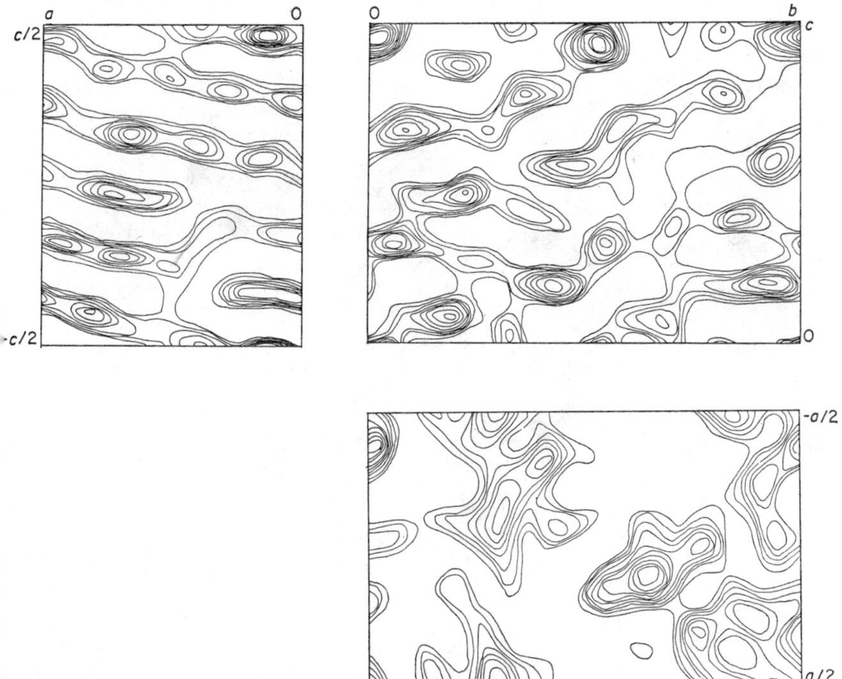

FIG. 1. Sections at $a/2$, $b/2$, $c/2$ through the translation function, utilizing the preliminary molecular orientation. Reflections with spacings between 6 and 12 Å were used. The sections are arranged so that the reader can easily search for consistent sets of peaks. The correct peaks are seen in the upper left-hand corner of the two right-hand sections, and in the upper-right hand corner of the left-hand section.

for the space group $P2_1$. The interpretation of these sections is strictly analogous to that of the Harker sections from a structure in space group $P2_12_12_1$ with one atom in the asymmetric unit. We found only one molecular position consistent with large peaks on all three sections: of these three peaks, however, only one was the largest within its own section (Fig. 1).

We then set up a model of the yellow fin tuna met-Mb crystal structure using the sperm whale molecule in the calculated position and orientation. Phases for this model were computed by appropriately sampling and phase-shifting the Fourier transform of the molecular electron density function of sperm whale Mb. A Fourier synthesis using these phases and observed yellow fin tuna met-Mb amplitudes showed myoglobin-like molecules which did not interpenetrate. This result was very encouraging, since most incorrect interpretations of the translation function generate physically unreasonable packing arrangements. In addition, an anomalous dispersion difference Patterson synthesis, to be discussed later, has confirmed the heme-iron co-ordinates.

We then undertook to refine these rotational and positional parameters. We first calculated coefficients for the model structure's Patterson function, simplified to contain only inter-molecular vectors. These coefficients, properly scaled, were subtracted from the observed intensities to give, to a first approximation, coefficients for

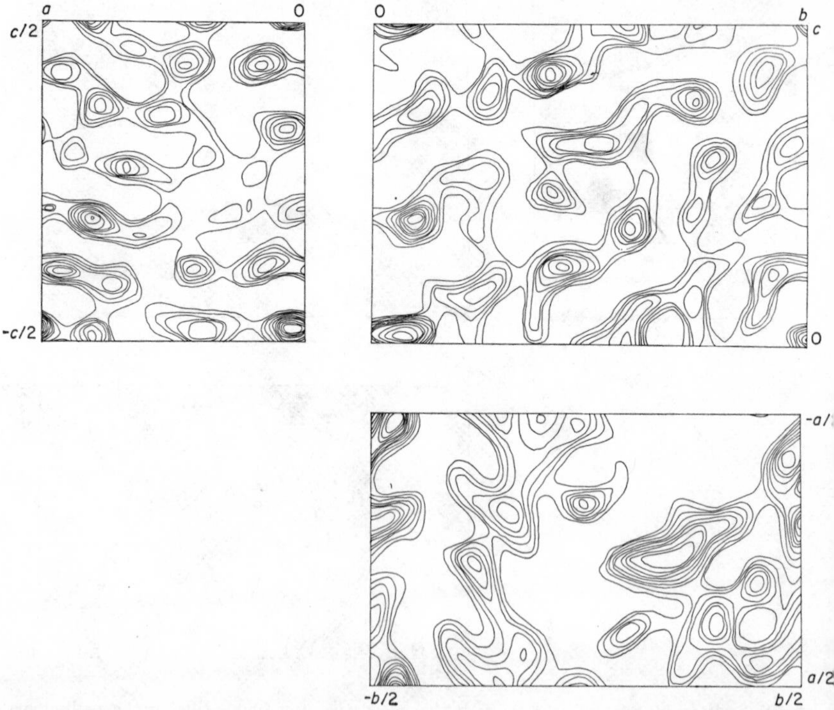

FIG. 2. Sections at $a/2$, $b/2$, $c/2$ through the translation function, utilizing the refined molecular orientations. Sections calculated and arranged as in Fig. 1. The correct peaks are slightly shifted, and are one or two contour levels higher, compared to other large peaks, than are the peaks in the preliminary map.

a met-Mb Patterson synthesis containing only intramolecular vectors. These coefficients are much more suitable than the observed intensities for an accurate rotation-fu t on calculation, which depends upon superposition of intramolecular vector sets. The rotation function, recalculated using these modified coefficients, showed the dominant peak shifted by a small amount to $\theta_1=195°$, $\theta_2=229°$, $\theta_3=297°$. Surprisingly, the relative height of the correct peak in the refined map was no higher than in the preliminary map; it was no sharper. We do not understand fully the reasons for this, but it may result from the very large errors occurring in the calculated coefficients for the intermolecular vectors. The refined value of $\boldsymbol{\theta}$ was used in another translation function calculation in which the previous molecular position was confirmed. The peaks corresponding to this solution, slightly shifted from their location in the preliminary map, are now the largest on their respective sections (Fig. 2).

These refined parameters were used, as explained previously, to calculate model structure factors. The phases from these were applied to the observed met-Mb structure amplitudes, and the resultant coefficients were used to synthesize our best estimate of the structure, which we will describe later.

4. Anomalous Dispersion Patterson Synthesis

For a mercury derivative of horse hemoglobin, Rossmann (1961) calculated the Patterson synthesis with coefficients $(F(\mathbf{h})-F(-\mathbf{h}))^2$. He was able to identify

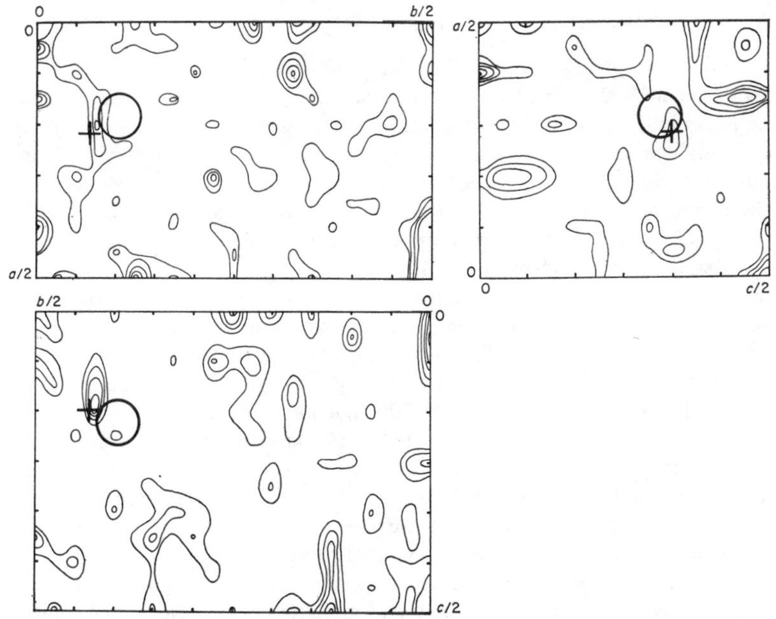

FIG. 3. Patterson synthesis based on anomalous scattering from yellow fin tuna metmyoglobin. The three Harker section at x, y, $z=1/2$ were calculated using the coefficients $(F(\mathbf{h})-F(-\mathbf{h}))^2$ from the 2·2 Å resolution data. The contour levels are the same on the three sections. The axes and origins have been arranged so that the viewer can easily compare peak positions. The iron–iron vector, as calculated from both the unrefined and the refined rotational and translational parameters, is indicated on each section by a cross (unrefined) and by a circle (refined). The radius of the circle is equivalent to 1 Å in Fourier space.

mercury–mercury atom vectors and, after applying the Buerger minimum function to locate mercury–iron atom vectors. Cullis *et al.* (1961) have shown that it is possible to use the anomalous dispersion effect of the iron atoms in hemoglobin to establish the absolute configuration of the molecule. Matthews (1966) found that the iodine–iodine atom vectors in pipsyl-α-chromotrypsin were almost as well resolved in a $(F(\mathbf{h})-F(-\mathbf{h}))^2$ synthesis as in the conventional difference Patterson, $(F_H-F)^2$. Kraut, Strahs & Freer (1968) were able to establish the position of the cluster of four iron atoms in the high potential iron protein of *Chromatium D* from an anomalous dispersion Patterson synthesis at 4 Å resolution. In myoglobin and hemoglobin the only atom with a significant anomalous dispersion component is the heme iron; for CuKα radiation $\Delta f''/(f+\Delta f') = 3{\cdot}4/(26-1{\cdot}1)$. It therefore seemed reasonable to apply this method to test the validity of our structure determination.

We calculate anomalous dispersion Patterson maps using both the complete set of 6 Å data, and the partially complete 2·2 Å set. Despite the difference of a factor of five in the number of terms used, the two maps were qualitatively quite similar indicating that the higher resolution data are meaningful. There are only two consistent sets of Harker peaks on the 6 Å map. These sets, among others, also occur on the noisier but more precise 2·2 Å map. One of these sets gives a position for the heme iron which is within 1 Å of that derived from the combined rotation–translation function calculations (see Fig. 3).

5. The Structure

Our synthesis indicates that yellow fin tuna met-Mb has the myoglobin fold. However, the method of structure determination employed is open to serious criticism. Strong peaks in the rotation and translation functions are encouraging by experience, but are not conclusive evidence of structural similarity. Further, a peak in the combined rotation–translation function implies at least modest agreement between calculated and observed intensity patterns. A Fourier synthesis calculated with test molecule phases and crudely correct amplitudes is bound to resemble the test molecule closely (Ramachandran & Srinivasan, 1961).

However, a number of factors suggest that our model for yellow fin tuna met-Mb is essentially correct. The most important evidence is the anomalous dispersion Patterson synthesis shown in Figure 3. The position of the anomalous scatterer determined from it coincides very well with the position of the heme iron in the model. This would be most unlikely if met-Mb did not have the myoglobin fold. Equally unlikely would be the physically reasonable packing arrangement we found. Taken together, these points provide strong evidence in favor of the proposed structure. The R-value for this structure is 46%, as calculated using all reflections with Bragg spacings between 10 and 6 Å. This compares favorably with the R-value of 38% calculated when our backbone model was used to approximate the published sperm whale Mb structure. Finally, we are encouraged because the refined value from the rotation function yielded a much sharper and more significant peak in the translation function.

The electron density map of yellow fin tuna met-Mb is very clear (Plate I), and it is easy to isolate one molecule. The course of the chain can be followed unambiguously, and there are no anomalous internal contacts. The C-D region (e.g. Watson 1969), has low electron density which falls, at one place, below the level used to define the

PLATE I. Models of two of the four molecules in the yellow fin tuna met-Mb unit cell, displaying the closest intermolecular contact observed. The screw axis parallel to a is vertical, and penetrates the region of contact. Note the gap in the C–D region.

molecule. This is known to be a variable region in the globins, and its diffuse appearance is not surprising. Measurement of the inter-helix angles in the met-Mb structure indicates that it resembles sperm whale Mb more closely than any of the hemoglobin subunits listed by Padlan & Love (1968). How much of this similarity is real, and how much is introduced by the use of model phases, we cannot say. These matters are discussed by Tollin (1969).

6. Conclusions

Using Patterson function searches we have shown that a globin from a bony fish has approximately the same structure as all of the other globins whose structures have been determined. We are exploring methods for refining the structure.

This research was supported at the University of Virginia by its Center for Advanced Studies and by National Institutes of Health grant no. 1-R01-GM 1578B-01, and at Johns Hopkins University by a computing grant from the Faculty of Arts and Sciences and by National Institutes of Health grant no. AM02528.

REFERENCES

Bodo, G., Dintzis, H. M., Kendrew, J. C. & Wyckoff, H. W. (1959). *Proc. Roy. Soc.* **A,253**, 70.
Brown, W. D., Martinez, M., Johnstone, M. & Olcott, H. S. (1962). *J. Biol. Chem.* **237**, 81.
Crowther, R. A. & Blow, D. M. (1967). *Acta Cryst.* **23**, 544.
Cullis, A. F., Muirhead, H., Perutz, M. F., Rossmann, M. G. & North, A. C. T. (1961). *Proc. Roy. Soc.* **A,265**, 15.
Huber, R., Formanek, H. & Epp, O. (1968). *Naturwissenschaften*, **2**, 75.
Kraut, J., Strahs, G. & Freer, S. T. (1968). In *Structural Chemistry and Molecular Biology*, ed. by A. Rich & N. Davidson, p. 55. San Francisco and London: W. H. Freeman & Co.
Kretsinger, R. H. (1968). *J. Mol. Biol.* **38**, 141.
Lattman, E. E. & Love, W. E. (1970). *Acta Cryst. B.* **26**, 1854.
Matthews, B. W. (1966). *Acta Cryst.* **20**, 230.
Muirhead, H., Cox, J. M., Mazzarella, L. & Perutz, M. F. (1967). *J. Mol. Biol.* **28**, 117.
Nockolds, C. E. & Kretsinger, R. H. (1970). *J. Phys. E. Sci. Instrum.* **3**, 842.
Padlan, E. A. & Love, W. E. (1968). *Nature*, **220**, 376.
Rae, A. D. & Blake, A. B. (1966). *Acta Cryst.* **20**, 586.
Ramachandran, G. N. & Srinivasan, R. (1961). *Nature,* **190**, 159.
Rossmann, M. G. (1961). *Acta Cryst.* **14**, 383.
Rossmann, M. G. & Blow, D. M. (1962). *Acta Cryst.* **15**, 24.
Scouloudi, H. (1969). *J. Mol. Biol.* **40**, 353.
Tollin, P. (1969). *J. Mol. Biol.* **45**, 481.
Watson, H. C. (1969). In *Progress in Stereochemistry*, ed. by W. Klyne & P. De La Mare, vol. 4, p. 299. New York: Academic Press.

J. Mol. Biol. (1970) **50**, 137–142

Low-resolution Studies on the Relationship between the Triclinic and Tetragonal Forms of Lysozyme

M. A. JOYNSON, A. C. T. NORTH, V. R. SARMA†

Laboratory of Molecular Biophysics, Department of Zoology
Oxford, England

R. E. DICKERSON‡ AND L. K. STEINRAUF§

W. A. Noyes Laboratory, University of Illinois
Urbana, Illinois, U.S.A.

(*Received 15 December 1969*)

The structure of the tetragonal form of lysozyme has been established and X-ray diffraction data have been measured for the triclinic form. The rotation function of Rossmann & Blow (1962) has been used to determine the orientation of the lysozyme molecule in the triclinic cell. The rotation function contains a single significant peak. An alternative approach, that may be used straightforwardly with a triclinic form having only one molecule in the unit cell, is by direct sampling of the molecular transform and this has yielded a similar value for the molecular orientation. The degree of agreement between the observed triclinic crystal structure factors and those calculated from the molecule determined from the tetragonal crystal data leaves no doubt that the molecule has a similar structure in the two crystal forms, at least to a resolution of 6 Å.

1. Introduction

Hen egg-white lysozyme is a basic enzyme which can be crystallized in a variety of forms by a proper choice of pH and the anion. Lysozyme chloride can be crystallized in a tetragonal and an orthorhombic form, the nitrate in a monoclinic and triclinic form and the sulphate and iodide in a monoclinic form (Steinrauf, 1959). The structure of the molecule in the tetragonal form has been solved to a resolution of 2 Å (Blake *et al.*, 1965) by the multiple isomorphous replacement method. The present paper describes the relationship between this structure and the structure of the molecule in the triclinic form at 6 Å resolution. The known structure has been used to derive the orientation of the molecule in the triclinic form by two essentially different methods. One is to calculate the rotation function (Rossmann & Blow, 1962), which compares the Patterson syntheses of the two structures. The second is more direct and compares the Fourier transforms of the two structures. The diffraction data for triclinic lysozyme were collected by two of the authors (R. E. D. and L. K. S.; Dickerson, Reddy, Pinkerton & Steinrauf, 1962, and unpublished work).

† Present address: National Institutes of Health, Bethesda, Md., U.S.A.
‡ Present address: Norman W. Church Laboratory of Chemical Biology, California Institute of Technology, Pasadena, Calif., U.S.A.
§ Present address: Department of Biochemistry, Indiana University School of Medicine, Indianapolis, Ind., U.S.A.

2. Rotation of the Patterson Synthesis

Rossmann & Blow (1962) developed a method of determining the orientation of a known or unknown group with respect to another identical group either in the same or in a different crystal by calculation of an overlap integral known as the rotation function, defined as

$$R = \int_U P_2(X_2)\, P_1(X_1)\, \mathrm{d}X_1 \tag{1}$$

where P_1 and P_2 are the Patterson functions of the two groups and the position vectors X_1 and X_2 are related by

$$X_2 = |\mathbf{C}|\, X_1 \tag{2}$$

where $|\mathbf{C}|$ represents a rotation matrix. Clearly, the function R has a maximum value when the rotation is such that peaks of the two vector sets coincide. The integral in equation (1) can be shown to be equal to

$$R = \sum_{\mathrm{h}} |F_h|^2 \{\sum_{\mathrm{p}} |F_p|^2\, G_{hh'}\} \tag{3}$$

where $|F_h|$ and $|F_p|$ are the structure amplitudes of structures (1) and (2), respectively, and $G_{hh'}$ is an interference function whose magnitude depends on the reciprocal lattice vectors h and h' as well as the volume U within which the integral in equation (1) is evaluated. The rotated reciprocal lattice point h' is related to p by

$$h' = |\mathbf{C}|^{\mathrm{T}} p \quad . \tag{4}$$

This in general takes non-integral values and the second summation in equation (3) is over all the integral reciprocal lattice points around h'. G is a maximum when h and h' coincide and falls off as the distance between them increases so that the number of points included in the summation depends on the rapidity with which G varies. For the volume U used in the present calculation, the inclusion of 27 points around the non-integral reciprocal lattice point ensured that all points with significant values of G were included. The rotation matrix $|\mathbf{C}|$ has been calculated in terms of the three Eulerian angles $\theta 1$, $\theta 2$ and $\theta 3$ (Rossmann & Blow, 1962).

The known molecule of lysozyme in the tetragonal form was placed in a hypothetical triclinic cell of dimensions $a = b = c = 80$ Å $\alpha = \beta = \gamma = 90°$ and its Fourier transform calculated at the reciprocal lattice points of this cell. This will be referred to as the calculated transform. Contributions were included from the 1001 non-hydrogen atoms in the enzyme molecule. Nitrogen atomic scattering factors were used for all atoms, together with an isotropic temperature factor $B = 15$ Å^2. The determination of the parameters of these atoms will be described elsewhere. Atomic co-ordinates are available from one of the authors (A. C. T. N.).

We have evaluated the rotation function between this calculated transform and the observed transform of the unknown triclinic structure. The hypothetical unit cell has dimensions that are at least twice as great as the dimensions of a single molecule in each direction. In the corresponding Patterson function there is no overlap between the set of (intramolecular) vectors arising from a single molecule and the (intermolecular) vectors between neighbouring molecules, and all vectors less than 40 Å long must be intramolecular in origin. In the Patterson function of the real triclinic crystal, in which adjacent molecules are of course in contact, intermolecular and intramolecular vectors are inextricably intermingled, but most of the vectors near the Patterson origin are intramolecular and the proportion decreases with increasing distance from the origin. Selection of the appropriate value for the volume U over which the rotation function is to be evaluated is therefore subject to two conflicting requirements. The larger the volume, the greater is the number of possible overlaps, but the greater also is the number of spurious overlaps with interatomic vectors. Experience has indicated that an optimum radius for U is about half the diameter of the molecule (the maximum intramolecular vector) and the volume U was taken to be a sphere of radius 20 Å in the present calculations.

The angular intervals at which the rotation function should be evaluated depends upon the inherent resolution of the Patterson functions, i.e. the highest order structure amplitudes included in the summation. The complete rotation function was calculated at 15°-intervals in each of the Eulerian angles but a finer interval (7½°), more appropriate to the available resolution, was used in the neighbourhood of the rotation function maximum. The calculations were done on the KDF9 computer of the Oxford University Computing Laboratory, by means of a FORTRAN program written by us for this purpose. The calculated transform has not been corrected for the presence of liquid in a real crystal, which alters the intensities of low-angle reflections to a very large extent. Such reflections were completely omitted from the rotation function calculations and only reflections with interplanar spacings between 6 and 10 Å were used. Further, in order to save computing time, only the strongest 165 observed reflections in this range were included in the summations.

The rotation function contains a single large peak of maximum height 360 units. The background level of the function appears to approximate to a normal distribution with a mean of 270 units and standard deviation (σ) of 12 units. The peak to background ratio is 1·33 and the peak is approximately 7·5 σ above background. The next highest point in the map is 3·7 σ above background and while this and the other smaller features must represent some relationships between different regions of the molecule, there is no doubt that the principal peak indicates the rotation for which the Patterson functions are brought into coincidence.

3. Direct Comparison of the Fourier Transforms

Since the triclinic crystal form contains only one molecule in the unit cell, the observed structure amplitudes $|F_{obs}|$ represent simply the Fourier transform of a single molecule sampled at the reciprocal lattice points. The correct orientation of the molecule in the unit cell may therefore be established by rotating the calculated Fourier transform of the lysozyme molecule with respect to the triclinic lysozyme reciprocal lattice. For each rotation angle, a residual R defined by

$$R = \sum \big|\, |F_{obs}| - |F_{calc}| \,\big| / |F_{obs}| \qquad (5)$$

is calculated after placing F_{obs} and F_{calc} on the same scale by equating $\sum F_{obs}$ and $\sum F_{calc}$

The points of the reciprocal lattice when rotated will not in general coincide with points at which the molecular transform has been evaluated, so the required values were found by interpolation in the real and imaginary parts of the structure amplitudes of the eight nearest reciprocal lattice points. By choice of suitably large cell dimensions, giving close sampling of the molecular transform, linear interpolation was found to be satisfactory. The above residual was calculated for all possible rotations at intervals of 15° in the three Eulerian angles, including all reflections with $d \geqslant 6$ Å (d = interplanar spacing.) A single minimum was found in the residual and its position was established more precisely by calculation at closer intervals in its neighbourhood. At the minimum, the residual has a value of 43·5%, compared with a general background level of the order of 68% (the residual for a randomly incorrect structure of equal atoms should be 59%). The residual obtained by comparison of the calculated structure factors with $d > 6$ Å for the lysozyme molecule with the tetragonal crystal data, from which the model was derived, is very closely similar (43%) to the above minimum residual for comparison with the triclinic crystal data.

The positions in spherical polar co-ordinates of the rotation function peak and

TABLE 1

Positions of rotation function peak and minimum residual

	χ	ψ	ϕ
Rotation function maximum	46	100	90
Fourier transform minimum residual	49	98	85

The angles χ, ψ, ϕ are defined in Figure 1, after Rossmann & Blow (1962).

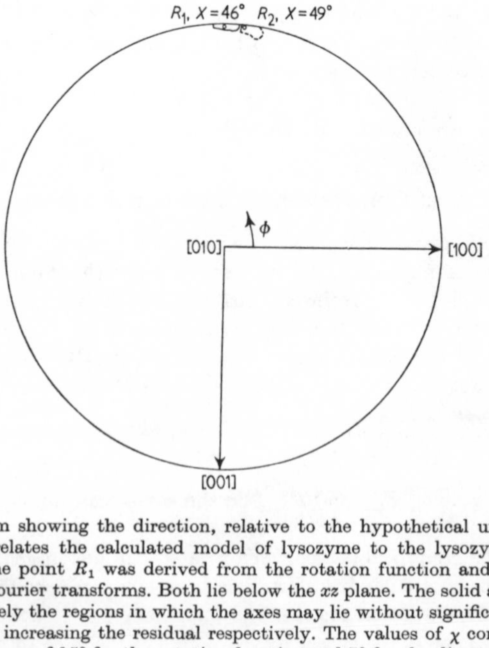

FIG. 1. Stereogram showing the direction, relative to the hypothetical unit cell axes, of the rotation axis that relates the calculated model of lysozyme to the lysozyme molecule in the triclinic crystals. The point R_1 was derived from the rotation function and R_2 from the direct comparison of the Fourier transforms. Both lie below the xz plane. The solid and dashed contours indicate approximately the regions in which the axes may lie without significantly decreasing the rotation function or increasing the residual respectively. The values of χ corresponding to these limits lie within a range of 15° for the rotation function and 7° for the direct comparison.

Fourier transform minimum residual are shown in Table 1 and illustrated in stereographic projection in Figure 1. A rotation of 5° about an axis passing through the centre of the molecule, which has a diameter of the order of 40 Å, implies a displacement of a point on the surface of the molecule through 2 Å at the most, so it can be seen that the angular range of the rotation function peak and the difference between its position and that of the minimum residual, are well within the range expected for the 6 Å resolution data.

Both the rotation function and the direct comparison of Fourier transforms indicate unequivocally the orientation of the lysozyme molecule in the triclinic crystal form. The fact that the residual R, a measure of the agreement between the model and the observed X-ray diffraction, is as good for the triclinic data as for the tetragonal data from which the model was derived, suggests moreover that the conformation of the enzyme in the triclinic crystals is similar to that in the tetragonal crystals at a resolution of 6 Å. This conclusion was examined further as follows. First, the calculated transform contains the phase information that is lacking in the observed X-ray diffraction pattern, so that it is now possible to calculate an electron density map of triclinic lysozyme from the observed triclinic structure amplitudes and the phases obtained from the calculated transform sampled at the appropriate rotation angle. All the significant features of the 6 Å resolution map of tetragonal lysozyme are in fact reproduced in the resulting map. An alternative way of searching for significant differences in such a situation is to calculate a difference electron density map from the same phase angles, but with amplitudes given by the difference between the observed triclinic values and those of the calculated transform. The largest peak in this "difference map" has a density of $0{\cdot}06e/Å^3$, compared to a maximum density of $0{\cdot}65e/Å^3$ in the electron density map itself. We therefore conclude that there is no major difference in conformation between the lysozyme molecules in the two crystal forms, recognizable at the present resolution of 6 Å. This reinforces our opinion that the molecular conformation of the lysozyme molecule seen in the tetragonal crystal represents the conformation of the free molecule and is not an artifact depending upon the crystal lattice forces. It is of course to be expected that small conformational differences, particularly of the peripheral side chains, would be revealed in a study at higher resolution.

The comparison of a known molecular structure with diffraction data from a triclinic crystal, containing only one molecular orientation, represents the simplest situation for the exploitation of the rotation function. While our result with lysozyme is unequivocal, the peak-to-background ratio is disappointingly small, though it is reasonable to expect that a more significant peak would be formed with higher resolution data. Our intention is to examine rather more complicated situations. One example is the orthorhombic crystal form of hen egg-white lysozyme, for which it is necessary to determine the translational parameters between symmetry-related molecules as well as their orientations. A second example is lysozyme from a different organism, e.g. human lysozyme, which can be expected to have a generally similar conformation to the hen egg-white molecule. A still further stage would be to compare molecules known to have a family resemblance to one another in amino-acid sequence and expected to have a rather similar conformation; α-lactalbumin bears such a relationship with lysozyme.

The direct comparison of the Fourier transform of the known molecule with the observed diffraction pattern gave a more clear-cut result and permitted a more precise determination of the molecular orientation than the rotation function. Unfortunately, however, this method cannot be used in this simple form with crystal lattices of higher symmetry and appropriate developments of it are being considered.

We are grateful to Professor D. C. Phillips for encouragement and many helpful discussions. Three of us (M. A. J., A. C. T. N. and V. R. S.) thank the Medical Research Council for support.

REFERENCES

Blake, C. C. F., Koenig, D. F., Mair, G. A., North, A. C. T., Phillips, D. C. & Sarma, V. R (1965). *Nature*, **206**, 757.
Dickerson, R. E., Reddy, J. M., Pinkerton, M. & Steinrauf, L. K. (1962). *Nature*, **196**, 1178.
Rossmann, M. G. & Blow, D. M. (1962). *Acta Cryst.* **15**, 24.
Steinrauf, L. K. (1959). *Acta Cryst.* **12**, 77.

Reprinted from *J. Mol. Biol.* (1971) **58**, 389–395

An X-ray Crystallographic Study of Demetallized Concanavalin A

A. Jack, J. Weinzierl and A. Joseph Kalb

J. Mol. Biol. (1971) **58**, 389–395

LETTERS TO THE EDITOR

An X-ray Crystallographic Study of Demetallized Concanavalin A

Demetallized concanavalin A crystallizes in space group $P2_122_1$ with unit cell dimensions $a = 85{\cdot}4$ Å, $b = 91{\cdot}5$ Å, $c = 61{\cdot}3$ Å. The asymmetric unit contains one protein molecule. The rotation and translation functions indicate the existence of a local dyad axis some 7° off the z-axis with a screw component leading to a relative subunit translation of about 6 Å. The demetallized crystals are converted to the native form on soaking in dilute solution of transition metal ions and Ca^{2+} ions.

Concanavalin A is a saccharide-binding protein of the Jack bean. The protein molecule, which weighs $5{\cdot}5 \times 10^4$ daltons, has two transition metal-binding sites, two calcium-binding sites and two saccharide-binding sites (Yariv, Kalb & Levitzki, 1968; Kalb & Levitzki, 1968; Kalb & Lustig, 1968). In solution, demetallized concanavalin A binds transition metal ions but Ca^{2+} is bound only if the transition metal sites are occupied. Saccharide binding can occur when both transition metal and Ca^{2+} sites are occupied. Concanavalin A, as isolated from the Jack bean, contains metal ions and crystallizes at low salt concentration in space group $I222$ with one half-molecule per asymmetric unit. Hence a molecule consists of two identical subunits related by a dyad axis (Greer, Kaufman & Kalb, 1970). The demetallized protein does not crystallize under the same conditions if adequate care is taken to exclude divalent metal ions.

We have now found conditions for crystallizing demetallized concanavalin A. The crystals belong to space group $P2_122_1$ with unit-cell parameters nearly equal to those of the native crystals (Table 1). The asymmetric unit in this case is a whole molecule. We have used the rotation and translation functions (Rossmann & Blow, 1962; Rossmann, Blow, Harding & Coller, 1964) to find the movements responsible for this symmetry change.

When a demetallized crystal is soaked in dilute solution of transition metal ions and Ca^{2+} ions, the X-ray diffraction pattern changes to one which is nearly identical to that of the native crystals (Plate I). Transition metals or calcium alone do not cause this change.

Demetallized concanavalin A was prepared by dialysis of acidified concanavalin A as previously described (Kalb & Levitzki, 1968). Crystals were grown at room temperature by dialysis of demetallized protein against 1·35 M-$(NH_4)_2SO_4$ containing 0·05 M-sodium acetate (pH 5·0). Dialysis tubing and all glassware were treated with boiling EDTA solution to remove trace metals, and solutions of $(NH_4)_2SO_4$ and sodium acetate were treated with a metal-sequestering resin (Dowex A–1).

For X-ray diffraction experiments, crystals were mounted in sealed, thin-walled quartz capillary tubes which had been rinsed with the dialysis solution described above and which contained some of that solution. Diffraction patterns of three centric projections were recorded with a Buerger precession camera (Ni-filtered CuKα radiation, precession angle 17°, crystal-to-film distance 75 mm) and from these the unit-cell dimensions were calculated. The space group was assigned on the basis of the symmetry of the observed reciprocal planes and the systematic absences along the a^* and c^* axes (Table 1). The weight of the protein in an asymmetric unit for the demetallized crystal is twice that in the asymmetric unit of the native crystal since the unit-cell volumes of the two crystal forms are nearly equal whereas $P2_122_1$ has four asymmetric units per unit cell and $I222$ has eight. The results of the soaking experiments described below exclude the possibility that demetallized and native crystals differ substantially in protein content.

TABLE 1

Concanavalin A

	Demetallized	Native†
Unit cell dimensions (Å)		
	a 85·4 ± 0·4	87·2 ± 0·4
	b 91·5 ± 0·4	89·2 ± 0·4
	c 61·3 ± 0·3	62·9 ± 0·3
Systematic absences		
	$h00$ for h odd	hkl for $h + k + l$ odd
	$00l$ for l odd	
Space group	$P2_122_1$	$I222$
Weight of protein in asymmetric unit (daltons)		
	$5{\cdot}2 \pm 0{\cdot}5 \times 10^4$	$2{\cdot}6 \pm 0{\cdot}3 \times 10^4$

† Data for native concanavalin A from Greer *et al.* (1970). A somewhat greater estimate of uncertainty in unit-cell dimensions is given here based on our experience that there is some variability in these dimensions from crystal to crystal. Space group $I222$ is to be preferred over $I2_12_12_1$ on the basis of peak positions in the three-dimensional difference Patterson of a $PtCl_4^{2-}$ derivative which we have prepared. Heavy-atom positions deduced from this Patterson have been refined to give R-factors of around 22% in the three centrosymmetric projections.

Soaking experiments were done by transferring a few crystals into 2 ml. of the dialysis solution described above but containing, in addition, 10^{-3} M-cadmium acetate, manganous chloride or calcium chloride, as required. After at least five days soaking, crystals were examined by X-ray diffraction. A precession angle of 9° was chosen since the soaked crystals were cracked and thus it was difficult to align them accurately enough for examination at greater precession angles. Crystals soaked in cadmium and calcium or manganese and calcium had diffraction patterns nearly identical to those of native crystals (Plate I). Crystals soaked in $MnCl_2$ alone or in $CaCl_2$ alone did not change noticeably.

Three-dimensional X-ray diffraction intensity data to 5·5 Å resolution were measured from a crystal of the demetallized protein as well as from one of the native protein with a Hilger–Watts 4-circle automatic diffractometer for use with the rotation and translation functions.

Consideration of the symmetry elements of the space groups $I222$ and $P2_122_1$ shows that the change of symmetry on demetallization can be accounted for by either a translation or a rotation of the molecules or a combination of both movements in the x–z plane (see Fig. 1). Translation of the molecules along the y-axis can also produce

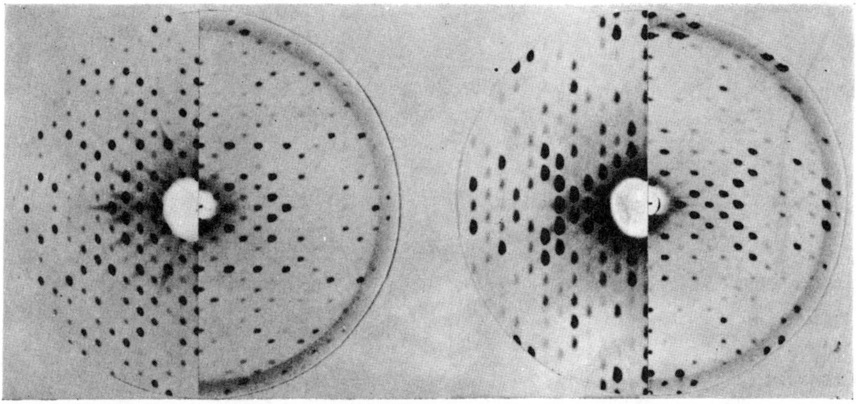

(a) (b)

PLATE I. Comparison of X-ray diffraction patterns of native concanavalin A and of demetallized concanavalin A soaked for 5 days in 1·35 M-$(NH_4)_2SO_4$, 0·05 M-sodium acetate (pH 5·0) containing 10^{-3} M-$MnCl_2$ and 10^{-3} M-$CaCl_2$.

(a) $0kl$: left half, native; right half, soaked demetallized. (b) $h0l$: left half, native; right half, soaked demetallized. c^* horizontal in both cases.

the required symmetry but as this treats two of the molecules in the cell differently from the other two it is not considered likely.

Rossmann & Blow (1962) have shown that when two identical or closely related molecules occur in different crystal forms, the relative orientation of the molecules in their respective cells can often be found without prior knowledge of the molecular structure. They define a rotation function calculated from observed intensities only, which is a measure of the overlap of all intramolecular Patterson vectors for any given rotation.

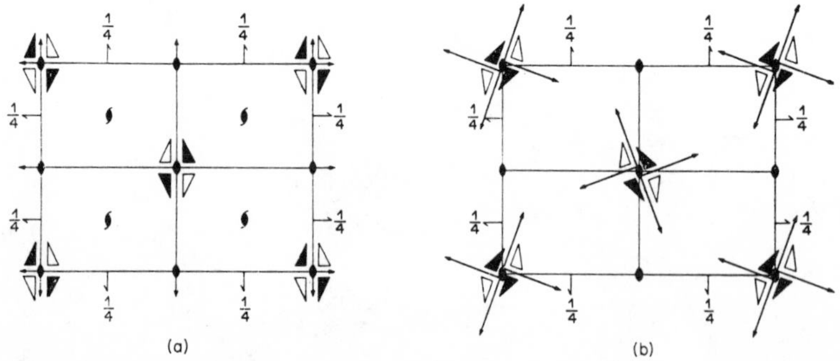

(a) (b)

FIG. 1. (a) y-Axis projection of space group $I222$. Each triangle represents one asymmetric unit, and the black and white triangles are crystallographically equivalent.

(b) Here the triangles have been rotated about the lines $x = z = 0$, $x = z = \frac{1}{2}$, and an arbitrary relative translation of black and white triangles added. The space group is reduced to $P2_122_1$, and black and white triangles are now crystallographically distinct.

From the cell dimensions of concanavalin A, 25 Å appears to be a reasonable molecular radius, if the molecules are assumed to be approximately spherical. Hence all the intramolecular vectors in the Patterson will occur within about 50 Å of the origin. However, a considerably smaller cut-off radius (35 Å) was chosen, since a 50 Å sphere will contain a very large number of unwanted, intermolecular vectors.

We have calculated a self-rotation function for the demetallized protein, using polar angles in the convention defined by Rossmann & Blow, with the crystallographic z-axis defined by $\psi = 0°$ (Fig. 2). Only the plane $\kappa = 180°$ was calculated: then for any values of ψ and ϕ, the value of the rotation function is a measure of the degree of 2-fold symmetry in that direction. The rotation function was computed using Patterson vectors of length 35 Å or less, and with only the largest 133 independent reflections out to a resolution of 6 Å (47% of the total observed intensity). No significant peaks were found away from the crystallographic dyad directions; however, since a small rotation is to be expected, a fine scan (2°-intervals) was carried out in the region of each peak corresponding to a crystallographic dyad. The resulting map showed definite shoulders to the peaks on the line $\phi = 0°$, at ψ approximately equal to 7° and 83° (Fig. 3(a)). The peak at $\phi = \psi = 90°$ showed no such shoulder, nor did any of the peaks in the self-rotation function of the native protein which was calculated under similar conditions.

For confirmation of these results we computed a cross-rotation function between the two crystal forms, using Eulerian angles in the convention described by Rossmann &

Blow, with the crystallographic z-axis pointing up. The value of the rotation function was calculated for all rotations in the asymmetric unit in 10°-intervals of the three angles θ_1, θ_2 and θ_3, using all the observed 6 Å data for the demetallized crystal, but only the largest 54 independent reflections (37% of the total observed intensity) for the native crystal. The highest peaks in the resulting map appeared to be at the origin

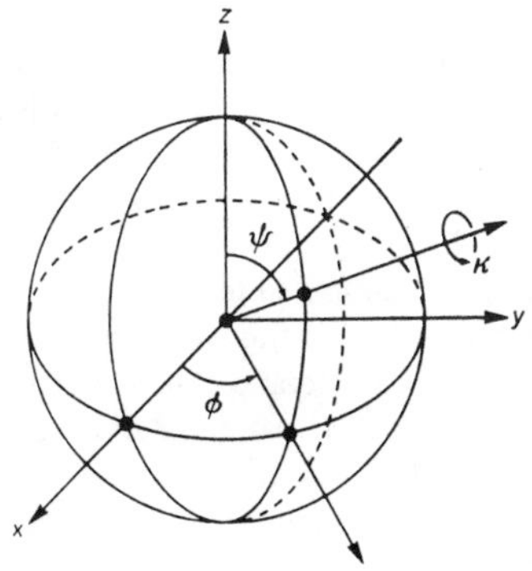

FIG. 2. The polar angles κ, ϕ, ψ used to define angular orientation.

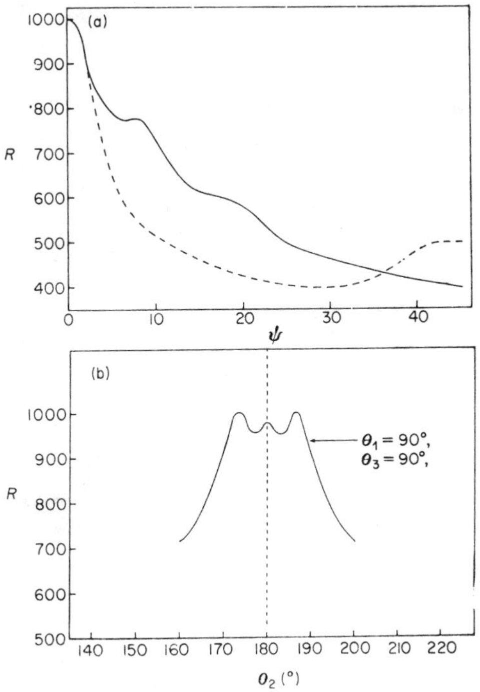

FIG. 3. (a) Self-rotation function of demetallized concanavalin A, showing the lines (———) $\kappa = 180°$, $\phi = 0°$ and (----) $\kappa = 180°$, $\phi = 90°$.
(b) Cross-rotation function, showing part of the line $\theta_1 = 90°$, $\theta_3 = 90°$.

($\theta_1 = \theta_2 = \theta_3 = 0°$) and its symmetry-related positions. The Eulerian angles corresponding to a rotation of 7° in the x–z plane are $\theta_1 = 90°$, $\theta_2 = 7°$ (or 173°), $\theta_3 = 90°$. On recalculating the function around the region $\theta_1 = \theta_3 = 90°$, $\theta_2 = 180°$, we did indeed find a definite peak corresponding to this rotation, with a slightly smaller peak at $\theta_2 = 180°$ (Fig. 3(b)). Since the line $\theta_2 = 180°$, $\theta_1 = 90°$ is a 2-fold axis in the rotation function, it seems likely that the peak at $\theta_2 = 180°$ is the result of imperfect resolution of two symmetry-related peaks (cf. the rotation of seal and sperm-whale myoglobin (Tollin, 1969)). The peak height is 1000 on an arbitrary scale. Away from the peak, the mean value of the rotation function is 540, with standard deviation ± 75. Because of the symmetry it is impossible to say whether the non-crystallographic dyad relating subunits corresponds to x or z in the native, but the transformation clearly involves a rotation of $7° \pm 2°$ in the x–z plane.

We next used the translation function to find whether there was any translational movement of the subunits coupled with the rotation. This function compares inter-subunit vectors within a region of a Patterson map centred at **S** with a rotated version of the same Patterson centred at −**S**. (Rossmann *et al.*, 1964). The function was first calculated using a rotation of 180° about the local axis 7° off z. The resulting Fourier map (Fig. 4) shows three principal features: streaks through the origin (maximum

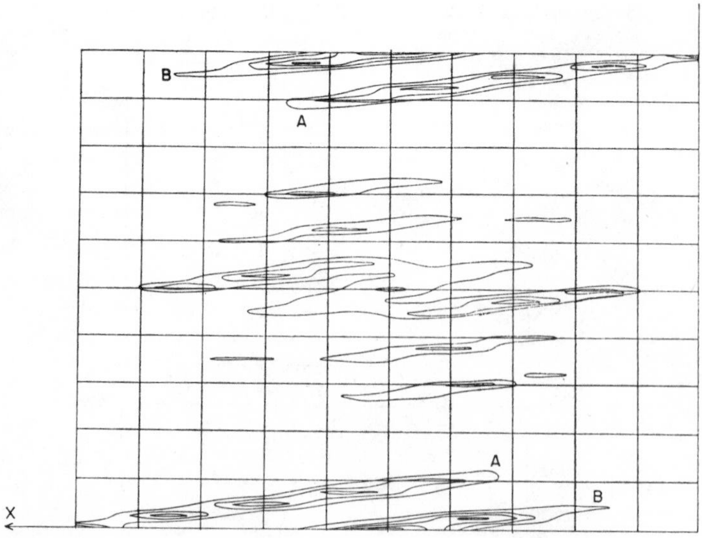

FIG. 4. Section $y = 0$ of the translation function. Rotation axis 7° off z. All data between 12 and 6 Å used; Patterson removed within 25 Å of origin; radius of integration 40 Å.

height 324) normal to the rotation axis (A), caused by imperfect removal of the self-Patterson; a parallel streak through $x = \frac{1}{2}$, $z = 0$, whose maximum value is 630 in the plane $y = \frac{1}{2}$ (B), and a parallel streak through $x = \frac{1}{2}$, $y = \frac{1}{2}$, $z = \frac{1}{2}$ (maximum height 752) arising from the pseudo-body-centring of the lattice.

A likely explanation of the streaks B through $x = \frac{1}{2}$, $z = 0$ is that there is a translation of the subunits relative to each other of 6 ± 2 Å parallel to the local axis, this distance being given by the perpendicular distance from A to B (see Fig. 1(b)).

The fact that these streaks have a maximum at $x = \frac{1}{2}$, $y = \frac{1}{2}$ indicates that the subunit centres are near $\frac{1}{4}, \frac{1}{4}, \frac{1}{4}$. In support of this explanation, the translation function calculated using the local axis 7° off x, instead of z, as rotation axis shows no prominent features other than a streak centred at $\frac{1}{2}, \frac{1}{2}, \frac{1}{2}$ caused by the pseudo-body-centring.

The rotation about the axis 7° off z, combined with the translation of the subunits along this axis, is equivalent to rotation of the subunits in pairs about axes parallel to y but displaced along x to either side of the crystallographic dyad.

The present study shows that the structures of native and demetallized concanavalin A are closely related although not isomorphous. Binding of metal ions changes the molecular packing which undoubtedly reflects a conformational change within the subunits. Calcium ions alone do not effect this change, a result which is consistent with the finding that, in solution, the demetallized protein does not interact with Ca^{2+} ions. Although the protein binds transition metal ions, soaking demetallized crystals in $MnCl_2$ solution does not bring about a change in space group. This suggests that a relatively small conformational change occurs on transition metal binding and that the major change occurs on subsequent Ca^{2+} ion binding. Recently, an electron spin resonance study of Mn^{2+} in concanavalin A has shown that Ca^{2+} ion binding is accompanied by an increase in the symmetry of the environment of the Mn^{2+} ion (Nicolau, Kalb & Yariv, 1969).

In order to learn the detailed mechanism of Ca^{2+} site formation upon binding of transition metal ions, the structure of concanavalin A in three states should be solved: demetallized, with transition metal only and with transition metal and Ca^{2+} ions. The present findings suggest that study of the three forms may be simplified since the first two appear to be isomorphous so that the solution of either structure would yield the other by use of difference Fourier methods. The relationship between the third structure and the first two is less straightforward but should be considerably simplified by knowledge of the rotational and translational relationships between these structures (see Tollin, 1969).

We would like to thank Drs J. Greer and D. M. Blow for many helpful discussions, and Miss Annette Snazle for preparing the drawings. The crystals were grown with the technical assistance of Mrs S. Tauber.

One of us (A.J.) holds a Medical Research Council Scholarship for Training in Research Methods whilst another of the authors (A.J.K.) was a European Molecular Biology Organization short term fellow at the Medical Research Council Laboratory of Molecular Biology during the course of most of this work.

All computations were done on the IBM360/44 computer at the Institute of Theoretical Astronomy, Cambridge University.

Medical Research Council
Laboratory of Molecular Biology
Hills Road, Cambridge, England

A. Jack
J. Weinzierl

Department of Biophysics
The Weizmann Institute of Science
Rehovot, Israel

A. Joseph Kalb

Received 5 February 1971

REFERENCES

Greer, J., Kaufman, H. W. & Kalb, A. J. (1970). *J. Mol. Biol.* **48**, 365.
Kalb, A. J. & Levitzki, A. (1968). *Biochem. J.* **109**, 659.
Kalb, A. J. & Lustig, A. (1968). *Biochim. biophys. Acta*, **168**, 366.
Nicolau, Cl., Kalb, A. J. & Yariv, J. (1969). *Biochim. biophys. Acta*, **194**, 71.

Rossmann, M. G. & Blow, D. M. (1962). *Acta Cryst.* **15,** 24.
Rossmann, M. G., Blow, D. M., Harding, M. M. & Coller, E. (1964). *Acta Cryst.* **17,** 338.
Tollin, P. (1969). *J. Mol. Biol.* **45,** 881.
Yariv, J., Kalb, A. J. & Levitzki, A. (1968). *Biochim. biophys. Acta,* **165,** 303.

J. Mol. Biol. (1969) **45**, 533–544

Subunit Structure of Aldolase: Chemical and Crystallographic Evidence

P. A. M. Eagles, L. N. Johnson, M. A. Joynson

Laboratory of Molecular Biophysics
Department of Zoology
Parks Road, Oxford, England

AND

C. H. McMurray and H. Gutfreund

Molecular Enzymology Laboratory, Department of Biochemistry
University of Bristol, England

(*Received 25 June 1969*)

Detailed studies of the reactivity of the sulphydryl groups of aldolase have resulted in evidence for a tetrameric structure of the enzyme. Several distinct classes of sulphydryl groups were found which differed (i) in their reactivities, (ii) in their involvement in the active form of the enzyme and (iii) in that some are protected by substrates while others are not. These studies of the sulphydryl groups also resulted in the preparation of a monoclinic crystalline derivative which contained four equivalents of *p*-chloromecuribenzoic acid per mole of protein.

X-ray diffraction studies on these crystals and on hexagonal bipyramid crystals obtained with native aldolase have provided information concerning the molecular symmetry of the aldolase molecule. In the hexagonal crystal form the molecule is situated on a crystallographic dyad axis which implies that the subunits are at least identical in pairs. In the monoclinic crystals non-crystallographic symmetry has been detected by Patterson and rotation function methods and shows the molecule to be a tetramer with pseudo-222 symmetry. These data provide unambiguous evidence for a four subunit structure of aldolase.

1. Introduction

The subunit structure of aldolase has been investigated by a variety of techniques in recent years and there is now compelling evidence for a tetrameric structure based on two pairs of non-identical subunits. Earlier evidence which had suggested a three subunit model was first brought into question by the ultracentrifugation studies of Kawahara & Tanford (1966) who showed that native aldolase with a molecular weight of 158,000 dissociated into units of 40,000 on treatment with guanidine hydrochloride. Their result, which has recently been confirmed by ultracentrifugation studies in other laboratories (Sia & Horecker, 1968; Szuchet & Yphantis, 1968), was strengthened by the demonstration of the formation of five isoenzymes, including three hybrid forms, in hybridization experiments using brain and muscle aldolases (Penhoet, Rajkumar & Rutter, 1966; Penhoet, Kochman, Valentine & Rutter, 1967) and observations in the electron microscope, which indicated a tetrahedral arrangement of subunits, each of which is approximately 40Å in diameter (Penhoet *et al.*, 1967). The presence of equal quantities of two non-identical subunits was suggested in 1967 (Chan, Morse & Horecker, 1967; Morse, Chan & Horecker, 1967) and an $\alpha_2\beta_2$ structure was proposed. Recent primary structure studies (Lai, 1968) have shown that cleavage with cyanogen bromide results in four peptide fragments, consistent with the presence of twelve methionines in the total molecule, and further examination of these fragments indicated that, although the subunits are, in general, closely similar, differences exist in the N-terminal and C-terminal portions of the two types of chains (Koida & Lai, 1969). Reports for the presence of only three substrate and inhibitor binding sites (Castellino & Barker, 1966; Ginsburg & Mehler, 1966; Ginsburg, 1966), which are discussed in a recent review by Morse & Horecker (1968), are at variance with the results for a four subunit model. There have been suggestions that the failure to detect four binding sites may be related to the presence of approximately one mole of organic phosphate in the enzyme (Kobashi, Lai & Horecker, 1966; Morse & Horecker, 1968).

Aldolase has a large number of sulphydryl groups, some of which are readily accessible to reagents while others react only after unfolding of the protein molecule. We were interested in studying the differences in the reactivities of sulphydryl groups of various proteins with a view to selective labelling and to investigating the effect of environment on reactivity. It was also expected that the number of sulphydryl groups within each class of reactivity would give information about the quaternary structure. Previous work on the sulphydryl groups of aldolase by Swenson & Boyer (1957), Rowley, Tchola & Horecker (1964), Kowal, Cremona & Horecker (1965) and Cremona, Kowal & Horecker (1965) had not given clear information supporting either a trimer or a tetramer model.

The reactivities of different sets of sulphydryls and the numbers of such groups within each set were studied with 5,5′-dithiobis-2-nitrobenzoic acid and chromophoric mercurials. The objective of selective labelling and the preparation of crystalline derivatives was achieved with mercurials.

In this paper we also wish to report our recent crystallographic experiments which provide unambiguous evidence for the four subunit structure. Two crystal forms have been studied both of which have provided information concerning the molecular symmetry of the aldolase molecule. In the hexagonal crystal form obtained with native aldolase, it was found that the molecule is situated on a crystallographic dyad axis which implies that the subunits are at least identical in pairs. In the case of the monoclinic crystals which were obtained after reacting one mole of aldolase with four equivalents of *p*-chloromercuribenzoic acid, the detection of non-crystallographic symmetry by Patterson and rotation function methods has shown the molecule to be a tetramer with pseudo-222 symmetry.

2. Materials and Methods

(a) *Preparation of rabbit muscle aldolase and its crystalline derivatives*

A large rabbit was anaesthetised with diethyl ether vapour, ensanguinated, skinned and eviscerated. White skeletal muscle was removed from the hind legs and back. The minced muscle was extracted twice with equal volumes (× 2 wet weight) of 5 mM-EDTA pH 6·0 for 45 min each. The supernatant fraction was obtained by spinning in the MSE 18 centrifuge at 22,000 *g* for 15 min. The combined supernatant fractions were diluted (× 2) with 5 mM-EDTA pH 6·0 and the aldolase removed quantitatively from solution with 1 kg of CM52 (Whatman) which had been previously equilibrated with the same buffer.

TABLE 1

Fractionation of rabbit muscle aldolase

	Total units $\times 10^{-4} \pm 5\%$	Specific activity μmoles/min/mg protein $\pm 5\%$
Extract	8·0	1·0
CM cellulose (0·3 M-NaCl)	7·5	7·3
$(NH_4)_2SO_4$ 60% P_1	5·7	8·74
Supernatant S_1	1·25	—
Supernatant S_2	4·5	10·0
Precipitate P_2	1·6	8·8
Precipitate P_3	3·0	14·6
Precipitate P_4	1·6	15·3

The CM52 was washed with 2 l. of 50 mM-NaCl, 5 mM-EDTA pH 6·0. Both the extract solutions and the washings were discarded. The cellulose was washed with 3·0 l. of 0·3 M-NaCl, 5 mM-EDTA pH 6·0 to remove the enzyme (see Table 1). The eluate was cooled to 4°C in the cold room and $(NH_4)_2SO_4$ added to 60% saturation, slowly with constant stirring over a 1-hr period. The pH was adjusted to 6·5. At this stage the preparation was left overnight. Centrifugation (22,000 ***g*** for 20 min MSE 18) yielded a supernatant S_1 and precipitate P_1 which contained the bulk of the enzyme. The precipitate P_1 was dissolved in 50 mM-triethanolamine–hydrochloride 5 mM-EDTA pH 6·5 and further fractionated by cautious addition of $(NH_4)_2SO_4$. The first precipitate contained little enzyme and the main bulk of the pure enzyme came in the second two fraction P_3 and P_4, which were obtained from the supernatant S_2.

Fractions P_3 and P_4 were combined and found to contain 53% of the original aldolase activity. However, this was found to be contaminated with lactic dehydrogenase, approx. 0·8% protein. The preparation was free from triose phosphate isomerase <0·001% and glycerol-1-phosphate dehydrogenase <0·01% on activity basis.

(i) *Crystallization*

Native hexagonal crystals. Hexagonal bipyramid crystals were grown from a solution of 5 mg aldolase/ml. pH 6·0 at 4°C. The protein solution was buffered with either 5 mM-EDTA or 0·1 M-citrate, 5 mM-EDTA. Ammonium sulphate was added until an amorphous protein precipitate appeared at which stage the salt concentration was estimated to be approximately 50% saturated. Crystals grew within 2 weeks.

Native monoclinic crystals. The protein was diluted to 5 mg/ml. by the addition of 0·1 M-triethanolamine–hydrochloride, 5 mM-EDTA pH 7·3. Saturated ammonium sulphate was then added at room temperature until the solution became turbid. The ammonium sulphate saturation was in the range of 44 to 49% saturation but the formation of crystals did not appear to be critically dependent on the salt concentration within this range. Large crystalline plates appeared within a few days.

p-Chloromercuribenzoate–aldolase monoclinic crystals. The enzyme was reacted with PCMB† (4 equivalents per mole of protein (mol. wt 160,000)) at pH 7·0. The percentage of the reactive sulphydryl group reacted (see discussion below) was checked by means of the DTNB titration. The protein was diluted to 5 mg/ml. in 0·1 M-citrate, 5 mM-EDTA pH 5·5 and saturated ammonium sulphate solution added in the cold (4°C) to approximately 48% saturation. The time for lozenge-shaped crystals to appear varied from 1 to 3 months but once nucleation had commenced growth was fairly rapid.

(ii) *Assay*

Aldolase was routinely assayed in pH 7·5, 0·2 M-triethanolamine–hydrochloride, 5 mM-EDTA, 25°C, as described previously by Trentham, McMurray & Pogson (1969).

† Abbreviations used: PCMB, p-chloromercuribenzoate; DTNB, 5,5′-dithiobis-2-nitrobenzoic acid

This is based on the linked assay of Racker (1947). Protein concentration was determined using $E_1^{1\%}$cm = 9·1 at 280 nm (Baranowski & Neiderland, 1949). The optimum specific activity obtained was 15 μmoles/min/mg enzyme. The molecular weight of the enzyme was assumed to be 160,000 (Kawahara & Tanford, 1966).

(b) *Titration of sulphydryl groups*

For the determination of the total number of sulphydryl groups, 0·33 mM-DTNB in pH 7·5 0·2 M-triethanolamine–hydrochloride, 5 mM-EDTA, 25°C, was incubated in a spectrophotometric cuvette, and the release of the 5-thio, 2-nitro benzoate anion E_{412nm} $1{\cdot}36\times10^4$ M^{-1} cm^{-1} (Ellman, 1959) being followed at 412 nm using a Uvispek H700 spectrophotometer (Hilger & Watts Ltd.), provided with a Gilford recording attachment and a Servoscribe recorder (type RE 54, Kelvin Electronics Co.)

For rapid reactions a stopped-flow apparatus with a 1 cm light path similar to that described by Gutfreund (1965) was used. The record of the reaction could be resolved into three distinct phases:

(a) Fast initial phase equivalent to 4 sulphydryl groups/molecule;

(b) Slow phase equivalent to a further 8 sulphydryl groups/molecule;

(c) Finally a further 16 sulphydryl groups per molecule were only exposed to DTNB when the enzyme was unfolded in the presence of 4 M-urea or 4 M-guanidine hydrochloride. Heating the enzyme at 40°C in the presence of DTNB also exposes these buried sulphydryl groups. However, this reation is difficult to monitor due to gradual precipitation of the protein.

Second-order rate constants were measured by varying the DTNB concentration and comparing them with that of cysteine under similar condition. These are summarized in Table 2.

TABLE 2

Stoichiometry and reactivity of aldolase sulphydryl groups

Sulphydryl group	No. of sulphydryl groups/ 160,000 mol. wt	k-mole^{-1} sec^{-1}
Cysteine	—	6000
(a) Native aldolase	4 ± 0·25	262
(b) Native aldolase	8 ± 0·25	2·5
(c) Total aldolase	28 ± 0·25	—

The total number of sulphydryl groups agrees well with that found by Benesch, Lardy & Benesch (1955) and Swenson & Boyer (1957). These numbers are clearly only compatible with a tetrameric structure of the aldolase molecule mol. wt 160,000. Each class of aldolase sulphydryl group (Table 2(a) and (b)) gives pseudo first-order kinetics. This indicates that within the accuracy of the experiments the groups in one monomer are identical to the respective groups in any other monomer and that there appears to be no interaction between them.

(i) *Protection with substrate*

When the sulphydryl titration is carried out in the presence of substrates then the number of sulphydryl groups titrated with DTNB changes. With fructose 1,6-diphosphate (2 mM) in the spectrophotometer cell in the presence of enzyme, the number of groups in the slow reaction (Table 2(b)) changes from 8 to 4. A similar effect is observed with glyceraldehyde-3-phosphate (5 mM) and dihydroxy-acetone phosphate (5 mM). Sulphate and phosphate also showed some protective effect.

After 12 residues in the native enzyme have reacted with DTNB the enzyme is inactive, the kinetics of the inactivation being similar to that of the slow release (Table 2(b)) of the thio-nitrobenzoate anion. When substrate is present the enzyme is still active after

8 residues have reacted. The kinetics of the reaction of these 8 residues is, however, not changed by the presence of substrate.

(ii) *Reactions with mercurials*

Swenson & Boyer (1957) studied the reaction of aldolase with *p*-chloromercuribenzoic acid. We have made use of the fact that when 2-chloromercuri-4-nitrophenol and 4-chloromercuri-2-nitrophenol react with sulphydryl groups, there is a change in the ionization of the phenol with a resultant chromophoric change at 410 nm, as shown by McMurray & Trentham (1969). Reaction of these compounds with native aldolase in the stopped-flow apparatus showed that the reaction proceeded in two distinct phases. A much slower reaction was also observed which was associated with precipitation of the protein. Unlike the reaction with DTNB the size and rate of the secondary phase was unaffected by fructose 1,6-diphosphate. It is possible that this different behaviour of the protein when protected with substrate towards the two different types of sulphydryl reagents indicates small conformational changes in the enzyme and it is interesting that there are considerable changes in the unit cell dimensions between native and PCMB-aldolase monoclinic crystals (see below), although no change in the activity of the enzyme after reaction with four equivalents of PCMB was observed.

3. Crystallographic Results and Discussion

(a) *Hexagonal bipyramid crystals*

The hexagonal bipyramid crystals were found to be extremely susceptible to radiation damage and an almost complete loss of the diffraction pattern was observed from a crystal approximately 0·5 mm × 0·1 mm after about six hours exposure to the X-ray beam from an Elliott rotating anode tube run at 2 kw. For this reason the maximum precession angle was limited to 6°. A 6° zero level precession photograph of the $hk0$ zone showed 6 mm symmetry and this symmetry was also observed in the first upper level photograph. The crystal system is therefore hexagonal with point group 622. A precession photograph of the $h0l$ zone showed $00l$ reflections to be present when $l = 6$, 12, 18 and 21. The space groups $P6_122$ and $P6_222$ (or their enantiomorphs) require that $00l$ reflections occur only when $l = 6n$ and $l = 3n$, respectively. Therefore the presence of the $002l$ reflection indicates that the space group is $P6_222$ with 12 general positions, although pseudo-$P6_122$ symmetry appears to exist for low-order reflections corresponding to spacings greater than 10 Å. The unit cell parameters were found to be:

$$a = 161.0 \pm 0.6 \text{ Å}, c = 169.0 \pm 1.0 \text{ Å}; V = 21.4 \times 10^5 \text{Å}^3.$$

The density of the crystals was measured with a bromobenzene–xylene density-gradient column as described by Low & Richards (1952). The column was calibrated with sodium bromide solutions of various densities. Crystals were blotted free of excess mother liquor on a microscope slide and quickly placed in the column with the aid of a pair of tweezers. The density was recorded within two minutes and found to be 1·250 ± 0·006 g/ml.

An estimate of the water content of the crystals was obtained from measurements on eight crystals whose wet weights varied between 0·09 and 0·03 mg. The crystals were blotted free of excess liquid and dried in air until constant weight was obtained. The mean value of the water content was found to be 31·7 ± 2·0% of the wet weight of the crystals. Crystals air dried in this manner have been shown to retain between 5 and 10% of the protein weight in water (Haurowitz, 1950) and hence 7·5% of the protein weight was added to the apparent weight of water in the crystal. Since the crystals are in nearly saturated ammonium sulphate solution, the air dried crystals still contain a considerable amount of salt. It has been shown (Perutz, 1946) that not all the water in a protein crystal is available to salt owing to an impermeable mono-molecular layer of water associated with the protein which, in the case of horse haemoglobin, amounted to 0·3 g/g of protein. Following the work of North (1959) on ox haemoglobin, we have assumed that of the estimated water content, 0·3 g/g of aldolase is salt free and the remainder has the same concentration as the mother liquor. This proportion of bound water is most likely an overestimate since the molecular weight of aldolase is almost twice that of haemoglobin. A drop of mother liquor was dried to constant weight and the weight of salt found to be 78% of the weight of water.

On the basis of the data given above, the protein content was calculated to be 48·5% of the wet weight of the crystals and hence the molecular weight of the asymmetric unit, assuming 12 general positions, is 65,000. The chief sources of error in this computation of the crystallographic molecular weight lie in the measurements and assumptions involved in the estimates of the water content and the salt content of the crystals and these errors may result in an apparent increase or decrease in the molecular weight of approximately 10 to 20%. Values for the molecular weight of aldolase obtained in the ultracentrifuge have been found to be between 140,000 and 160,000 (Morse & Horecker, 1968). Thus our value of 65,000 might either represent approximately one-half an aldolase molecule, or, allowing for extreme errors in measurement, might possibly represent one-third of the molecule. However the symmetry elements of space group $P6_222$ only permit a molecule to be placed at 12 general positions, or at six special positions on twofold axes or at three special positions on two twofold axes normal to each other. There is no site at which a molecule having trigonal symmetry can be placed so as to exploit such symmetry (*International Tables for X-ray Crystallography*, Vol. I, p. 287). Hence, although our value for the molecular weight is somewhat lower than the commonly accepted value, we conclude that the hexagonal crystals contain half an aldolase molecule per asymmetric unit and that the complete molecule is situated on a dyad axis of symmetry.

Values of V_m, the volume of the asymmetric unit per molecular weight of protein, are calculated to be 2·75 Å^3 per dalton and 2·23 Å^3 per dalton for half-molecular weights of 65,000 and 80,000, respectively. These values are consistent with values found for other proteins which have been tabulated by Matthews (1968), while estimates of V_m for one aldolase molecule per asymmetric unit or one-quarter molecule per asymmetric unit lie outside this range. These observations support our conclusion that the molecule is situated on a dyad axis of symmetry.

The packing of various arrangements of the molecules in the hexagonal cell has been studied with the aid of models. We assumed that the molecule is a tetramer and that the subunits are roughly spherical with diameter 40 Å (Penhoet *et al.*, 1967), and imposed the condition that one dyad axis of the molecule be parallel to a crystallographic dyad axis. It was found that a tetrahedral or pseudo-tetrahedral arrangement of subunits provided a more plausible structure which was consistent with the unit cell dimensions (a:c = 0·71) and the low order $P6_122$ symmetry than a square planar arrangement. This result is in agreement with the observations made by Valentine from electron micrographs of aldolase (Penhoet *et al.*, 1967).

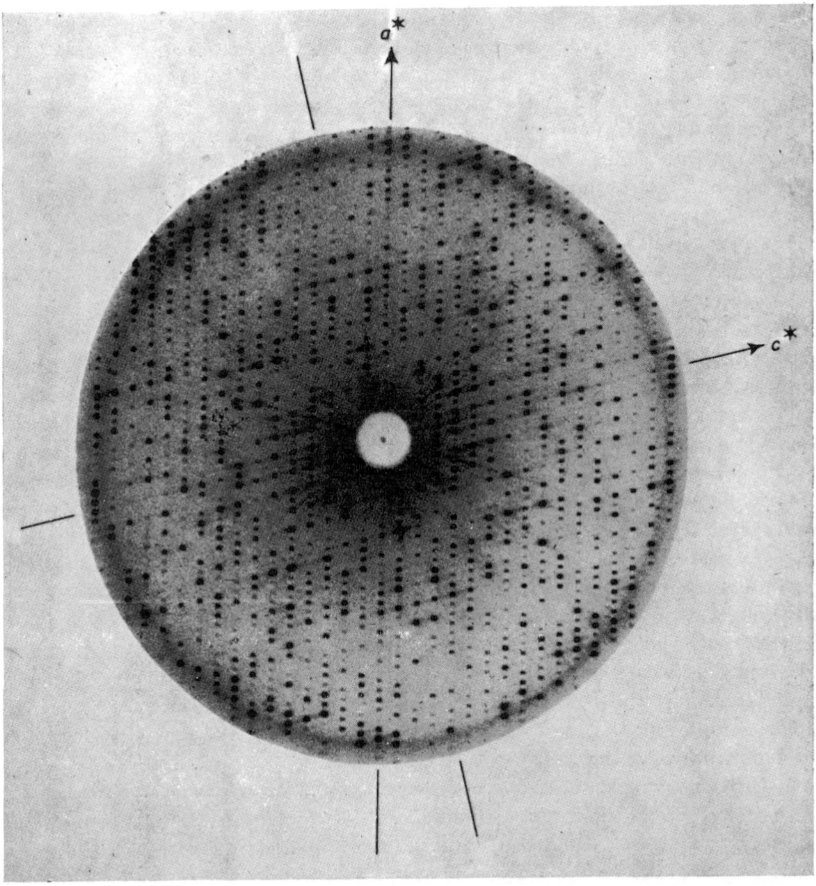

PLATE I. A 9° precession photograph of the $h0l$ zone of the monoclinic PCMB–aldolase crystals. The reciprocal lattice axes a^* and c^*, and the non-crystallographic mirror planes are indicated. This crystal has been soaked in 3 mM-uranyl acetate solution and the intensities are slightly different from the native protein.

(b) *Monoclinic crystals*

The PCMB–aldolase crystals were found to be monoclinic, space group $P2_1$ and unit cell dimensions $a = 163{\cdot}7$ Å, $b = 61{\cdot}4$ Å, $c = 81{\cdot}6$ Å, $\beta = 103{\cdot}74$ Å, and $V = 7{\cdot}94 \times 10^5$ Å^3. The density of the crystals, measured by the density gradient method, was found to be 1·26 g/ml. Estimates of the water content of these crystals were found to depend very critically on the manner in which the crystals were blotted before weighing and for this reason no measurement of the molecular weight was obtained. The volume of the asymmetric unit per molecular weight of protein of 160,000 is 2·5 Å^3 per dalton which is well within the range of V_{m} tabulated for other proteins (Matthews, 1968). Hence it is assumed that the unit cell contains one aldolase molecule per asymmetric unit.

Very recently monoclinic crystals have been obtained from native aldolase. The unit cell dimensions were found to be: $a = 164{\cdot}5$ Å, $b = 57{\cdot}3$ Å, $c = 85{\cdot}0$ Å, $\beta = 102°40'$. Unfortunately these crystals are significantly non-isomorphous with the PCMB–aldolase crystals and do not enable the mercury to be used as a heavy atom derivative at this stage. However, there are several possible modification experiments, based on the different reactivities of the sulphydryl groups, which we hope will result in an isomorphous series of derivatives. The monoclinic crystals are considerably more resistant to radiation damage than the hexagonal crystals and withstand at least 50 hours exposure in the X-ray beam. Both the native and the PCMB–aldolase monoclinic crystals showed a tendency for twinning about *a*. The following results and discussion refer to data obtained from the PCMB–aldolase crystals which were obtained in advance of the native monoclinic crystals and which appear to grow more readily to an appreciable size (approximately 1 mm × 0·2 mm).

A 9° precession photograph of the *h0l* zone shows indications of non-crystallographic mm symmetry in which one mirror plane is normal to c^* and the other, by Friedel's law, to *a* (Plate I). Since the observed X-ray diffraction pattern is the result of sampling the molecular transform of the asymmetric unit of the crystal at the appropriate reciprocal lattice points, any non-crystallographic symmetry represents a manifestation of the symmetry of the molecule itself. Naturally occurring proteins cannot contain mirror planes and hence we conclude that the non-crystallographic mm symmetry observed in the *h0l* photograph is due to the projection of a local twofold rotation axis of the aldolase molecule onto the (010) plane.

In order to probe these symmetry properties further by means of Patterson and rotation functions, three-dimensional data to a resolution of 8·5 Å were collected from a single crystal on the Hilger and Watts PDP8 computer-controlled four-circle diffractometer. The data, comprising some 1470 reflections together with their Friedel pairs, were processed and corrected for absorption in the usual way (North, 1965; North, Phillips & Mathews, 1968). Data from such a large unit cell necessarily contain a fair proportion of weak reflections. In the present case 19·3% of a total 2802 measurements were found to be below the minimum observable intensity, σ_{N_0}, where σ_{N_0} represents the standard deviation in the background corrected intensity N_0. For those reflections for which $\sigma_{N_0}/|N_0|$ exceeded a limiting value of unity, the measured N_0 was rejected and replaced by a value $0{\cdot}5 \times \sigma_{N_0}$ (Hamilton, 1955), while reflections for which statistical fluctuations or errors in measurement had resulted in a negative value of N_0 greater in magnitude than σ_{N_0}, were assigned zero intensity.

The angular relationships between the subunits in the aldolase molecule were then investigated by means of the rotation function (Rossmann & Blow, 1962). This function represents the amount of overlap when the Patterson summation is superimposed, within a sphere around the origin, on a rotated version of the same summation. It is anticipated that the function will have a large value when the rotation is such as to superimpose all the vectors relating electrons in one subunit (the self-Patterson function) on all such vectors within another subunit. The vectors will tend to be located within a sphere around the origin, which was taken to be 40 Å for aldolase. The rotation may be specified by the three Eulerian angles (θ_1, θ_2, θ_3) or by the spherical polar co-ordinates (χ, ψ, ϕ) where ψ and ϕ fix the direction of the rotation axis and χ denotes the angular rotation about this axis. For monoclinic aldolase a Cartesian co-ordinate system (X_1, X_2, X_3) was chosen such that X_2 is parallel to b, X_3 to c and hence X_1 is parallel to a^*. Initially the 74 largest reflections within the limit of 8·5 Å resolution were used to calculate the rotation function $R(\theta_1, \theta_2, \theta_3)$ at intervals of 15° in each angle. Only one prominent peak was observed and an investigation of the region around this maximum using the 167 largest reflections within the limit of 8·5 Å resolution and angular intervals of 10° showed that the maximum value of R occurred at $\theta_1 = 90°$, $\theta_2 = 30°$ and $\theta_3 = 90°$. The height of the origin peak of R, corresponding to no rotation, is 735 units and the peak at (90°, 30°, 90°) is 690 units. The background level of the function has a mean value of 338 units and a standard deviation (σ) of 27 units. Thus the maximum peak is 13 standard deviations above background whilst the next highest peak is only $2{\cdot}8 \times \sigma$ above background.

The corresponding spherical polar co-ordinates of the maximum and its symmetry related equivalents are: $\chi = 180°, \phi = 105°, \psi = 90°$ and $\chi = 180°, \phi = 15°, \psi = 90°$, which represent two twofold rotation axes, one of which is parallel to c^* and the other to a, as was suggested by the $h0l$ photograph. The combination of a local twofold rotation axis perpendicular to the crystallographic twofold screw axis with the crystallographic twofold screw axis automatically produces a second local twofold normal to the other two due to the Friedel symmetry of the X-ray diffraction pattern, so that although we may conclude that the aldolase molecule in the monoclinic unit cell contains at least one local twofold rotation axis which is parallel to a or to c^*, we cannot determine at this stage whether the tetrameric molecule is utilising both local twofold axes. Also it is feasible, from the present evidence, for these twofold rotation axes to be associated with translations parallel to the rotation axes. This possibility seems extremely unlikely in view of the arguments put forward by Monod, Wyman & Changeux (1965) and Hanson (1966) in favour of closed oligomeric structures resulting from exclusive isologous association of subunits but we are at present investigating this possibility by means of the translation function (Rossmann, Blow, Harding & Coller, 1964).

It is interesting that very similar arrangements of non-crystallographic symmetry have been observed in several other proteins which crystallize in monoclinic space groups. Haemoglobin (Perutz, Rossmann, Cullis, Muirhead, Will & North, 1960), β-lactoglobulin (Green & Aschaffenburg, 1959), α-chymotrypsin (Blow, Rossman & Jeffrey, 1964), pig muscle lactate dehydrogenase (Pickles, Jeffrey & Rossmann, 1964), α-lactalbumin (Aschaffenburg, Handford, Joynson, North, & Phillips, unpublished results) and the 2*Zn* and 4*Zn* rhombohedral crystals of insulin (Dodson, Harding, Hodgkin & Rossmann, 1966) all contain local dyad axes which are perpendicular to the unique crystallographic axis. This arrangement for the combination of crystallographic and non-crystallographic rotation axes is evidently highly favourable.

The rotation function investigates the symmetry of the Patterson summation within the region in which self vectors between atoms in one subunit are likely to occur. In the case of aldolase, a visual examination of the regions of the Patterson, which contain the cross vectors between one molecule and the symmetry related molecule, revealed the presence of an additional local symmetry element. The Patterson synthesis, computed from the complete 8·5 Å resolution data, contains only one significant peak which occurs on the Harker section, $V = \frac{1}{2}$, with co-ordinates $U = 0{\cdot}488$, $W = 0{\cdot}926$ (Fig. 1) (where the co-ordinates are expressed according

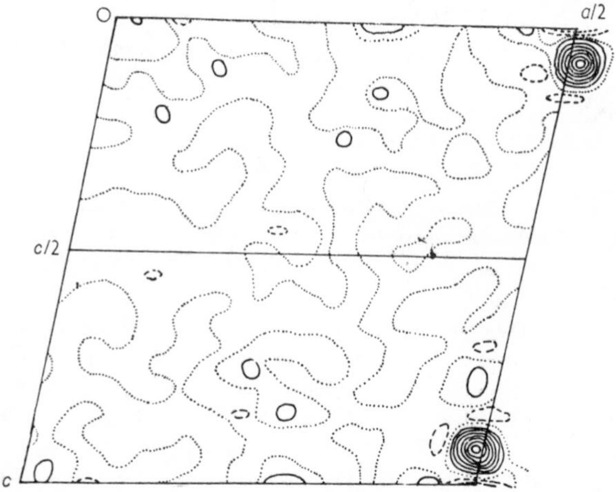

FIG. 1. The Harker section, $V = \frac{1}{2}$, of the 8·5 Å three-dimensional native Patterson. The zero contour is shown dotted and negative contours are dashed. The contour interval is ten arbitrary units.

to the convention described in *International Tables for X-ray Crystallography*, vol. I, page xi). The peak is outside the region of the self-Patterson function investigated by the rotation function and is five times the height of any other feature in the map and 0·345 times the height of the origin. Patterson (1949, 1952) has shown that centro-symmetrical structures which are related by a centre of symmetry, give rise to a peak in the Patterson synthesis with height half that of the origin peak and at a position corresponding to the vector between the molecular centres. In the space group $P2_1$ a similar peak will be generated on the Harker section, if the molecule itself contains a local dyad axis parallel to the crystallographic screw dyad axis, as is shown in the diagram (Fig. 2). Such symmetry would not be detected in the rotation function because it is superimposed on the crystallographic symmetry. The height of the molecular symmetry peak in aldolase is approximately 70% of the height anticipated on the basis of the above arguments. This may be partly due to uncertainties in the data for when the Patterson synthesis was recomputed with the intensities weighted according to the squares of the reciprocals of their standard deviations, the height of the molecular symmetry peak improved to a value 0·375 times the height of the

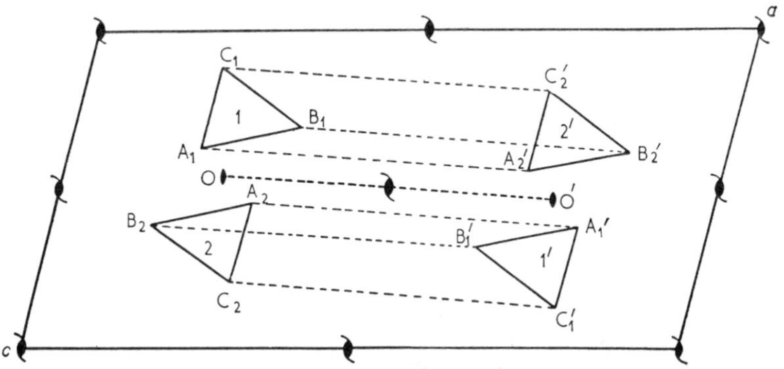

FIG. 2. A diagram to demonstrate the formation of the peak on the Harker section $V = \frac{1}{2}$, in the three-dimensional Patterson synthesis resulting from the presence of a local twofold rotation axis parallel to the crystallographic twofold screw axis.

A point A_1 at height Y in subunit 1 is taken into point A_2, height Y, in subunit 2 by operation of the local dyad axis which intersects the (010) plane at 0. Points A_1 and A_2 are transformed to points A_1' and A_2', respectively, both at height $Y + \frac{1}{2}$ by operation of the crystallographic two-fold screw. Vectors A_1A_2' and A_2A_1' are equal in length to each other and to $00'$ and superimpose on the section $V = \frac{1}{2}$ of the three dimensional Patterson. For each point in subunit 1 a similar set of vectors is generated. If there are N equal atoms in subunit 1 then the height of the origin peak in the Patterson synthesis is proportional to $4N$ (the total number of atoms in the unit cell) and the height of the molecular symmetry peak to $2N$.

origin, i.e. approximately 75% of the height anticipated. Slight differences in the tertiary structures of the subunits, arising from their chemical non-identity, would also result in a relative lowering of the molecular symmetry peak but, due to the low resolution of our data, it is not possible to obtain a quantitative estimate of this effect. However, the high significance of molecular symmetry peak in relation to other features in the map, its compact shape and the approach to the value expected from theory provide strong evidence for the existence of a local dyad axis parallel to the crystallographic dyad which intersects the (010) plane at $X = 0{\cdot}244$, $Z = 0{\cdot}463$ or the related positions $X = 0{\cdot}244$, $Z = 0{\cdot}037$; $X = 0{\cdot}256$, $Z = 0{\cdot}037$; $X = 0{\cdot}256$, $Z = 0{\cdot}563$.

The combination of this result with the results from the rotation function lead to the conclusion that the aldolase molecule is a tetramer possessing a fair degree of 222 symmetry. A schematic diagram for the arrangement of the subunits in the monoclinic cell is shown in Figure 3. Although we have shown the subunits to be arranged with perfect tetrahedral symmetry in the diagram we know that the 222 symmetry cannot be precise and must be pseudo-tetrahedral since the subunits are chemically non-identical. The results on the hexagonal crystal form have shown that aldolase possesses one true dyad axis of symmetry and hence we conclude that the four subunits are arranged in a pseudo-tetrahedral structure in which the true dyad relates the $\alpha\beta$ pairs, as in haemoglobin (Perutz, Muirhead, Cox & Goaman, 1968). Due to the low resolution of our data we cannot determine at this stage which of the local twofold axes in the monoclinic crystal cell represents the true dyad axis of the molecule and therefore we have shown them all to be equivalent in Figure 3.

A search for suitable isomorphous heavy atom derivatives is now in progress and

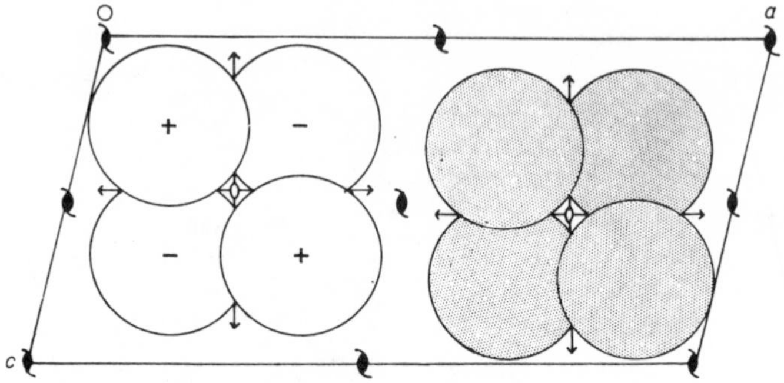

FIG. 3. A schematic diagram of the arrangement of the aldolase molecules in the monoclinic unit cell.

The subunits are represented as spheres 40 Å in diameter and are arranged in a tetrahedral structure with local dyads parallel to a, c^* and b. At the present time we cannot distinguish between the α and β subunits and have shown them to be identical. The molecular centre is at $X = 0{\cdot}244$, $Y = 0$, $Z = 0{\cdot}463$ (the choice of the Y co-ordinate is arbitrary in this space group). The shaded molecule is generated from the non-shaded molecule by the operation of the crystallographic twofold screw axis and its molecular centre is therefore at $Y = \frac{1}{2}$. There are three other related positions for the X, Z co-ordinates of the molecular centre (see text) and all of these give equally plausible packing arrangements. The choice of this particular position out of the four possibilities is arbitrary.

we hope that this will lead to a confirmation of the symmetry properties expressed here and eventually to a three-dimensional model of the aldolase molecule.

Note. While this work was in progress we have learnt that the unit cell dimensions and space group of the hexagonal crystals have also been determined by Dr N. Andreeva and her colleagues in Moscow and those of the monoclinic crystals by Dr F. S. Mathews in Washington University Medical School, St. Louis, U.S.A.

We are most grateful to Professor D. C. Phillips for his unfailing advice and encouragement and to Dr. A. C. T. North for his most helpful discussions. We are also indebted to Dr E. N. Baker for his help with the diffractometer measurements. We wish to acknowledge the support of the Medical Research Council (P.A.M.E.) and the Science Research Council (M.A.J. and C.H.McM.).

REFERENCES

Baranowski, T. & Neiderland, T. R. (1949). *J. Biol. Chem.* **180**, 543.
Benesch, R. E., Lardy, H. A. & Benesch, R. (1955). *J. Biol. Chem.* **216**, 663.
Blow, D. M., Rossmann, M. G. & Jeffrey, B. A. (1964). *J. Mol. Biol.* **8**, 65.
Castellino, F. J. & Barker, R. (1966). *Biochem. Biophys. Res. Commun.* **23**, 182.
Chan, W., Morse, D. & Horecker, B. L. (1967). *Proc. Nat. Acad. Sci., Wash.* **57**, 1013.
Cremona, T., Kowal, J. & Horecker, B. L. (1965). *Proc. Nat. Acad. Sci., Wash.* **53**, 1395.
Dodson, E., Harding, M. M., Hodgkin, D. C. & Rossmann, M. G. (1966). *J. Mol. Biol.* **16**, 227.
Ellman, G. L. (1959). *Arch. Biochem. Biophys.* **82**, 70.
Ginsburg, A. (1966). *Arch. Biochem. Biophys.* **117**, 445.
Ginsburg, A. & Mehler, A. H. (1966). *Biochemistry*, **5**, 2623.
Green, D. W. & Aschaffenburg, R. (1959). *J. Mol. Biol.* **1**, 54.
Gutfreund, H. (1965). *An Introduction to the Study of Enzymes*, p. 123. Oxford and Edinburgh; Blackwell Scientific Publications.
Hamilton, W. C. (1955). *Acta Cryst.* **8**, 185.

Hanson, K. R. (1966). *J. Mol. Biol.* **22**, 405.
Haurowitz, F. (1950). *Chemistry and Biology of Proteins*, p. 91. New York: Academic Press.
Kawahara, K. & Tanford, C. (1966). *Biochemistry*, **5**, 1578.
Kobashi, K., Lai, C. Y. & Horecker, B. L. (1966). *Arch. Biochem. Biophys.* **117**, 437.
Koida, M. & Lai, C. Y. (1969). *Fed. Proc.* **28**, 3416.
Kowal, J., Cremona, T. & Horecker, B. L. (1965). *J. Biol. Chem.* **240**, 2485.
Lai, C. Y. (1968). *Arch. Biochem. Biophys.* **128**, 202.
Lia, C. Y. (1968). *Arch. Biochem. Biophys.* **128**, 212.
Low, B. W. & Richards, F. M. (1952). *J. Amer. Chem. Soc.* **74**, 1660.
Matthews, B. W. (1968). *J. Mol. Biol.* **33**, 491.
McMurray, C. H. & Trentham, D. R. (1969). *Biochem. J.* in the press.
Monod J., Wyman, J. & Changeux, J-P. (1965). *J. Mol. Biol*, **12**, 88.
Morse, D. E., Chan, W. & Horecker, B. L. (1967). *Proc. Nat. Acad. Sci., Wash.* **58**, 628.
Morse, D. E. & Horecker, B. L. (1968). *Advanc. Enzymol.* **31**, 125.
North, A. C. T. (1959). *Acta Cryst.* **12**, 512.
North, A. C. T. (1965). *J. Sci. Instr.* **41**, 42.
North, A. C. T. Phillips, D. C. & Mathews, F. S. (1968). *Acta Cryst.* **24**, 251.
Patterson, A. L. (1949). *Acta Cryst.* **2**, 339.
Patterson, A. L. (1952). In *Computing Methods and the Phase Problem.* p. 29. Pennsylvania State College.
Penhoet, E., Kochman, M., Valentine, R. & Rutter, W. J. (1967). *Biochemistry*, **6**, 2940.
Penhoet, E., Rajkumar, T. & Rutter, W. J. (1966). *Proc. Nat. Acad. Sci., Wash.* **56**, 1275.
Perutz, M. F. (1946). *Trans. Faraday Soc.* B, **42**, 187.
Perutz, M. F., Muirhead, H., Cox, J. M. & Goaman, L. C. G. (1968). *Nature*, **219**, 131.
Perutz, M. F., Rossmann, M. G., Cullis, A. F., Muirhead, H., Will, G. & North, A. C. T. (1960). *Nature*, **185**, 416.
Pickles, B., Jeffrey, B. A. & Rossmann, M. G. (1964). *J. Mol. Biol.* **9**, 598.
Racker, E. (1947). *J. Mol. Chem.* **167**, 843.
Rossmann, M. G. & Blow, D. M. (1962). *Acta Cryst.* **15**, 24.
Rossmann, M. G., Blow, D. M., Harding, M. M. & Coller, E. (1964). *Acta Cryst.* **17**, 338.
Rowley, P. T., Tchola, O. & Horecker, B. L. (1964). *Arch. Biochem. Biophys.* **107**, 305.
Sia, C. L. & Horecker, B. L. (1968). *Arch. Biochem. Biophys.* **123**, 186.
Swenson, A. D. & Boyer, P. D. (1957). *J. Amer. Chem. Soc.* **79**, 2147.
Szuchet, S. & Yphantis, D. A. (1968). *Fed. Proc.* **27**, 521.
Trentham, D. R., McMurray, C. H. & Pogson, C. I. (1969). *Biochem. J.* **114**, 19.